In Your Face

An Insider's Explosive Account Of the Takata Airbag Scandal

Kevin Fitzgerald
and
David Schumann

PUBLISHED BY RECALL AWARENESS

Edited by Caroline Pincus
Illustrations by Ryan Fitzgerald
Cover Art by Annalisa Feliz Loevenguth
Book Design by David Schumann

Second Edition – September 2019

Paperback ISBN – 978-0-578-57329-8
eBook ISBN – 978-0-9975610-8-1

To order, contact publisher or visit www.RecallAwareness.com.

Disclaimer: The material in this book is offered to provide helpful information on the subjects discussed. The publisher and authors are not responsible for any specific damages or negative consequences resulting from any actions taken based on the content presented herein.

IN YOUR FACE

An Insider's Explosive Account of the Takata Airbag Scandal

Preface

by David Schumann

As I wrote this book with Kevin, friends and colleagues would often ask what we were working on. We had both left our jobs to focus on it full-time, and they wondered what was so important.

I would tell them I was writing a book on Takata – an explosive account of fraud and failure – or something like that. Most of the time, I would have to explain myself further because Takata isn't a company whose name most people recognize. I would ask them if they'd heard about the exploding airbags that were maiming and killing people across the world. Some had a vague sense of the story, from a news report or two, but no sense of the present scope and urgency. I would give them a quick summary of the tragedy and the largest automotive recall in history. Then the light would go on, and nearly everyone would say that they or someone close had received a recall notice for their airbag. All too frequently they would ask, "Is it really that serious?!"

It is that serious. These experiences highlighted why we had to write this book quickly. Takata manufactured airbags that have killed twenty-four people and injured hundreds as of June 2019. After more than a decade of recalls and deaths, the end of this nightmare cannot come soon enough. The reports of failures continue unabated. More innocent people will succumb to the hidden danger that sits directly in front of their faces, within arm's reach, every time they get into the wrong car or truck.

This isn't just any automotive component. Takata manufactured devices that fail violently, like a grenade, sending metal shrapnel into faces, necks, and chests. Even those who don't die from their injuries have their lives significantly altered with crippling and disfiguring traumas. Efforts to stem the tide of exploding airbags has continued to fail and time is not on our side. This largest of automotive recall efforts to remedy the horrors, nearly 70 million inflators in the United States alone, and more than 120 million worldwide, isn't close to completion. Less than a third of the potentially lethal airbags are off the road today, and not enough of the driving public know how real the danger is.

There are places in the world that haven't even started to recall. Some airbags have more than a 50% chance of exploding in the most minor of accidents. Our purpose is to change this significantly, leaving our reader with the same sense of urgency we feel. We must speed up the global recall. This is just the tip of the iceberg, however, and while we hope to raise awareness, our true purpose is to change the finish line entirely.

We spent more than two years bringing Kevin's shocking story about the incompetence and fraud he encountered at Takata as one of its leading airbag engineers, not only to get recalled cars repaired faster, but primarily to indict tens of millions more that the regulatory agencies believe are safe. Takata has claimed these airbags are immune to the same safety problems of their past, and automakers are steadfastly clinging to it. Nobody wants to expand an already complex and massive recall, except the future victims and a few others like us. We know the deaths will not stop until we do. There are another hundred million inflators not under recall that have the same weaknesses – the same Achilles tendon – and unless we do something about that, more innocent lives will be ruined.

The scandal grew because of obscured facts, misrepresentations, lies, and a basic ignorance of the science behind airbags. Only truth can redeem these mistakes. We must reorient a conversation that is and has been too focused on liabilities, profits, and probabilities, to one that puts consumers first, framed around accountability, responsibility, and certainty.

This is Kevin's account of his experiences working for Takata for nearly fifteen years as an engineer and executive. His story is of a long and defining struggle to persistently fix the rot at the heart of the company, where his personal pains became inseparable from those at work. His testimony contains the keys to understanding the Takata failures, and the poignant reasons why we had to share his explosive revelations. The company's persistent shortcomings will be weighed against a crucial missing requirement that every airbag should have met before going into our vehicles. Missed by airbag manufacturers, automakers, and regulatory agencies of the world, the oversight will seal our case and make clear the horror of what has been let loose.

Ultimately, this is a story about one man who made a difference, and his continuing efforts to engage others to help make a bigger impact yet. Every day counts as millions of airbags creep closer to failure. Eight people died while we wrote this book. This is our prayer – our way of focusing our hopes and intentions around this issue, in the certain faith they will be realized by the higher power in humanity. Something needs to change, not just in relation to this scandal and aftermath, but something else, perhaps more fundamental and elusive that we hint at. This is our way of introducing the problem. The solution, we hope, is with all of us.

I joined Takata as an engineer fresh from college in 2004. There I met and eventually worked for Kevin. He was a mentor to me, we became good friends, and I came to know his family as mine. I left Takata in 2008, but we stayed in touch and would talk about his struggles as an executive there, continuing the same battles we had shared. I moved from Michigan to Arizona and the years passed. We talked less and my Takata memories slowly faded. I continued to work in the pyrotechnic business, on a few start-ups of my own, and life was busy. Kevin attended my wedding in 2014 and we caught up briefly. Later that year, I learned that he resigned. I knew little about the circumstances of his departure until later, when he took a job with the same company I had been working with. This would bring us back together again and lead to something we could have scarcely imagined at the time.

The Takata recall went from large to massive in 2015. The numbers of everything kept rising: deaths, injuries, news reports, and the total number of recalled vehicles. Kevin started his new life in California as a Director of Operations with my company. Then in 2016, while I was visiting his facility, the two of us had dinner and talked about old times and the scandal that continued to erupt. At one point he became serious and agitated. It wasn't a light conversation to begin with but became heavier as we talked about the deaths. He told me that night that the scope of the recall was far larger than anyone imagined, and he shared with me the incredible ending of the story you're reading, that I won't dare reveal at this point. He told me then, however, that he would not rest until all Takata airbags were off the road. Every news report affected him deeply, he was angry, and I could see it was affecting his life. He had left the company but hadn't relinquished his struggle with it. Like the returned soldier, the battle he spent so much time fighting was still raging in his soul.

As we talked that evening, I saw in him what I have often felt in my own work: the terrible frustration of wanting change and being unable to affect it. A heavy burden of knowledge so consequential, but ineffectual, and dwarfed by the enormity of the systems and institutions that keep grinding despite it. I could sense this compelling force in him with no place to go, and it was tearing him apart. I worried for my friend. This concern and the heavy facts he laid on me that evening were the sparks for the idea to write this book together and share his powerful story – a story I was certain needed to be told – for everyone and for Kevin.

I called him after letting this thought simmer and told him so. Having recently finished my first book, I assured him we could be successful and that it would help him create the change he wanted. He said no and described more of the suffering and personal scars. Going back into that world threatened his current goal of putting his life back together, and he was scared to think about what could happen if he did. I let it go but also asked him if he would think about it while I went on vacation with my family.

As we vacationed on Lake Michigan, I couldn't stop thinking about the book and different scenes of his story. A day after returning, I sent him a text asking if he wanted to talk about it.

His reply was typical Kevin – clear and to the point – and I will never forget it.

"No need to talk. I'm in. Let's do this."

That was the beginning.

But how to tell the tale of the largest automotive recall from our insider's perspective? It wasn't an easy task, we discovered, and it took us a few takes before we settled on a format we were happy with. We agreed it made the most sense to tell his story in his voice. His first-person perspective on circumstances was the only way to convey him accurately, in his shoes and words. This is Kevin's story – truthful and purposeful – but one we wanted our reader to enjoy and connect with. We structured it into three main Acts that span the fifteen years he stood in the middle of it all, witnessing the scandal unfold from the first mistakes to the last.

I always knew Kevin had a great memory but working with him again I found myself constantly in awe of his ability to recall a richness of detail and dialogue in each situation over the years. A testament to a depth and attachment to his feelings, and certainly to his Irish ancestry, a land of wizened old storytellers. Certainly, he can't remember the exact words from every conversation, but we wanted it to be about the people, and dialogue was an important part of that. Some conversations he remembers spot on and for the rest we provide meaning and intent, allowing the story to flow.

I helped him write his story some, but my main task was to write the Introduction and Conclusion to establish the greater perspectives and set the background. Kevin is the protagonist and I'm the narrator. My neutral voice gives the preface and connects his account to our purpose and the bigger dots along the way. I also have a small interlude to introduce my part in the drama, but then it's all Kevin until the end.

We also developed illustrations and glossaries of terms and sources that are shared in the Appendices and on our website. These help with the technical aspects we included.

What we want readers to know is that our tale is a deeply human saga, and one we strove to tell with integrity, respect, and compassion for the people who played their parts. While we must highlight lies, mistakes, unethical conduct, and corporate malfeasance, we also shine light on the friendships, successes, and resistance that formed at the root of it all. From the victims and villains, to the complicit and the heroes, our story is about real people and the decisions that shaped the course of this tragedy. We name names and we seek those most responsible. This is not vendetta, but a need to bring the truth out, not just to prevent similar failures from happening again, but also to absolve the many from the faults of the few. The people who lived and worked for Takata came to work each day doing their best to uphold Takata's vision of "a world with zero traffic fatalities." Where that went wrong is the trail we must illuminate lest we retread.

Naturally, we want the reader to enjoy Kevin's story, but this shouldn't be an invitation to see everything as he does, or as we do. The people he fought against have their version of events and motivations. This is not about judgement, but about the complex relationships and decision-making processes that unleashed millions of deadly airbags into the world, snuffed innocent lives, maimed and disfigured hundreds, and is not finished yet. Kevin offers us a front seat ride to see what went wrong because he was truly in the middle of it, as the reader will soon be too.

INTRODUCTION

From Textiles to Explosives

TAKATA IS the company. Takada is the family. This is their story.

East of Kyoto, in Shiga Prefecture, sits Lake Biwa, the largest freshwater lake in Japan. Around this mystical body of water in 1933, Takezo Takada founded his company in the town of Hikone, famous for one of Japan's oldest surviving castles of the same name. Takata Company was a textile business that got its start producing specialty fabrics and high-strength lifelines for military parachutes. The whole world had been fighting since before the First World War, and Japan was no different, fighting with Russia and conquering Korea and Manchuria. As the Great Depression hit, Japan was expanding its colonial reach throughout Asia, both militarily and economically. The voices calling for a grander Empire where the sun never set rose in a grand crescendo.

In 1937, Takezo's heir was born – Juichiro – the same year Japan invaded China to start the second Sino-Japanese War. Demand for Takata's parachutes and fabrics soared as the battles escalated and the war economy grew. In 1938, Japan began fighting France in Indochina and renewed hostilities with Russia. Then Germany attacked Poland in 1939 and war in Europe started again. By the spring of 1940, the Nazi Blitzkrieg rolled across Europe in six brutal weeks, capturing France and everything between. By the fall of 1940, Japanese delegates convened in Berlin with Germany and Italy to sign the Tripartite military alliance. Victorious in their own regional conquests, the three nations agreed to split the world and align. America waited and armed her allies as Great Britain fought desperately to repel the Luftwaffe. Japan overwhelmed China and Greater Asia and their economy boomed. With the bombing of Pearl Harbor at the end of 1941, Japan brought America into the sway.

The Great War desolated Japan by 1945, leaving its industry and infrastructure ruined, and the future of its people uncertain. Nuclear holocaust and total defeat left only a few cities and factories standing. Demand for industrial goods plummeted and economic depression followed. There were no more Takata parachutes or Toyota military trucks. The economy that had been so efficiently yoked to the war effort was dead and the U.S. occupation followed defeat with times of great upheaval and uncertainty. The Americans wrote a new constitution, ended the rule of emperor Hirohito, though allowed him to remain a symbolic figurehead, and formed a new government. Women were given equal rights and new laws promoted the freedom of speech, local governance, and reduced the powers of the police. Importantly, Japan was prohibited from building or maintaining a military force indefinitely.

Surviving companies struggled to re-identify themselves and many closed for good. Toyota designed a new automobile in 1947, started to rebuild, but by 1949 couldn't meet payroll and their employees went on strike. Workers unions were springing up everywhere. A young democracy, busy at the grass-roots, was being established. Farmland owned by the aristocracy was appropriated to the families that had been farming it generationally. Economic and political freedoms expanded, and commerce began to churn. A seed had been planted in the ashes, the soil was fertile, and the rising sun would sprout a national renaissance that would take the world by storm.

Forced to build their economy from scratch, Japan became a manufacturing nation again. Processing imports into high value exports became the national strategy as it had been before. The government was business and export friendly, working closely with industry to research, innovate and develop new technologies rapidly. Business returned slowly by the middle of the 1950's. A surviving Takata sought new opportunities in the post-war economy.

Then in 1952, as the U.S. occupation of Japan was ending, Takezo Takada found his own lifeline – a product to build his company's future upon. Following early American developments in auto seatbelts, Takata began researching how to apply their parachute weaving technology to the newest automobile feature. The safety restraint would come to dominate the focus and fortune of the Takada business.

Seatbelts

The first safety-belt patent was issued in 1885, but it took seventy more years before being adopted into cars. The earliest restraints went into the flying machines at the turn of the century. Orville Wright installed a belt in 1908 to help him control his bi-wing aircraft as he bounced wildly across the rough-cleared fields that served for runways. A decade later, the first seatbelts were used in race-cars and became mandatory for pilots beginning to fly upside-down. For these dare-devils, the need for proper restraint was born through experience, but the real need was to protect the amateurs taking to the new roads in greater numbers and speeds. The Model-T was two-decades old at this point as war-engines were converted into cruisers for the masses.

The problem that became quickly clear is that too many injuries and deaths were resulting from all the new makes and models of vehicles crashing. Dangerous new roads, faster cars, and the end of prohibition meant by 1937 there were already 40,000 motorist deaths a year in America. Groups of medical professionals began to install restraints in their own cars and urged manufacturers to do the same. The automakers wouldn't yet. They were worried they might lose business with the unfashionable features and resisted seatbelts as long as possible.

The push came strongly in the 1950's. Influential California neurologist Dr. Shelden published his research on the deaths and head-trauma injuries from motor vehicle accidents. An early advocate for improved vehicle safety, his presentations highlighted the staggering reality while offering most of the solutions. He and others argued that companies should include the safety features we take for granted today: recessed or collapsible steering wheels, reinforced roofs, retractable seatbelts, and even airbags. The writing was on the wall.

Ford and Chrysler offered safety restraints as options in 1956. Two years later Saab introduced them as standard and Volvo patented the first three-point belting configurations. The era of the seatbelt had dawned, and beside it was also born the idea for the airbag. Ford and GM worked on inflating protective cushions as early as 1955, but it would take another two decades for the industry to figure out how to make them work well enough.

In 1960, Takata started selling their two-point seatbelts. Two years later they helped establish Japan's first crash-test facilities. Takezo Takada was proud when the company received national attention in 1965 as his engineers began testing with crash-test dummies, measuring and demonstrating the life-saving power of the safety belt. Takata was well-positioned as the nation's auto industry surged through the 60's and as the Japanese economic miracle unfolded, their cars and trucks began to storm the globe. Then in 1966, the U.S. Congress passed the National Traffic and Motor Vehicle Safety Act, establishing automobile safety standards the world would adopt. Seatbelts became mandatory in the U.S. Nothing could have been better for the Takada's and business surged.

Through the 1970's Japan had the third largest GDP in the world and a thriving economy built around vehicles, steel, ships, electronics, and chemicals. Twenty years after defeat they were dominating trade in the world, even as most other industrial nations recessed. In 1973, Takata began selling child car-seats and they participated in National Highway Traffic Safety Administration (NHTSA) crash-tests, where they out-performed other major manufacturers. Their restraints were winning customers and they invested heavily in the latest research and development (R&D) for the rapidly evolving safety systems market. They started to investigate airbag fabrics and cushions.

In 1974, Takezo Takada passed the baton to his son Juichiro, or Jim, as the world would come to know him. Takezo steered his company for forty years to become a major automotive brand and scion of business in Japan. The way was clear, and his son's purpose was to expand this dynasty internationally. Jim Takada was charismatic, intelligent, worldly, and hard-working. In his mid-twenties when his father's first seatbelts went into cars, his time was the post-war era. At the age of thirty-eight, he assumed the helm and began to chart a new destiny for the company.

In 1984, he established his foothold in the United States, the center of global automotive business, and incorporated Takata Restraint Systems (TRSI). He established a joint-venture in Michigan called Takata-Fisher Corporation and began making seatbelts for the Big Three in Motor City. At the same time, he was shaking hands with the biggest textile companies in the South and establishing strong relationships with the people that would eventually manage his North American operations. But while growing his company globally, a connected nascent technology was suddenly taking off. The era of the airbag was approaching, and it would confront Jim with a difficult decision.

Airbags

By the mid-eighties, the inevitability of airbag mandates was becoming clear, and the market began to heat up. Only a few companies were positioned to serve the niche market well because it was so specialized. As a textile company, Takata had already made airbag cushions and seat-belts. Their best customer, Honda, had requested that they become their full safety systems supplier and dive into airbags and crash electronics. It made sense.

Jim wasn't sure, however, and decided against airbags. At a New Year's party in 1985, he relayed his fears to his best customer and friend, telling Saburo Kobayashi, the head of Honda's new airbag team he could not "cross a bridge that is so dangerous."[1] He reasoned that a single mistake could wipe his company out and that if anything happened to the airbags, he would go bankrupt. Here, at the inflection point of his company, Jim's first instinct was to pass. For the reader to understand why, we first must explore the basis of our tale – the technology that makes airbags tick.

Art follows nature, giving us a way to relate to the life-saving advancement our story revolves around. An airbag can be understood by analogy to our reflex responses, such as blinking, flinching, or leaping heroically to the rescue. Nerves and senses detect a sequence that triggers some assault or threat in our environment. This crucial information is relayed through our central nervous system where deep in the brain, a near-instantaneous decision takes place. An autonomic response takes over and our nerves fire commands through the body, quickly deploying our best countermeasures to the danger. We throw our hands up in front of our face and protect the head at all costs.

In the hurtling vehicle, crash sensors relay the news of collision through the car's wiring to a simple computer. This electronic control unit takes a few measured attributes from the accident and decides the appropriate programmed response. Electric commands are sent to airbags, coordinated features, and seatbelt pretensioners to protect the occupant depending on the threat assessment. Within each airbag, a device called the inflator is activated. The heart of the airbag, it quickly releases gases into the cushion. The bag inflates rapidly to be in place in time to protect the occupants from the peril of their own momentum. As fast as a human response, a literal blink of an eye, the whole sequence takes less than 50 milliseconds – or 5% of one second. One instant the steering wheel or dash is before you, and the next moment a cushion greets you.

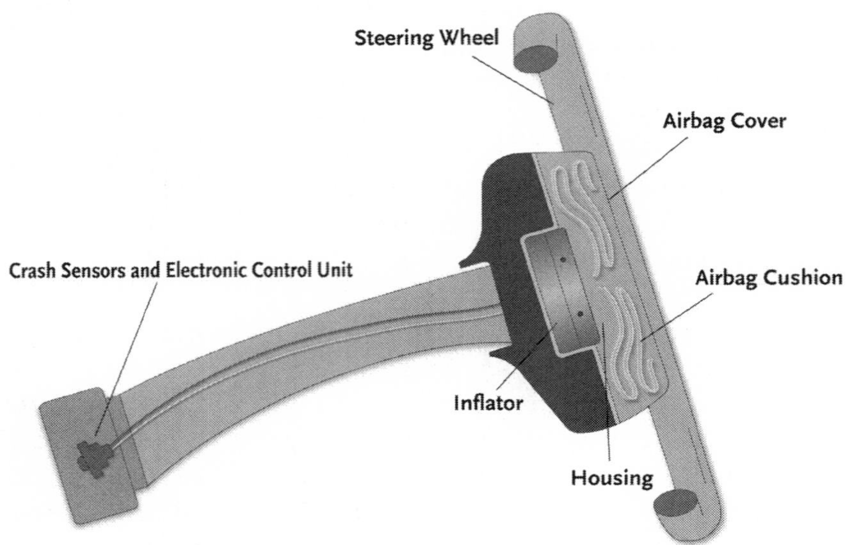

FIGURE ONE: BASIC AIRBAG SCHEMATIC

The sketch above shows a driver airbag module in a steering wheel, but the same concept applies to wherever the airbag is located, whether passenger dash, driver knee panel, or the various side-impact and roof locations found in modern cars. The shape and design of the cushion, inflator, and housing accommodate the variations, but the basic function is the same. A bigger bag is needed for the passenger because there is more space to cushion and the steering wheel is much closer to the driver.

There are a few nuances worth mentioning. Frontal airbags are vented so they don't retain any substantial pressures. When the occupant engages the bag, it begins to deflate as gases are pushed through the vents. This provides a slower deceleration and softer cushion. Additionally, most frontal airbags have dual-stage inflators. Also called 'smart' inflators, they have two main chambers that allow the output of gas to be varied, depending on the speed of the accident, and the weight and belted-status of the occupants. This prevents too forceful of a bag deployment against smaller people and in slower speed accidents. The earlier airbags injured or killed a few, mostly small women and children, until the improved inflators were introduced. The technology is effective and saves lives. NHTSA estimates that from 1987 to 2017, airbags saved nearly 51,000 people in the United States.[2] While we take airbags for granted now, the technology took the better of four decades to perfect, and most importantly for our story, it required the inclusion of a defense-industry technology that had never gone into vehicles before. This is the reason they work and the reason for our whole story.

Takata had already been producing bags – the fabric cushion – since around 1976. A decade later, Honda wanted them to go a step further, and supply complete airbag modules. The module is the plug and play assembly that is sold to the automaker. It is comprised of the airbag folded and packed into a housing, a cover that integrates into the car's interior trim, and the inflator – that makes it a dynamic system.

The first airbags were tested in the 1950's. They used pressurized tanks of gas that were released when commanded. They worked and filled the bags but were too slow to be of any help in a real collision. Driving at 60 miles an hour is equivalent to travelling through space at eighty-eight feet per second. If you are a foot from the steering wheel, then in just over 10 milliseconds (0.01 seconds) you'll hit the wheel after a dead-stop.[3] There are factors that slow this, like the dampening forces of our spine and the metal crumpling around us. The early companies determined that around 40 milliseconds was needed from the time of collision to a fully deployed airbag, ready and in place. Two advancements would need to happen before this could be achieved: accurate and reliable crash-sensors, and gas-generators that could deliver fast enough.

Pyrotechnic is two Greek words meaning 'fire,' and 'art.' The science of fireworks and rockets, using the energy from chemical reactions to make fire, light, gas, smoke, or sound is an old and mysterious trade. Pyrotechnic inflators became the standard for airbags when Talley Defense Company first developed them for Chrysler in 1968. Only the chemistry of energetics was fast enough, so the automakers went to the defense industry to solve the problem. Talley chemist John Pietz formulated a propellant around a chemical called sodium azide. The engineers adapted gas-generators originally used for jet ejection-seats around the unique constraints of the airbag. These sodium-azide inflators were the breakthrough that would enable the era of the airbag.

Propellants are a type of pyrotechnic chemistry used to propel or provide thrust. That was their primary use for the militaries of the world, rapidly generating lots of hot gases to push missiles, torpedoes, ejection seats, and more. There are many flavors and applications, but with airbags, propulsion isn't good. Inflation is all that is needed and so the ports that direct the gas are balanced to cancel any net forces. A key need for airbag propellants is that the gases produced must not suffocate, poison, or burn the occupants. Sodium-azide was perfect because it could produce gas quickly that was safe enough to breathe. But it had the most important criteria met – environmental and aging stability proven through decades of various military programs. Cars are surprisingly harsh environments for pyrotechnics and sodium-azide was known to be safe and reliable.

Propellants are not explosives. They can become explosive under certain circumstances but are considered one of the safer chemistries used in the industry. Other energetic materials are meant to explode and detonate. Typically, propellant cannot sustain combustion in open air. It needs both increased heat and pressure to ignite. A gas-generator then is fairly simple. Pyrotechnic formulations are loaded into metal housings that are sealed. Then they are ignited with electric-matches and a smaller sequence of pyrotechnic charges. If the inflator is the heart of the airbag, the propellant is the heart of the inflator. It must withstand decades of exposure and then when called upon deliver a precise flash of magic. Chemists and engineers specialize here and are the professionals at the center of our story.

Figure Two is a cross-section of a typical Takata driver inflator – a dual-chamber design that is relevant to our story, called PSDI. The two chambers each function identically, but with different propellant loads and volumes. The housing is comprised of two steel caps and a divider plate. The three are welded together to form the internal chambers. Inside there are two small cylinders where initiators sit, each with a booster charge beneath. The initiator has two contact pins that connect to the crash-system and receive the electrical signal to operate the airbag.

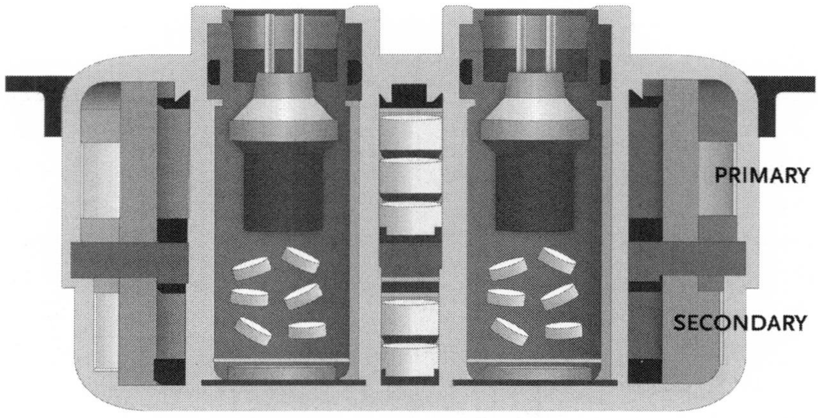

FIGURE TWO: CROSS-SECTION OF 'PSDI' INFLATOR

Blink and you miss it but save your life it can. For a company producing seatbelts for thirty years, nothing could have been more foreign, and yet so compelling. The technology was rooted in an industry Japan had been prevented from participating in since 1945. These were pyrotechnic specialty devices produced by a handful of niche defense companies. Saving lives is always serious business, but this was more so, and the real root of Jim's hesitation.

Takata Inflators

If first Jim refused Honda, it didn't take long for him to change his mind. By 1987, just two years after the New Year's party 'no,' his marching orders were full-speed ahead with Takata's new airbag program.

We can speculate that the lure of the growing market and the insistence of his best customers helped sway him. There are rumors that even after he declined, the Honda airbag team worked with his team clandestinely until he relented. But there were also economic factors that made it harder to resist diving into the precarious world of pyrotechnics, and the cutting edge of automotive safety systems. By the mid-eighties, the Japanese trade surplus had reached a pinnacle, creating currency imbalances and political unrest within Germany and the U.S. This led to the Plaza Accord in 1985 and the agreement to devalue the Dollar against the Yen. The overwhelming Japanese exports were curbed as intended, but an immediate opportunity to buy American investments and operations at a discount of nearly fifty percent resulted. The Japanese bought Pebble Beach, and the Takada's healthy balance sheet from two decades of growth gave Jim even more incentive to expand.

The airbag capability had to come from the defense companies, either Americans or Europeans. There were only a few specialists who had propellants and gas-generators and some experience adapting them to cars. In the U.S. there were three primary airbag pioneers. Talley Defense was the first with the original sodium-azide inflators, but would decide to license their technology to TRW, one of three big safety restraint companies. Morton-Thiokol Chemical Corporation had the propellant background and would seed Autoliv, the market leader today. This left Rocket Research, a longstanding defense company in Washington State, and that's where Jim went to make a deal.

Concurrently, Takata launched their research and development (R&D) center. On Earth Day of 1987, Automotive Systems Laboratory (ASL) was established in Michigan with three divisions framed around airbag modules, electronic controls and crash-sensors, and inflators and propellants. ASL and Rocket Research began to develop the first Takata airbags, leaning on proven sodium-azide technology and initial production lines were set-up in Moses Lake, WA. Inflation Systems Inc. (ISI) was established in 1988 as the inflator operations organization, and shortly after that the first Takata inflators were installed into modules. Honda was eager to test.

Takata made the leap, but Jim was not finished yet. He had even bigger plans and shortly after, entered into a second joint-venture with a German defense company called Bayern-Chemie. Bayern had helped Daimler-Benz with their early airbag program and developed sodium-azide inflators as early as 1972, just a few years behind Talley. Variations of these would become Takata's first driver inflators. The joint-venture established an operation in LaGrange, Georgia – under the ISI badge – and it became Takata's first center of inflator production and the setting for Act one ahead.

To finish his push into airbags, Jim purchased the fabrics division of Burlington Industries in 1988 for $80 million. Headquartered in Greensboro, North Carolina, it was renamed Takata-Highland Industries and would become the springboard for further North American expansion. The following year, Takata acquired two more American companies to grow their expanding seatbelt, fabrics, trim, and airbag capacities. TK Holdings Inc. was established officially as the North-American subsidiary and the early executive team was hired from these burgeoning relationships.[4]

The first driver and passenger modules were in production by 1990. Takata was officially an airbag supplier and in 1992 they bought out Rocket Research's interest in the Moses Lake facility. The joint-ventures were being wound down and soon Takata would have their own team and foundation ready to build one of the largest safety system companies. The ASL and Rocket Research partnership were still busy finalizing the patents that would ensure future innovation while training of the new team of specialists that would carry the banner forward pressed on. All the wheels were in motion, but who would run it?

Propellant

Paresh Khandhadia is a chemical engineering executive at the heart of our drama. A small man with dark hair, and round glasses that give him an almost 'Poindexter' look. As a key character and the father of the inflators central to our saga, a proper introduction is in order.

Born and raised in India, Paresh received his Chemical Engineering degree in 1978 from the Indian Institute of Technology, in Bombay. He continued his education in the U. S. and completed his Master's in 1981 from the University of Akron in Ohio. From there he went to work as a chemical processing engineer for the Canadian government and then a subsidiary of the major company Imperial Chemical Industries (ICI)[5]. Here he would discover the focus of his career in airbag propellants. In 1987, just as Jim was partnering on his airbag program, a joint-venture between ICI and TRW was announced. Called SABAG, the operation would manufacture large volumes of sodium-azide propellants for the market's growing demand. Paresh became a technical manager for the joint-venture in 1988, rapidly learning the challenges of the new and growing industry.

Sodium-azide was robust but like everything had its downsides. It was notoriously difficult to handle, prone to exploding from small mishaps and toxic for the workers on the line. Most of the early companies producing the chemical had incidents, but SABAG had the worst of it. As they scaled up there were five major accidents and fires, and Paresh's team worked diligently to improve safe processing methods. In 1990, they suffered their worst fire and were forced to close the plant down for most of the year.

It was clear the pursuit of a better propellant was highly lucrative, and the industry chemists were intently focused there, including ASL and Rocket Research. Scientists were racing to develop the next better, safer, and cheaper propellants. Patents began to churn out from the competitors at a dizzying pace. There was a sense of urgency, something new to invent for the car again. The rewards were obvious, but not the propellants. They had to burn fast, clean, and efficiently, while being safe and stable for decades in the demanding environments of the world. The Rocket team had a strong start with a variety of other formulations they were optimizing and investigating. Here is where Paresh enters.

With his propellant production experience, he is hired in late 1991 to become the eventual lead for Takata's inflator and propellant R&D. His role is to take the Rocket and Bayern foundations, and launch his own team and facilities, responsible for the future of the company's inflators. It was the opportunity of a lifetime to say the least. Some of the team he inherited were incredibly seasoned, having worked in the 60's and 70's on rockets, munitions, and explosives. This was the seed of Takata's propellant research and they all kept busy on the next generation of propellants.

The future for inflator R&D was in Detroit, however, and Paresh soon opened a propellant and inflator technical center in Armada, Michigan, about an hour away. Here he set out to find the chemistry breakthroughs and innovations that would propel the industry. Paresh worked for Tsuneo Chikaraishi, the global inflator boss in Echigawa, Japan.

By 1994, Paresh's team was conducting the final feasibility tests of a new and improved formulation. The propellant was safer to handle than sodium-azide and it was much cleaner, producing gases that were safe to breathe "even for asthmatics." Based on a Rocket formulation used originally for fire suppression, Paresh's team patented an improved chemistry around it. Their breakthrough was to incorporate chemicals that would scavenge undesirable and harmful gases, transforming them into cleaner effluents. This was a breakthrough. They named it '3110' and marketed it as 'Envirosure.'

The innovation spawned a new family of inflators and Takata's first non-azide airbags went into production in 1998 to much fanfare from their core Japanese customers. The following year they took ten percent of the North American market. Envirosure was a hit, and Takata had every reason to be happy with Paresh and his new team. Awards and industry recognition followed.

Still, there's rarely a 'golden bullet' with propellants. Paresh's breakthrough did not have the best gas yield.[6] Higher yields means less propellant is needed to produce the same amount of gas, and with the Japanese focus on being best in size and weight, Paresh needed to do better. Additionally, the specialty chemicals required to scavenge the propellant's harmful gases were expensive and rare. There were only a few companies that made them in small batches, and that would eventually create supply-chain uncertainties and costlier inflators. Both were bad for the automotive markets and meant the new formulation would be short-lived. But Takata made promises for future volumes, and they counted on Paresh to deliver his next breakthrough. He was keenly aware of this and already busy investigating another option.

The Rocket team had also filed a patent for propellants built around a fuel called PSAN – or 'phase-stabilized' ammonium-nitrate. Ammonium nitrate is a common chemical and had been used in propellants for decades. Other inflator companies were also investigating PSAN because of its gas efficiency. The promises were many but there were also risks, as ammonium nitrate was not known to be particularly stable. The Rocket team had looked at PSAN, but like most in the industry, developed other options first.

Paresh took the safer route too, putting most of his team on Envirosure first and quickly bringing it to market, but he couldn't resist the temptation of

PSAN. In parallel, he tasked one of his chemists named Sean Burns to work on it and in 1996, a year after Rocket was issued their patent on PSAN, Paresh and Sean filed their own on behalf of Armada. They called the new propellant "smokeless" because it burned so clean it produced very little airborne particulate. Their newest breakthrough promised inflators that would be the smallest and lightest – the cutting edge – and would dominate the market for decades to come. More work was needed, but Paresh was determined. By 1999, ASL's smokeless inflators were developed and validations were in process in Armada.

Now let's meet our protagonist, also working on PSAN propellants, but at one of Takata's competitors.

A Pyrotechnic Expert

To know Kevin is to know that Sandy is his rock and sanity. Without her, he is certain to have crashed into the shoals somewhere along the way and been unable to muster the courage to weather life's storms. She is the most important character in our story that will have but few scenes. Like Akiko is to Jim Takada, Sandy's presence is always there as a part of Kevin's character – his wife and his life. I can attest that she helps guide his wild and intelligent spirit always closer to paths of grace, gentleness, and greatness.

Kevin was born in the Bronx, New York, in August of 1962 to Joseph and Patricia Fitzgerald. Both were from Ireland, living just miles away from each other in Dublin, but they would meet on Rockaway Beach in Queens, after immigrating to the U.S. in the 1950's. They got married and had three children, Kevin was the middle son. Settling in Haverstraw, about thirty miles north of the city, both of his parents made the two-hour commute every day to work for the *New York Times.* He spent a good childhood in the majestic beauty of the lower Hudson Valley and as a teenager enjoyed running messages for the *Times* and mastering the intricate city subways.

Kevin's parents were straight-off the boat Irish Catholics and he was raised in the church. Schooled by a combination of nuns, brothers, laymen, and priests, he often grappled with his heavy religious upbringing, sometimes considering it more a burden and chore. Later, he came to realize it set a strong foundation for his life.

His parents emigrated to give their future children more opportunities. They worked hard and put their three kids through college. Kevin attended Bucknell University in Lewisburg, Pennsylvania where he received his B.S.

in Mechanical Engineering, in 1984. At Bucknell, he would meet Sandy Greenly, destined to become his wife. They were close friends at first, but their relationship deepened when they both started life in New York City after graduating.

There his first job was an engineer for the U.S. Government at Picatinny Arsenal, in New Jersey. Fresh out of school, he was working in the Mines, Countermines, and Demolitions Department, experimenting with explosives on behalf of the soldier. He loved it, but the slow pace and rigid mentality of government work didn't fit him. Two years later, he and Sandy moved across the country to California, where he took a new job with a company called Marquardt, in Van Nuys. Shortly after moving, the two returned together to their Alma Mater chapel at Bucknell and exchanged their vows in a small ceremony of friends and family. They loved the West Coast and he started working on the early development of MPIM, short for multi-purpose individual munition. For the Army, it was a portable, shoulder-launched weapon for close-combat, designed to smash through triple thick brick walls and penetrate light-armored vehicles.

The job went well, but while there he learned of an opportunity with Martin Marietta, a major defense company. They needed help advancing the Army's latest tank-killing weapon called Javelin. One of their top programs, it would take more than a decade to develop fully. Kevin started work on the missile's warhead and they moved to Texas. Martin Marietta had teamed with Texas Instruments in Dallas to develop the infrared targeting and seeking system, and that became home. Their first son was born there and then in 1990 the growing family moved to Martin Marietta's headquarters in Orlando, Florida.

1991 saw the first successful Javelin flight test. Kevin still recounts the moment vividly, describing as he stood anxiously with colleagues, listening to the countdown and live test over a speakerphone. He narrates the missile's flight as it leaves the launcher in a blast, and hovers there just a moment before the main motor is ignited. Turning upward, the rocket engine shoots it high into the sky above. At the zenith, it turns down and locks onto the target, diving straight down at the tank, like a bird of prey. The warhead smashes through the armor with a complicated sequence of pyrotechnic-driven explosions, culminating in a molten-metal, armor-piercing arrow that penetrates the tank like a fire hose through sand.

Kevin worked on Javelin until it went into production in 1993. He knew the defense industry rose and fell on big programs like this one and so he started looking for new work. He found a position as an engineer for Talley Defense Systems, and the family moved back West, this time to Mesa, Arizona. Talley had pursued Kevin aggressively because of his experience with Javelin and MPIM and a desire to expand their portfolio of similar systems.

Sandy and Kevin made the move to Arizona in the summer of 1993, already expecting the birth of their second son. They bought a home near Red Mountain and fell in love with the desert. Kevin started work on a 'bunker-busting' missile, and thoroughly enjoyed the family-like feel of Talley. When the program finished, he was reassigned to Talley's newly rejuvenated airbag division. Talley had been out of the airbag business for a while now, having licensed their technology to TRW, but the non-compete was soon to expire and they wanted back in. Kevin went from making missiles to airbags and loved the fast-paced and competitive automotive business. This was his cup of tea.

Talley formed a partnership with Delphi Automotive called Aegis, and with a new high gas yield Talley propellant, the team developed what was arguably the world's smallest driver inflator. It was called D60 and was in a class of its own, but it wouldn't sell. Its small package was desirable, but its gas temperature was too high, leaving the module engineers to deal with the heat. The novelty of its size wore thin quickly. The D60 went into limited production but Delphi reverted to more traditional inflators and disbanded the venture in 1998.

Kevin had come to love the business, so he looked to competitors for new opportunities, eventually securing an offer from BREED Technologies in Lakeland, FL. The family of now three children crisscrossed the country again. Alan Breed invented the crash-sensor that enabled the airbag industry in 1967 and built a large safety systems company from its success. BREED expanded from there into seatbelts and airbags, and, when Kevin arrived, they were experimenting with PSAN propellants.

Experienced ballisticians and engineers from the defense industry knew of the difficulties with ammonium-nitrate, especially moisture sensitivity and a tendency to explode. Many warned of the potential hazards and pitfalls, but the push for smaller inflators was strong. Kevin managed development for their side-impact PSAN inflator, and then moved onto a dual-stage passenger program as they expanded his responsibilities.

BREED found themselves in financial trouble, however. They had purchased Allied Signal's seatbelt division for too much money. That, coupled with the increasing cost pressures of the automotive industry, had them in a vise, and when GM demanded deeper cost reductions, BREED refused, quickly learning that you don't say no to the largest American company.[7] Kevin left in 1999 as the company sought Chapter 11 protection, but not before he was fortunate enough to meet Alan Breed, who was sadly passing from cancer.

At this point, Kevin had been designing airbag inflators for half a decade and wanted to stay in the business. He found a job as an Engineering Manager, with a company called ISI, in LaGrange, Georgia. It was a new and growing operation that was looking for experts and offered Kevin a promotion. As he boxed up his things at BREED, Paresh's team in Armada was just finishing the first design validations of their PSAN inflators. The new designs were being transferred to the production teams in LaGrange where Kevin and Sandy were shopping for a new home.

And now, let Kevin tell his story.

Act One

Kevin and ISI

1999 to 2001

(KEVIN)

1

A Takata Engineering Manager

LIFE STARTED out well for us in LaGrange in the summer of 1999, as well as any relocation of the family can go. Following a short spell in apartments, we bought our new home. LaGrange is a charming southern town, located around West Lake, a muddy and murky body of water home to deadly water moccasins. With a shoreline of thick and slick red mud, the lake was surrounded by forests and homes and the colors contrasted beautifully.

My home was on one side of the lake with a large wooded yard and a big back porch for entertaining. There were no fences between neighbors, and everyone kept their homes and yards well-manicured. Textiles was a major business for the city and many homes were built around the old Milliken mills to house their workers. There were more than a dozen churches throughout town that were always full on Sunday, and University of Georgia sports – the 'Georgia Bulldogs' – was the next closest thing to religion. We liked our new home and appreciated many of the aspects of life in LaGrange, and the south.

I had only a short drive into the office each day, usually dropping my sons off at school on the way. Back then, before changing to their red logo, Takata-ISI was blue and white. Driving into the side parking lot, I would see their flagship inflator facility, sparkling white, with blue trim everywhere. Large masonry columns framed the front-entrance, which was set past hedges and flagpoles. I always badged-in through the side entrance, took the stairs to the second floor, and made my way past the purchasing cubicles, beyond which was my engineering office area.

The facility was mostly open shop floor with two stories of office areas and a test lab straddling the corner closest to the main entrance. Just past the receptionist were the HR and finance departments. Inflator engineering, purchasing, program management and Greg Lightle, the General Manager, were all on the floor above them. None of these offices had a line of sight to the production floor. The quality and manufacturing engineers, along with the plant manager, Tommy Calloway, were on the floor above the test area, which had large windows overlooking the assembly lines. This let them keep an eye on the bustling activity below. All the walls were a freshly painted white, but railings, rafters, and accents with royal blue gave the space a clean look. The cafeteria was lined with windows looking out at the production floor.

The inflators Takata produced at the time were many and the varied assembly lines were tightly fit into the sprawling shop floor. Walking past the cafeteria clockwise, the first line you'd come to was a massive relic that came with the purchase of the building. It took up so much space, there was only one more that could fit beside it, and it made Takata's breakthrough first-generation driver inflator. Continuing around the floor were three more assembly lines, producing assorted driver, passenger and side airbag inflators of the same technology.

Filling up the rest of the space were two lines that were still under construction. These would build Takata's next generation of driver and passenger inflators, the ones at the heat of our story. Right in the middle of the floor, between all the lines, was a main area full of finished goods, where the daily production meetings were held.

As Engineering Manager in the Inflator Applications Group, I reported to Bob Schubert, who was the Director responsible for plant engineering support. Bob reported to Greg Lightle, and Greg reported directly to Frank Roe, President of Takata North American Operations. I was given responsibility first for the non-azide, or '3110', family of inflators, called NADI, NAPI, and NASI. While this generation of inflators had only been in production a brief time, already by 2000 they were planned to be superseded by Paresh's latest designs, utilizing his PSAN propellant, called PSDI, PSPI, and SPI. The other engineering manager reporting to Schubert, was Robert Thibodeau, who was responsible for the process validations and launch of the new product lines. My team was small, and Robert's even smaller, but Schubert reassured us that we would both soon grow. The Takata sales teams were pushing the new PSAN technology aggressively and I knew the smaller, lighter inflators would be competitive. The future looked bright.

Schubert coached me early that there were two camps of application engineers in LaGrange. The first was his team of Robert and I, responsible for moving new designs into production and maintaining them throughout their life cycle. We kept the assembly lines humming, pushing design changes that improved productivity, and working with the customers on new variants. Then there were the two Japanese engineers – the liaisons – who lived and worked in LaGrange. We referred to them as the "residents." Their job was to act as intermediaries for our Japanese customers, but their real duties were unclear to us. Their names were Hideo Nakajima and Shinichi Tanaka, and they reported directly to Tsuneo Chikaraishi in Japan. Tsuneo was only one step removed from Jim Takada.

I first met my new group in a meet-and-greet arranged by Schubert. I talked about myself and my background, and then opened it up to the engineers. They were eager to speak, explaining the workings of the group and how they interacted with our residents. They went through who was who, and who did what, but as they shared more, I began to sense an undercurrent of distrust – and frustration. I put it aside for the moment, but it was unmistakable. One thing for certain was my young team was hungry and excited. They wanted to learn the fundamentals of pyro-device engineering, and as we talked, their desire for the technical tools they were lacking became clear. When one of them mentioned Hideo Nakajima, I thought it would be a good time to break the ice.

"Hideo, didn't he kill the radio star?" I got a few chuckles, but mostly only perplexed stares. I realized how young they were and continued,

"Come on, *Video Killed the Radio Star*?" Still more stares.

"The first video ever on MTV?!" I said incredulously.

"Oh yeah, now we get it!" They all said and laughed – tossing a bone to the new boss.

It wasn't long before I was getting the hang of the place, familiarizing myself with the designs, and working those ever-important relationships. I taught my team the skills they needed to level the playing field and prodded them to question. This made life more difficult for our residents whose eagerness to please the customer often led to difficult designs for the plant.

The least happy with my engineers' new independence was Shin Tanaka, the resident ringleader. I began to understand that his job was really to enforce the will of Japan, and their customers, on the plant. This was not an easy role, especially once I entered the picture. The more I recognized that their agenda was not always in Takata's best interest, the more I started to push back.

I will never forget the time Shin lost his temper at Peter Holland, my

NADI engineer. Peter was finding himself more and more on the receiving end of Shin's frustrations. Takata was already in production with far too many NADI variants, and rather than convincing customers to take inflators already in Takata's portfolio, Chikaraishi and Shin were creating new ones at a dizzying pace. This constant customizing made production much more difficult, not to mention it was just plain lazy and foolish. I coached Peter to start pushing back more and that led to a most memorable incident.

I was sitting at my desk when I heard a terrible commotion coming from Peter's cubicle. When I raced in, Shin was standing on a chair towering over Peter, who was leaning as far back as he could in his own and looking up at him in disbelief. I stopped in my tracks at the sight. Shin was screaming at the top of his lungs and shaking his finger at Peter. Harry Trimble, the PSDI engineer, was standing next to them, looking on in a sheer panic.

"Shin! Get down off that chair!" I yelled, somewhat aggressively, and came closer.

This caught his attention. He turned his head towards me and realized I wasn't kidding and dismounted the chair.

"In the conference room – now," I said to him.

He obliged and followed me into the private room. I closed the door and could see instantly he was ready to do battle – still hot and red – but I quickly cut him off.

"Don't you ever do that to one of my guys again," I said. "Are we clear?"

He looked at me with a mix of shock and anger, clearly not accustomed to being confronted. Before he could answer, I defused the situation, saying quickly that if he had a problem with one of my folks again, he should please come see me and we would straighten it out together. He nodded angrily and stomped out of the room.

I was starting to understand where the undercurrent of distrust was coming from. The tug-of-war was constant between the interests of my engineers, responsible to the plant, and our residents, responsible to Japan. The operation was a struggle of different forces that the growing company was grappling with. Shin and Hideo were living a new life in the United States. They were pyrotechnic novices but were charged with delivering by their leaders back home. Their mission could be summed up easily: please Honda, Toyota, and Nissan, their core customers, at any cost. They worked hard and very late into the night, with compulsory phone calls to Japan starting just as we were packing up and calling it a day. Tokyo and Echigawa were fourteen hours ahead of LaGrange, and they suffered for it.

A Visit from Jim

As a former TRW inflator executive, Greg Lightle knew these competing interests were hurting his operations. Configuration after unnecessary configuration had him constantly at Frank Roe's ear to intervene. This occurred so frequently, in fact, that when Jim Takada planned an upcoming trip to the States, Frank made sure to add the 'NADI variant issue' to the agenda.

When Greg got word of Jim's impending visit, he charged right down to Schubert's office. As he passed my cube, he motioned for me to follow and we barged in on my boss. Bob's office was like a professor's and he acted the part. There were books and papers stacked in corners, and his Georgia Tech diploma was hung on the wall. He was a brilliant ballistician with a deep understanding of inflators. Just as my guys were soaking up information from me, I was doing the same with him.

"Good morning, Greg and Kevin," Bob said.

"I just got off the phone with Frank," Greg boomed. "Mr. Takada will be visiting the plant in two weeks. I have been on Frank about the NADI problem for some time now and he wants us to get it out in front of Jim."

"OK, what do you suggest?" Bob replied.

"I want to make it visual. I want Jim to feel our pain. I want to monetize it. In two weeks, we should be able to put something together that accurately conveys the issue. A big board, right outside the test department, so that when we take Jim out to the floor for the plant tour, we stop there first. Point of impact!" Greg said.

Excited about the opportunity to pitch our case, I jumped in,

"We can do that. It will take some work, but two weeks is enough time, and this is important. I'll take care of it."

"Good, Kevin. Bob, you know we are going to have to paint the whole damn place again, don't you?" Greg said on his way out.

The next two weeks the factory was swarming with work crews cleaning and painting in advance of the big visit. I'd never seen anything like it, but apparently it was not uncommon. A visit by Frank had everyone on edge. The Plant Manager, Tommy Calloway, and his deputy were running overtime to polish everything. The place had to look good.

I arrived at my desk the morning of the big day, set my briefcase down, and made my way over to Peter's cubicle. He and the team had worked tirelessly getting the display board ready.

"Good morning, Peter. Were you guys here most of the weekend?" I asked.

"Yeah, but we got it done. Come take a look."

The board was huge. Eight feet by four feet, it listed all the different NADI part numbers LaGrange manufactured on the left-hand side and on the right, their corresponding performance ranges. Overlaps jumped out and the redundant inflators that never should have gone into production were circled in red. An estimation and explanation of the financial losses associated with the folly was summarized in the upper right-hand corner. It was great.

"Well done, Peter! This is exactly what Greg was after. It conveys the issue perfectly. Please thank the team for me."

"Will do, Kevin. They are pretty proud of it."

"They should be! It's a perfect representation of what happens when Shin and Hideo unilaterally enforce their will on the plant," I added. "Frank will be here any minute. Jim is still another hour or so out. As soon as Frank gets here, I'll bring him and Schubert by to have a look. He's going to love it. Let's just hope it has the impact on Jim we are looking for."

Frank was just getting settled when Peter and I walked back into the engineering area.

"Hello, Frank. Nice to see you." I said.

I had only met Frank on two occasions prior but felt comfortable around him. I understood why some feared him, but not why they disliked him. He was always genuine to me and I could see he respected Schubert. The three of us got along well together.

Frank looked at me. "Hey, Fitzgerald, you guys ready?"

"Yes sir. Do you have a brief moment to look at the NADI board before Mr. Takada gets here?"

"Sure, but we need to make it quick," he said, unpacking his briefcase.

"Great, I'll go get Bob."

When the three of us arrived at the board, Frank was silent as he looked it over carefully. Finally, after what seemed like an eternity, he turned to me, smiled, and said "I expect you to be vocal today about this problem, all these backdoor designs being facilitated by Echigawa. You need to put your mudcat on the table."

"Yes sir," I replied, looking up at him towering over me.

I had absolutely no idea what a mudcat was, but I was buoyed by the feeling that he already trusted me and respected my candor.

Mr. Takada arrived about an hour later and we started almost immediately. This was the first I'd met him, and I could instantly see why people were drawn to him. The man was pure charisma. When it was time to begin, Greg first reviewed the plant's financial and quality performance before pivoting to the NADI discussion. Gathering everyone around the board, he walked through the financial and operational impacts the different configurations were having on the plant. Mr. Takada appreciated the visuals and zeroed in on the overlaps, but he was concerned more with the potential quality pitfalls than with the redundancies presented. Jim understood the problem, but his customers were not complaining. In fact, they were happy and buying more. He thanked us, clearly considering it further as we went back into the meeting room.

The message was completely lost on the remainder of the audience. Tommy Calloway and his crew were ex-Milliken. They knew carpets, not pyrotechnics. As high-end fabric producers, their world was all about variants. Different colors, different materials, different coating weights. They didn't understand what all the fuss was about. In my prior jobs, it was the plant managers leading the charge, lecturing in excruciating detail about the burdens each new inflator placed on the operations. We took that to heart, limiting inflator families to just three variants, a high, medium and low output. That was enough in our experience, and the module engineers did their best to work within those constraints. We weren't always successful, but adding a new configuration was the last resort. The NADI product line comprehended none of this. It was the Baskin Robbins of inflator outputs, with so many flavors we had to hand out little, plastic spoons to sample them all. It was wasteful, but worse, it invited mistakes.

Frank, seeing the message wasn't resonating, glanced at me to say something and just as I was about to speak up, Hideo shuffled into the room with a box of parts under his arm, seemingly oblivious that a meeting with Mr. Takada was in progress. I knew right away that box contained hardware just in from Japan for more clandestine testing.

I spoke up. "Mr. Takada, there is a lot of merit to the discussion. At a minimum, LaGrange engineering should be consulted on all non-standard output requests. With all due respect, we are the experts, and we cannot help you if we are not in the loop."

"That seems to be a reasonable request," he replied.

In that moment, I figured out what my mudcat was, and said, "Thank you, sir. Then would you please speak to Hideo about the box of parts under his seat? This is how it starts and if it continues to go unchecked, there will be another inflator running down the NADI line with its contents."

Jim nodded his appreciation. Frank leaned back in his chair with a wide grin, and Hideo shifted uncomfortably in his seat. Frank got the tension in the system he was after. Whether the effort would have any lasting effect would remain to be seen, but the day had been won.

Leadership Highlights

I'd been in LaGrange for almost three months now and as I became more immersed in the operations, I increasingly began to realize the plant manager was out of his element and should not be overseeing explosive operations. Tommy was a tall, lanky man with a serious southern drawl and an elevator that stopped short of the top. He had a short and wiry assistant who was in a constant state of panic. When the two were paired they resembled the cartoon characters Deputy Dog and Ricochet Rabbit. It was an unsettling picture for any plant, let alone a pyrotechnic one.

One morning at daily management, Greg was reviewing the numbers and status of different departments. In a process called MRB, or material review board, inflators that fail an operation or inspection for one reason or another are put aside. It could be nothing, but they could also all be built completely wrong. In LaGrange, the suspect inflators were locked in a chain link cage, about the size of a large conference room, that could only be opened by the quality team.

Greg asked Tommy how we were doing clearing up the MRB backlog.

Tommy replied nonchalantly, "Well Greg, the MRB cage done gone missing."

Greg's eyes squinted as he looked at Tommy in disbelief and said,

"What the hell do you mean the MRB cage 'done gone' missing!?"

"Well, it was over in the corner there yesterday and today, it's gone."

Incredible, I thought.

"Tommy – MRB cages just don't get up and leave. Where the hell is it?"

After a short pause he replied, "I'll get back to you on that one, Greg."

Greg just shook his head. I was dumbfounded. I refused to even look at Schubert for fear of breaking out in laughter. Something like this just wasn't possible in this industry. The plant manager didn't know the location of potentially defective parts – nay – the very cage that should contain them. Worse, he didn't seem to be all that concerned. There wasn't the discipline required.

Another incident only a few weeks later further underscored Tommy's lack of respect for the devices he was charged with manufacturing. He asked me to meet him at the end of the NASI side-impact inflator line. When I arrived, he was standing next to several pallets with 'HOLD' stickers on them.

"Why are these here?" He asked.

I picked up the quality folder on top and leafed through it, finding the reason.

"This lot failed its pressure output test and needs to be moved to the MRB cage,"

I replied, showing him the discrepancies in performance.

Tommy looked back at the parts, thought a moment and then replied, "Why can't we just salt them in?"

"Salt them in?" I asked quizzically.

"Yeah, just put a few in the bottom of a good box until they are all gone."

Absolute disbelief. 'Salt them in?!' I thought to myself.

I looked at him. "Tommy. These aren't carpet remnants!"

I walked away shaking my head, realizing these guys had no business running pyrotechnic operations and that my job duties would have to expand.

Paresh Takes Notice

Shortly after Mr. Takada's visit, Robert Thibodeau surprised everyone by resigning. Days before his announcement, I was sitting at my desk when he stopped by with some parts in his hand, from the new PSAN passenger inflator. He pulled up a seat next to me and showed me the ignition closure. As he described it, it was clear he was not a fan of the design and listed what he saw as issues. Then he showed me how the various parts fit together, saying,

"This is not going to work. They won't listen to me. They won't listen to anyone and there's no stopping them. So, I will be leaving. I am giving you a heads up, because it will be coming your way."

He was dead serious, and I took him that way. This was his warning. Robert showed me the ignition closure because he knew I would understand. An unstable ignition process would mean all sorts of issues for high-volume consistency. The closure is where the whole event starts – the booster. Careful design of it prevents so many possible issues.

"But why will it be coming my way? I have my own group and we have plenty of work," I asked, somewhat startled.

Robert stood up, shook my hand and wished me the best of luck.

The new passenger inflator he was showing me was still in design validation at Takata's inflator development center in Armada, MI, and I hoped some of these issues would be addressed before it came to the plant. The new driver inflator, PSDI, was already past that gate and Robert was also responsible for its validation. Product launch was six short months away. This was a terrible time to lose him, but I had to stay focused on filling out my group. Still, it shook me that he would rather resign than inherit responsibility for this new design. It spelled trouble and it was becoming clearer to me that Paresh Khandhadia and Japan told the plant what to do and expected us to fall in line. But what if we were the real experts and nobody was listening?

Rolling up my sleeves and fixing inflators became my job, and there was no shortage of work. Although the '3110' inflators I was responsible for were respectable, they were not without problems. I was finding design issues that highlighted Takata's inexperience but also presented opportunities.

An early one was with our dual-stage passenger inflator. BMW was complaining loudly that its gases could choke a horse and after looking into it, we discovered that the design was operating at only half of the internal pressure required. It was chugging, not combusting, and that was producing lousy effluents. The root cause was evident. Takata had sold BMW a dirty inflator, their engineers eventually discovered it, and now it was up to us to fix it. Raising the operating pressure was one way to clean the gases so that's where we started. We were able to meet BMW's requirements, but too large a pressure increase was required, and the inflator's output raised above limits. It was becoming an impossible problem when I noted something strange in the design.

The filter used to trap particulate formed during combustion was lined with a thin aluminum shim. Its purpose was to prevent the inflator's ignition gases from losing too much heat to the filter and failing to light the propellant. What a terrible design, I thought. The shim worked, but as aluminum it also burned and made the effluent problem worse. I had the engineer call Paresh's chemists to ask if the propellant was compatible with copper and the answer was yes.

A copper shim worked and, with no more burning aluminum, a slight increase in operating pressure made the design fully compliant. Unfortunately, the changes proved too much for BMW. They insisted on more crash-testing, which was cost prohibitive, but they were interested in understanding why we handed them such a pig to begin with. That answer I knew but politely side-stepped, simply ensuring them it wouldn't happen again.

This was the same issue Takata had faced with the NADI-variants. They would make new inflators to please customers, like Honda or BMW, without a basic understanding of the science. There were serious issues with inflator engineering know-how at Takata, but Schubert was an expert, and together we were out to make a change. It gave me a sense of purpose.

Times were busy, the job was intense, and we needed help to manage the workload, so I asked Bob for a couple more engineers to assist with all the '3110' inflator programs. He didn't hesitate. Just the opposite. With each engineer, he also let me hire a technician to help them build parts, run tests, and create reports. This freed the engineers to challenge, which is right where I wanted them.

We interviewed a young-graduate named Stephen Kimmich who, like Bob, attended Georgia Tech. I thought someone coming out of the same school as Schubert was going to be a nice pick-up. During his interview, Stephen was great, and we hired him on the spot. He was beyond good at work. So, when another opportunity arose to improve an existing production inflator, I was confident Stephen was up to the task.

Takata's BMW module-engineers in Ulm, Germany were demanding improvements to the NASI side-impact inflator, a design I was not enamored with. They wanted a higher gas generation rate with cleaner gases and I wanted to change the design completely. Udo Bendig, who ran Ulm's side-impact team, called me and asked if there was anything we could do. We, of course, said yes!

Bob, Stephen and I gathered around a small table in Bob's office to discuss a few ideas.

"Bob, I think we need a clean piece of paper," I started.

Staring at the drawings, he nodded in agreement, "What do you have in mind?"

"Instead of this costly, wrapped filter, which isn't doing much, why don't we run the gas straight through a crushed wire filter and right out the other end? It's dead simple and I experimented with it while I was at BREED."

I could see Schubert wince, "that's a complete redesign. Paresh will construe that as being outside our charter."

"Give us three months, Bob. If we're successful, no one will care about the charter. We'll call it NASI-2. Paresh will love that," I said joking.

"OK, you have three months."

Stephen led the project and we tore it up. We achieved the higher gas generation rates with a granular booster and the crushed filter concept decimated the cost targets. Several trips to Ulm to coordinate the effort and Udo's team was ecstatic. They loved the finished product. Shige Takada, Jim's son who was being groomed for the eventual handover, even flew in from Japan to see it personally. The inflator was nominated for an award and with this recognition came new opportunities for Stephen.

As the last of the validation data was coming in, I pulled up a seat next to him, "Good morning, bud, how are you?"

"Good morning, boss. I am doing well."

"The NASI-2 results look great," I said. "I was just discussing them with Udo and they are going to want this inflator quickly. It's a go for production. Congratulations, Stephen!"

"That is awesome!" he said, tilting back in his chair and clasping his hands around the back of his head, rightfully pleased with his performance.

"That's not all," I continued. "We took note of how you loved your trips to Ulm and your interest in an assignment in Germany..." He wasn't leaning back in his chair anymore.

"The inflator will not launch in LaGrange. All the initial volumes are in Europe and it makes no sense to pay the added freight." I gave him a moment to savor the realization.

"So, it will launch in Freiberg?" he asked, now leaning forward in his chair.

"Yes, and Udo wants to know if you would like to take that assignment in Germany a little earlier than you had anticipated."

"Holy shit! You're kidding, right?" He stood up, smiling.

"No, sir," I got up from my chair and reached out to shake his hand, but he was having none of that. He gave me a big bear hug instead, spinning me around a couple of times before putting me back down.

"It will be a month or two before we can get you over there, but it appears you are fine with us getting the arrangements underway," I said laughing, happy for him. This is what we wanted.

"Yes, yes, of course I am. Thank you, Kevin, you won't regret this!"

We all went out for drinks afterwards to celebrate. Our workdays usually ended with me strolling into the engineering area, around 5:00, clapping my hands together and saying, "suds time." And when I did, you wanted to make sure you weren't blocking an exit because my team enjoyed their happy hours. The local Ruby Tuesday would almost always be waiting for us and have our first-round ready to go as we filed into the bar. Sandy and I would also host regular porch parties on weekends and the crew were often there. This was my engineering team and I was proud. We had grown in capability, both in personnel and technical competency, and we had just put two big wins on the board. With Schubert behind me and a hungry team in front of me, we were a force to be reckoned with.

Paresh started making noise, just as Bob predicted, that we had overstepped our boundaries. He wasn't happy with the recognition we received for NASI-2, certainly, and was still smarting over the earlier spotlight we put on the BMW inflator. He was frustrated but had more pressing matters to deal with than us Cowboys in LaGrange. His new baby, PSDI, was in process validation at the plant and the results of that crucial milestone were just starting to roll in.

2

Red Sky in Morning

A PROCESS VALIDATION for Honda takes about three months to complete and for PSDI it was started in late January of 2000. To ensure an inflator is ready to go into vehicles, each automaker has its own test series the manufacturer must pass, typically first with parts produced by the design team, called design validations (DV), and then always with parts produced on the lines, called process validation (PV). For Honda, this included high and low temperature soaks, vibration and drop, and thermal-cycling (back and forth between temp-extremes) tests, all intended to simulate an extended life in the vehicle. As each environment, or combination of environments, is completed, the parts are functionally tested by deploying them in a 60 liter tank, or closed volume, and recording their pressure outputs. All tests in the PV must meet these limits after the environments to pass and be allowed to proceed into production. This is the industry standard.

As the tests are completed, results slowly come in, and the application engineer in LaGrange tabulates the data and begins the report. Most engineers keep a running account so when the final tests finish, those results are inserted, and the report is finalized quickly after. Harry Trimble, the PSDI engineer, however, was not like most. He was an eccentric, free spirit, infamous for having dropped an expensive, rebuilt engine into an old, wood-paneled station wagon. Harry was the type of individual that needed special attention and now that his boss, Robert Thibodeau, had left, Schubert had a problem. Process validations typically don't require much oversight, so Bob decided to manage things himself while he searched for Robert's replacement.

For some reason though, he never got that chance. Just as some of the first PSDI validation data started rolling in, the LaGrange team was broadsided by word of his departure. He was in Auburn Hills on a business trip when the news leaked, and we were stunned. Only days earlier, I had been in his office discussing a new hire that would be starting in a few weeks, and now he was on his way out with no logical explanation. He was being reassigned to the quality department in Auburn Hills, to report to Al Bernat, who will become an important character in our story.

Later, after the news was shared with the group, I ran into Stephen in the stairwell as I was returning from the shop floor. He had been looking for me.

"What the hell is going on?" he said. "I really liked Schubert!"

"I have no clue. I am speechless," I said. "I really liked him too."

"You don't think it has anything to do with the NASI-2, do you?"

"No, of course not. At most, that would amount to a slap on the wrist. This must be much bigger. This is not a promotion for Bob. This is a lateral, and to me, that seems like some sort of punishment. Come on, let's get back to work," I said.

Just as we reached the top of the stairwell, we were startled by a loud 'BOOM' coming from the direction of the test area!

"What the hell was that?!" asked Stephen.

"An inflator just came apart!" I said, turning to run down the stairs to the lab.

"Are you sure? Should I follow you?"

"No, I'm just going to make sure everyone is alright. No sense in us both barging in and scaring people any further," I yelled back, running through the door and across the hall to the lab.

I'd heard that sound before while at BREED – working on PSAN inflators. We were conducting margin tests on dual stage passenger inflators and were curious what would happen if one were mistakenly fired backward. Let's just say it was a good thing we checked that box. It had made that same sickening sound, putting an end to that design concept in a hurry.

There was already a small crowd gathered outside the test bay when I walked into the lab. I was comforted to see it had been a closed tank test. That meant the bay door would have locked automatically when the anomaly occurred, and everybody would be safe. That was a relief, but it also meant it would be a half hour before we would learn anything from inside. I walked over to Hideo who was at the edge of the crowd with the test paperwork in his hand.

"That was a rupture. I'm sure of it. What inflator was it, Hideo?" I asked.

He didn't say a word. A grunt was all he offered as he stared at the paperwork he was holding, and then shuffled off in the opposite direction. As he did, I spied PSDI written across the top of the test request.

That was significant. Did a process validation part just explode? Hideo wasn't offering any information, but at a minimum, one of Paresh's new inflators just ruptured at its intended production facility and that was a big deal. With twenty minutes still left on the test bay lock out and everything under control, I turned to head back to the office area, and bumped right into Mike Jewel, the Test Lab Manager and a good friend.

"That gave the test technicians quite a scare," he said. "This doesn't normally happen around here."

"That's a good thing, Mike. Keep me posted, will you?"

"Sure thing, Kevin." Mike was a good man.

The news of Schubert's unexplained and strange departure, and now a PSDI rupture had the team on edge, myself included. Just two weeks later things settled down a bit with the announcement of a new boss, Bill Martin, who would assume Bob's role as Director of Engineering. He was from Takata's Moses Lake facility and was instrumental in bringing that plant online, and he bled Takata blue.

From the day he arrived in LaGrange, Bill had one mission and that was to put Paresh's new inflators into production, so I was hopeful he would get PSDI back on track. He showed little interest in my '3110' product line. His mission was to obsolete it. He was an industrial engineer, whose expertise lay in equipment, not interior ballistics like Bob. When he arrived in LaGrange, he immediately abandoned Bob's old office in favor of one downstairs alongside the manufacturing engineers. I was a practical mixture of both disciplines, so I was confident Bill and I would get along just fine.

A Most Damning Report

The new hire I had been discussing with Schubert was an old friend of mine from Talley, Tom Sheridan. A graduate from the University of Hard Knocks who knew gas generators, he immediately began attacking the job with awe-inspiring ferocity. He worked hard for this shot and was not going to let himself or me down. I assigned him a technician, the position he had occupied for so many years, and he graciously paid it forward. As he settled into his new role, the swirl of Schubert's departure and the PSDI failure began to fade into the background. I became hopeful that the rupture was an isolated incident and that Bill, and the development engineers had it figured out and were pressing ahead with the PV. That hope vanished when the 'booms' started again.

It was late June, 2000, and the PSDI inflator was scheduled to go into production in a matter of weeks, so when another explosion startled everyone in the office area, I was concerned, but also puzzled as to its source. The earlier PSDI issues must have been resolved if production was looming. And when I say startled, I am not kidding. We sat upstairs, sealed off from the test department noise. A normal inflator tank deployment sounds like a 'ting', barely distinguishable from inside the test lab. But, when this part exploded in the hollow steel test-tank, it was so loud I jumped out of my seat. Since I was already up, I poked my head out and motioned for Tom to come over.

"What the hell was that?!" he asked.

"You know what that was, Tom. Go find out what inflator it is," I told him.

"What, no please?" he said lowering his safety glasses and heading out the door.

A few minutes later he was back in my office, panting.

"You are out of shape, my friend," I laughed.

"It was an SPI."

"An SPI?" I was puzzled.

"Yeah, Bill said we are helping Armada out with some of their design validation testing and it was an SPI that failed."

"Tom, listen up. Before you arrived, the same thing happened with a PSDI inflator. I am not sure if it was part of the PV or not. I probably should have told you earlier, but your wheels were already up."

"Come on, Kevin, you know me better than that. No worries," he said. "But, let me guess, it's time we find out if that PSDI was a validation inflator or not, right?"

"Yes, it's high time. Too many parts are rupturing around here and PSDI is going into production for Honda in weeks. Find a copy of the validation report Japan must have submitted to Honda. I never saw it, so let's start there." Then I added, "And Tom, don't let anyone know what we are up to. Understand?"

"10-4 boss," he said as we locked eyes.

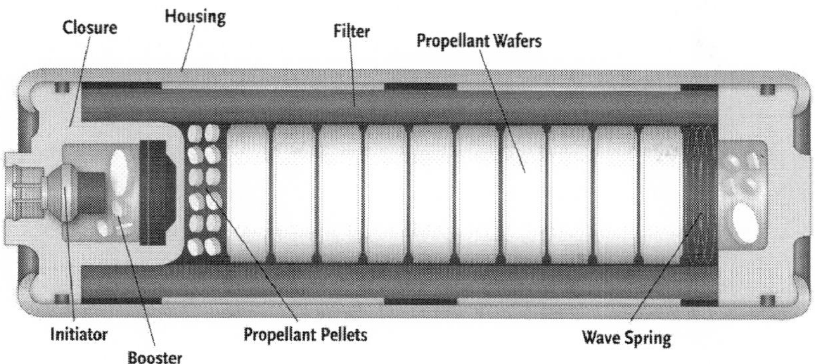

FIGURE THREE: CROSS-SECTION OF 'SPI' INFLATOR

Tom managed to find a copy of the report without raising any suspicion and we met in a conference room after most people had gone home for the day. We had to cancel suds time which did not go over well, but this was important. I picked up a copy of the report and leafed through it slowly, Tom doing the same with his copy.

"It's perfect. It's just too perfect. There is absolutely no shift in performance after environments. No inflator is this good, and we know parts are exploding," I said.

"Yeah, I agree," said Tom. "I can cross reference every test number in the report with the raw data on the server. It will take some doing, but if there are discrepancies, I'll find them."

"You can if we still have access. Check a few test numbers and see," I said pushing my chair back and getting up to look over his shoulder.

He signed into the network from the conference room PC and a minute later he was scrolling through the data. I leaned in closer to him.

"We are going to have to check every one of those for accuracy," I said. "There are too many strange things going on around here. Start with the toughest tests, like heat aging, and environments that include temperature cycling and moisture. If we are going to find parts that failed, it will be there. Work only after hours and if you come across anything out of the ordinary, holler."

"Got it, Kevin. If there is something fishy going on, we'll get to the bottom of it."

"Right, but let's not jump to any conclusions," I cautioned. It felt great to be working with my old colleague, trained on the defense side of the industry. He knew what to do.

The next day we had our answer. Tom went right to the hardest tests and began his search. Initially, the report seemed to match the test numbers on the server. The first level looked clean. As he dug deeper, he discovered that some of the data was substituted. The raw data on the server would not always match the perfect curve in the report. In one case, there was the clear signature of an inflator that had ruptured, which is unique and unmistakable. I almost spilled my coffee picking up the plots to look closer.

"Holy shit! What environmental is that from?" The inflator had clearly exploded!

"Vibration/Moisture/Thermal Cycle, just like you said," he replied.

"I would have rather been wrong. Shin and Hideo must have hidden this from everyone!" I exclaimed.

"I'll plot every single deployment from the server and match it to the report," Tom said stoically. "When I am finished, I'll wrap it up in a new report that will show what really happened."

"We need to do this as quickly as possible, Tom. You and I both know what a hand grenade this is. I don't want to accuse anyone of something like this until we are sure. I also don't know who to trust anymore, so we need to be careful, as we discussed earlier. Put the accurate report together, every test, and if it confirms our worst fears, I will run it up the ladder."

"Will do, Kevin."

"I need to get Harry's take on this, too. The inflator is about to go into production based on this fake report," I said shaking it angrily. "Harry signed it, along with Hideo and Chikaraishi. Why would he do that? And how the hell did Shin keep his fingerprints off it?"

"Look, Paresh signed it too!" Tom said.

"Holy shit, you're right, and look closely up here in the right-hand corner. Chikaraishi and Furusawa signatures are there as well. This is unbelievable!" Chikaraishi reported to Furusawa who reported to Jim Takada.

I walked immediately over to Harry's desk with the report in my hand but didn't find him there. What I did find just added to my exasperation. Lying on his desk was his own version of the PSDI validation report. It was a mess and he was still plodding through it – still massively incomplete – but it seemed like the makings of a truthful report. At least everything wasn't as perfect as the one I had in my hand. But why make another report? He had already signed the fake report. I was sure Shin had goaded him into it, but regardless, he signed the damn thing and that meant he was compromised. It was probably best he wasn't there. I relayed what I found to Tom and reminded him again to be discreet. We did not want the data disappearing from the server until at least one valid report was in the bank.

No Turning Back

The train left the station. PSDI was pushed into production and as the summer progressed, the plant struggled to meet Honda's ramp-up schedule. There were serious quality issues. Too many were being rejected for failing the helium leak test at the end of the line. It was killing production and the situation was worsening.

Helium leak is a standard inspection in the industry to make sure the inflator is moisture-proof. The air in the inflator is extracted and replaced with helium just before final assembly. The finished inflator is then placed in a chamber, a vacuum is drawn, and a measurement device sniffs to see if helium is being pulled out and at what rate. Helium is used because it's a tiny molecule well suited for detecting even the smallest leaks.

This was not a production issue, but a major design flaw. Armada located the final weld right next to the second chamber's exit nozzles, which were sealed by an adhesive backed aluminum shim. Because it was so close to the joint, the heat from the weld was breaking down the shim's adhesive, resulting in inflators that just poured out helium.

It was so bad that Honda's production was in serious jeopardy. Bill told me about the issue, but I didn't realize how big the problem was until I went down to the cafeteria one morning to grab a cup of coffee. All around the PSDI line were stacks of trays of partially-assembled inflators with rubber stoppers shoved into the booster tubes. Immediately drawn to the spectacle, the cup of coffee would have to wait. This is crazy, I thought to myself. Bill saw me walking dumbfounded in that direction and intercepted me.

"Yeah, I know," he said. "Engineering is working on a permanent fix, but until then, this is the best Paresh's guys could come up with."

"What the hell is it?" I asked him.

"The idea is to let the inflator sit overnight after the final weld, so the adhesive can re-harden before we perform the leak inspection," he answered. "The rubber stoppers are to prevent moisture from getting to the propellant that's already loaded."

I turned and looked at him, astonished by what I had just heard, and said,

"Bill, this is so out of process. There is no way to properly control this and parts will undoubtedly be exposed. Did we conduct a delta process validation?"

Bill just shrugged and moved on and I went back to the cafeteria for my coffee, grabbing a seat by myself to think. It wasn't just Paresh's PSDI that was giving the plant fits. The SPI and PSPI design validations Bill was helping Armada with were also failing, and badly. Exposure to the heat aging environment, a 40-day test at elevated temperature, was causing the new passenger inflators to explode and Moses Lake was frantically trying to figure out what was wrong with the propellant.

There was a new formulation or process change, or combination of both, arriving on our doorstep almost weekly, and each time, it was immediately assembled into SPI inflators and thrown into an oven. They were regularly cycling out of the environment and the frequent explosions were wearing on people's nerves. I put my face in my hands. With what Tom and I were discovering, the rubber stoppers, the SPI explosions, there was no way the PSDI should be in production and I knew it. Tom was making slow, steady progress on the report, but there was still a month of work left. No matter how difficult, we needed to work quietly until it was complete or there would be no slowing this train. Shin and Chikaraishi had already shown they would stop at nothing to please Honda.

The booms started to taper off towards the end of that summer and by September they had stopped completely. Something Moses Lake had done was working and the new passenger inflators were not exploding anymore. Everyone in the office was appreciative of how quiet things had become and, being curious, I went down to Bill's office to see what he knew. He was on the phone when I arrived and motioned for me to come in and sit down. When he hung up I asked him,

"So, what did Moses Lake change? It sounds like the passenger inflator is passing heat-age now."

"Yes, it is, and thank God. They stopped milling the BHT, the fuel," he answered.

There is a story behind why the BHT was being milled, or ground, in the first place that needs telling. Just before the PSDI validations were to start in LaGrange, Paresh unforgivably sent a new propellant geometry, called a 'batwing,' to Honda for sled test evaluations. The shape the propellant is pressed into determines how it will burn and changes how quickly gas is produced. The batwing was not the propellant geometry his team had used throughout development that supposedly passed the DV. The original design used a 'shark-fin' but Honda was so enamored with the batwing sled-test results that they asked Takata to make a last-minute change – just weeks before the PV! What was Paresh thinking? He knew Japan would acquiesce, and worse, he knew Takata did not have the production assets in place to make the batwing.

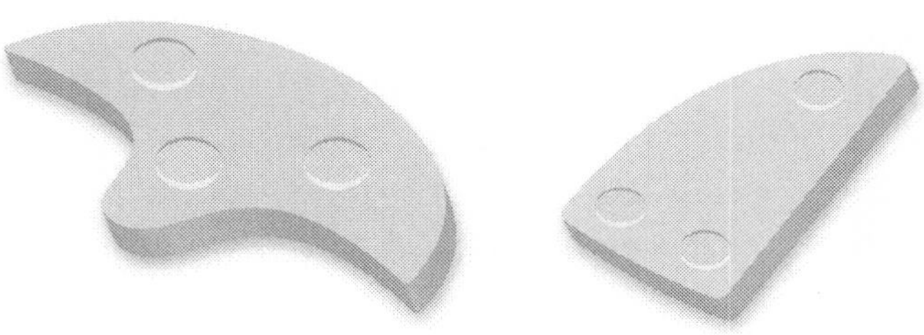

FIGURE FOUR: BATWING (LEFT) VS. SHARKFIN WAFERS

There was only one propellant press in the company that could make the batwing, and it was in Armada, not Moses Lake. That forced Paresh to supply the PV propellant to LaGrange and Moses Lake to suddenly figure out how one press was going to keep up with Honda's production. The only thing that could be done was to operate the press as quickly as possible, and to do that Paresh had the BHT milled to make it flow into the press dies faster. With no time to validate the change, he bet it all on the PV in LaGrange. As soon as Armada finished making the PV 'batwings,' the press was crated up and shipped to Moses Lake, where it was never capable of keeping up with production, literally jumping off the floor trying to do so.

"That's all it was?" I asked Bill. "Just stop milling the BHT? Seems so simple."

"Yep, that was it. Apparently, the material's needle-like particles help bind things together. Milling it may have helped the press run keep up with production, but it removed that benefit. Listen, I need your help. Please order three lots of batwings with BHT that has not been milled from Moses Lake and run another Honda PSDI PV with it. Understand?"

"Yes sir, got it. Hey, I also wanted to remind you that we have a new hire coming in next week. Another friend of mine from Talley, Bob Hardenburg. He's also a good friend of Tom's."

"Great, another Sheridan!" he chuckled. "I am glad you mentioned that though. With SPI and PSPI in better shape, I am going to need your team to fully engage in the new product line. We will not be replacing Robert. You and I will have to manage both product lines."

"That sounds great, Bill. I'll assign the delta PSDI PV to Tom and have Hardenburg shadow him. Bob will come up to speed quickly."

"Great. Thanks, Kevin."

I knew where Bill was going. Since milling the BHT was being fingered as the source of the passenger inflator problems, it only made sense to remove it from PSDI batwing production as well. If it worked, Takata would finally have a successful PSDI validation under its belt. A clean slate, so to speak, providing appropriate action was taken with everything produced before the process change. Tom and I just had to finish the report, and everything could work out, I thought. Cooler heads just had to prevail.

Unlike Sheridan, Hardenburg knew what he was getting into. Tom and I told him what we had found with PSDI and the problems with the new passenger inflators while we were recruiting him, but it was a good promotion and Bob trusted in what we were doing. His infusion helped tremendously, finally putting us at full strength. Together, they started the delta-PV of PSDI and with Bob helping, Tom found himself with the time needed to finish the report.

It was a huge job. He plotted all the data, inserting the actual test results behind every sheet in the original report and what it showed was not pretty. There had been three total ruptures in the PV and more. The entire validation was misrepresented and that is what took time to piece together. There were improper deployments after almost every environment. The inflator was completely unstable yet represented as normal. When Tom finished, I reviewed the document with him, helped him to finalize it, and then together, we wrote an e-mail from Tom to myself so that he could officially send me the finished document.

"I want this one paragraph to be firmer," I told him as I grabbed a pen and made a final edit. "I don't want anyone to think that our group had anything to do with this. I want it to say, 'the original report was assembled by our resident engineers, misrepresenting LaGrange's data for the express purpose of presenting a passing validation to Honda engineers.' Understood?"

"Got it. Anything else need changing?"

"No, let's get it wrapped up. Paresh is flying in next week and I want to present it to him and Bill at the same time."

"Bill will be blindsided," Tom said.

"I know. I'm not happy about that but am prepared for the consequences.

I am going to ask Bill to approve it as our boss, but it is more important to me that the people who signed the fake report see this 'corrected' one and sign it, acknowledging the truth. Bill was not one of them. After he approves it, I am going to ask for Paresh to sign it and then Hideo."

"What about Chikaraishi and Furusawa. They are in Japan. How will you get them to sign?"

"The best we can do is enter the report into document control and send them copies, so we have a record they received them," I answered.

There was no one left in the office as we made our way to the parking lot and left for home. It was the weekend, the leaves were changing color, and I had two more days to think about it all and what I had to do on Monday when Paresh arrived. It was time.

Retaliation and Resignation

Paresh arrived the following Monday evening and was scheduled to be in the plant first thing the next morning. While there, he always used the small conference room at the end of our hallway. When I came up from the cafeteria, he was unpacking his briefcase. I stopped by and said a quick hello before returning to my office where the report was sitting on my desk. I needed to collect my thoughts before tackling this. Fat chance. Just as I sat down, Bill walked by heading right for Paresh's room. It was now or never. I grabbed the report, following closely behind him, and once we were both in the room, I closed the door behind me.

It was an oversized office converted to a conference room with a rectangular table in the center. The sound of the door startled Bill and he glanced over his shoulder at me but continued to walk to the side of the table where Paresh was and shook his hand. I went to the opposite side and slid the 'corrected' report across the table towards Paresh, the only North American executive who approved it. The document came to a stop right in front of him. He looked down at it but made no move to pick it up. He just stared at it as I proceeded,

"Paresh, you need to read this. This is what really happened in the PSDI PV. It is imperative that you are aware, because the version you signed that went to Honda was falsified. There were post-environmental ruptures and the performance was all over the place."

Paresh looked at me in disbelief and said,

"I didn't read the original report. I just signed it."

"Well, you need to read this one, Paresh. We never passed the validation.

There were explosions and we are putting inflators in boxes to ship as we speak."

Bill was in shock as he listened to me continue,

"I'm sorry, Bill. I wanted to tell you, but Schubert evaporated into thin air, you were new, and I didn't know who to trust. It was a confusing time and we didn't want our access to the network cut off. I understand if you are upset with me, but let's please deal with this first."

You could hear a pin drop. Bill nodded and asked if he could speak to Paresh privately. I turned and quickly left, the report still on the table and Paresh's eyes dead-fixed on it.

Later in the day, Bill returned the report to me with his signature on it. He was not outwardly angry with me or Tom. Honestly, the report protected him. He came to LaGrange after the fact and his guys just put a wrong right. He should have been proud of us, but it was impossible to get a good read. Paresh refused to sign the 'corrected' report. I saw no more of him.

Hideo Nakajima was next and when I approached him with the report and a pen in hand, word must have already circulated. He didn't say a word to me. With his head bowed, he took the report, quickly signed it and gave it back to me.

The next day he approached me on the shop floor and said, "I'm sorry, Kevin, we had no choice."

I stopped, squared myself to him and replied, "yes, you did, Hideo."

Hideo was not a bad guy and I felt somewhat sorry for him. His eyes told the story of a man trapped in a job, and a culture, that were making him do things he knew were not right. He had become a man of his circumstances, not his decisions.

The report went nowhere after Hideo signed. We made sure we documented what happened and notified management. We sent hard copies by intra-company mail to the authors, the people who signed it, Chikaraishi's group in Echigawa, and of course Paresh. We put the names of those individuals it was distributed to on the front cover and locked a copy in our document control file cabinet. I would not see the report again for many years.

At this point, I was not quite sure who knew what, or what the plan was for all the PSDIs that had been shipped under false pretense. It was late 2000 and the delta PV that Bill had asked us to run with un-milled BHT batwings was nearing its conclusion. We had made sure to add a control group with the original process to get a direct comparison and were eager to start seeing results. I desperately wanted it to be successful, to have this part of the slate cleaned, even if I didn't know what was going to be done about the last four months of production.

To our surprise, no ruptures occurred in either group. The performance of the un-milled BHT was more stable, but neither group passed. Aggressive and out-of-specification deployments persisted in both. Un-milled BHT just pulled the system back from the edge a little, a scary place to live. Takata had already stopped the milling process back in October, before we even had our results. They knew it had to be as detrimental to batwings as it was for the wafers and made the change as soon as Moses Lake was ready. With no ruptures this second go-around, the lie about the first PSDI report seemed less important to management and we never heard anything more about it. The inflator's performance bar was lowered from meeting the customer's specification to less likely to explode. Takata just pushed on.

As Paresh's new inflators started to settle down, so did life in LaGrange. Like Tom, Bob made the step up to engineer in the move and was busy mentoring his new technician and learning the ropes. He and his family purchased a nice home near the lake, not too far from Sandy and me, and they seemed happy. Tom and Bob joined the rest of the gang at our regular porch parties and we began rotating them to different homes around the lake as they grew. Stephen was in Germany readying NASI-2 for production. We entered a period of stability, but by early 2001, the ground beneath us was moving again.

First, Greg Lightle was replaced as General Manager of the LaGrange facility by Chris Holloway, another former Frank Roe associate. No warning or explanation. I wondered why, but what happened next completely caught me by surprise. I was sitting in my office one morning when Holloway entered, closing the door behind him and sitting down. I didn't know Chris well yet, and to say I was wary of him would be an understatement. He was another 'yarn head' textile executive that didn't know shit about pyrotechnics, and worse, he had horses printed all over his button-down shirt.

"Kevin, we need to talk," he said with a ripe southern accent.

"OK, Chris," I responded tentatively.

"I don't have good news, so I'm just going to say it. Takata is relocating inflator applications engineering to Armada under Paresh. It makes sense. This facility is not going to be around forever. We are going to be relocating operations to Mexico over the next couple of years." He said all of this almost robotically. Delivering bad news didn't bother Chris.

"That's quite a bit to absorb," I said to him trying to buy some time.

"Yes, it is."

"So, the function is being moved to Armada. What's happening to the people?"

"Some will be made offers to relocate. Some will not. You and Tom will not be going. I want you here with me. I don't expect you to say anything now. Take some time. We will be making a formal announcement next week, so please keep tight-lipped about it until then," he said getting up.

"What about Hardenburg? We just moved him here. He just closed on his new home for Christ's sake," I said, a little annoyed.

"Bob will be offered a package to join the team in Michigan." He left the room, ending the conversation there.

What was I going to tell Bob? His family had just moved across country and bought a new home and now we were going to ask him to do it all over again. Damn it, just as it seemed like we were over the hump.

I found Bob and Tom in the cafeteria having coffee with their technicians. They saw me come in and waved me over.

"Good morning, boss," said Tom.

"What a motley crew," I said. "Do you guys mind if I borrow Tom and Bob for a minute?"

The technicians scooped up their coffees and hurried away. There was no one occupying the surrounding tables and I sat down across from the pair.

"What's wrong Kevin? You are white as a ghost," Bob implored, "Just spill it."

"Our team is being moved to Armada under Paresh. Physically moved. Bob, I know you just bought a home here, but you are on the list being asked to relocate to Michigan," I told them, obviously ignoring the tight-lip mandate from Chris.

"What about us, Kevin?" Tom asked.

"You and I will stay behind. That's all I know right now, Tom. I am so sorry, Bob. I had no idea they were contemplating this when I extended the offer...."

He cut me off. "Stop, Kevin. I know you would never do something like that, but wow," he paused and took a deep breath. "Well, this is actually not as bad as you think. Kathy and I are Michiganders. The thought of eventually making it back there was part of the reason we took the job. We just never thought LaGrange would be this short of a lay-over," Bob said, trying to make me feel better.

"Takata will take care of everything. I promise you that," I said. "As soon as I have any more information, I will let you know. Sorry again, Bob. I feel awful."

"It will work out, Kevin," Bob said. These guys were truly good friends.

The formal announcement came the following week. I was named LaGrange Plant Engineer, which meant I would be required to sign off on all inflator shipments leaving the plant, including the inflator I had just reported to management that didn't pass its validation. I would report directly to Chris Holloway. Tom was moved to plant manufacturing engineering and Bob was off to Michigan. I spent the next couple of months helping everyone get relocated, finding my team new jobs in the company, or outside too, and at the same time, I started looking for a job myself. Asking me to sign off on all PSDIs leaving the plant was the same thing as letting me go too.

My family's lives were about to be upset once more. We had been in LaGrange for almost two years now and my next job would not be here. I found employment a few months later, back in Arizona, with a company called Simula. An acquaintance of mine who was Simula's Director of Engineering wanted to move to Sales and Marketing and pursued me to fill the vacancy that would create. I accepted the position and submitted my resignation, but then something strange began to happen during my two-week notice.

Immediately I received pressure from Holloway, who raised Takata's non-compete clause of my contract and threatened me with legal action if I left. Simula was in the automotive safety restraint business, but they didn't make inflators. I pushed back, telling Chris it was absurd to consider Simula a threat. That led to a call from Al Bernat, Takata's Vice President of Quality, whom I had met on several occasions as he traveled in and out of LaGrange but didn't know very well. Mostly I knew Schubert had been transferred under him when he left.

"Kevin, this is Al Bernat," he said. "How are you?"

"I'm fine, Mr. Bernat, how can I help you?" I was puzzled as to why he would be calling.

"Chris tells me of your intention to leave Takata for Simula," he continued. "You are aware that you signed a non-complete clause that prohibits you from leaving Takata to join a competitor, are you not?"

"Yes, I am, Mr. Bernat, but Simula is not a competitor of Takata. You and

I both know that."

"Well, that is where we disagree. We will pursue legal action if you insist on going there," he said dispassionately.

I couldn't believe what I was hearing. I paused for a moment, trying to hold back my anger and said, "What is going on here Mr. Bernat? I have no intention of taking anything I learned from Takata with me to Simula. They have no use for it. Would you please just let me leave?" I said and placed the phone back on the receiver. I didn't hang up on him, but the conversation was over.

I reached out to Simula about the non-compete and the pressure I was receiving. Their lawyers reviewed it and then told me it wasn't worth the piece of paper it was written on. Unless Takata was going to pay me not to work, they couldn't deprive me of my livelihood. So, I cordially told Chris I would be leaving to work for Simula and I finished my two weeks. I never heard anything further and we moved back to Arizona in the spring of 2001.

Interlude

Kevin and David

2001-2005

(DAVID)

3

Dominoes

EIGHT YEARS after Kevin resigned his position in LaGrange, in May of 2009, a tragic event unfolds that needs to be absorbed here. A recent high school graduate was driving a Honda Accord to pick up her brother from a football practice in May of 2009. Ashley Parham was a cheerleader, active in her community, and was described by friends and family as popular and full of smiles. She hoped to become a teacher, so that she could "give back to the children of Oklahoma."

For one reason or another she became distracted as she drove across the parking lot to where her brother waited. One can imagine her day-dreaming or glancing over to the school, smiling about a memory. Whatever the reason, she accidentally crashed into another car. It was a minor accident, the kind that everyone walks away from wiser. But this time the car was going just fast enough to activate the airbag upon impact, and a chain reaction was initiated that resulted in her death.

The crash sensors relayed the impact and the driver airbag was activated. Five milliseconds later, the inflator's batwing shaped, PSAN wafers were roaring to life and expelling gas. The nylon cushion began to inflate and then burst through the module cover, filling the space between Ashley and her steering wheel. Everything looked fine from the outside, but like the Challenger disaster, Ashley's flight was doomed from the start.[8] An engineering disaster was unfolding inside.

Exactly one hundred milliseconds after she made contact, the crash computer sent another command, this one to the inflator's secondary chamber. It wasn't needed to protect Ashley from her minor accident and was being disposed of. This time however, the pressure inside the housing started to rise out of control. In time-scales impossible to witness, the inflator began to deform and then ruptured with a ferocious sound that Ashley would never hear. Exploded metal fragments, hot gases, and burning propellant blasted into her face and body. With the airbag cushion already inflated and out of the way by the primary chamber, there was an unimpeded path for the metal that tore into her neck and face, severing crucial arteries. She died from massive bleeding and trauma moments later and became the first victim of a defective Takata airbag.

In her hometown, in Oklahoma, her family and friends shared an emotional memorial service. A non-profit was started on her behalf called the Ashley Parham Foundation.[9] Very few people knew of the tragedy, even within Takata. Honda settled with the Parham family for an undisclosed amount of money and issued the following statement:

> **"Our deepest condolences to the Parham family for their great loss. In any vehicle accident, it is important that a full investigation be completed before attempting to theorize the exact causes of damage or injuries. It is too early in this process to draw any conclusions."**

But it's not too early for us to connect the dots. The PSDI inflator that Kevin reported to Paresh in 2000 as entering production fraudulently was the same that killed Ashley. Her Honda Accord was produced the year Kevin resigned from LaGrange and moved to Arizona.

Growth and Malignancy

Nothing seemed right in Kevin's eyes for the two years he watched the root of our tragedy develop in LaGrange. The plant managers were incompetent, if not unethical, Armada was poor at designing inflators and making 'rookie' mistakes, and the Japanese bosses would stop at nothing to please the customer – even if it meant fraud. He was happy to leave – relieved even – and his family enjoyed being back in Arizona.

Starting as Simula's Director of Engineering in 2001, Kevin managed the development of side-impact head protection airbags but yearned for more operations experience. Simula was bought by Zodiac in 2003 and Kevin got his chance when he was promoted to Vice-President of Operations, managing production over a variety of airbag 'cut-and-sew' operations. After bemoaning the number of 'yarn-heads' at Takata, he was now one himself. He loved the new work, but it meant time apart from the family too.

His first assignment was running a plant in the United Kingdom, in a town called Ashington, just outside of Newcastle, where Maggie Thatcher broke the coal mining unions in 1985. People were tough and wary of outsiders, and Kevin was confronted by menacing-looking, tattooed men that ran sewing machines and spoke with a Jordie dialect it took him more than a month to understand. He came to love those coal mining sewing machine operators and they helped him turn the operation around.

Following his UK stint, Kevin opened a plant in Mexico, much closer to home. The family enjoyed Arizona and their home, and life was as close to normal as possible. Takata was the furthest thing from his mind, certainly, as Kevin shared one too many pints with the workers in Ashington or Nogales, but if it's not clear at this point, he is not done with Takata yet. Nope, he's played two innings at most. Soon he will be back in circumstances only he can relate. First, however, let's revisit Takata from 2001, when Kevin leaves, until I enter our story.

The first generation of the smaller and lighter PSAN Takata inflators went into vehicles. PSDI was followed by SPI and PSPI, which also struggled during their validations. Close was good enough and the new designs had hungry customers. For Takata, the first years of the century were all about growth and the struggles that came with it. Times were fast. From 2000 to 2005, Takata's global production grew nearly 40% to 3.4 million vehicles.[10] Production was ramping in LaGrange, and Armada was developing the company's next generation of PSAN inflators. Making them work was a constant struggle.

In a bold move, Frank Roe and Chris Holloway were concurrently transitioning inflator production from LaGrange to Monclova, Mexico. Takata would become one of the first companies to move their pyrotechnic operations to the low-wage country and the savings would be dramatic. A new team was assembled, and LaGrange personnel traveled back-and-forth, living there for extended periods to train the new workers while the Mexican operations sprang to life.

Paresh kept advancing PSAN designs, all the while encountering new obstacles. Automaker's specifications were evolving, getting tougher, and further challenging PSAN's viability. He was also overseeing construction of a new building to house the essential ISI staff that would be heading north as LaGrange shuttered. For now, it was still just his team, which was growing. R&D and applications engineering were busy. Customers were lining up for new variations and the next generation designs. PSDI was the first to be refreshed because of serious manufacturing and design issues. Only in production for two years, it was replaced by PSDI-4 in 2002 and then again by PSDI-5 in 2004. SPI and PSPI remained the passenger designs, but new variations and improvements were being made.

The Japanese liaisons also relocated from LaGrange to Armada. Hideo was the primary resident there for Japan, and Shin Tanaka also came through Armada often but worked out of Echigawa. There were also four or five younger engineering residents living and working alongside Paresh's team, learning the trade and following the direction of their Japanese bosses.

And Jim Takada kept growing his company. In 2000, he purchased Petri – a massive European steering wheel manufacturer, and in 2001 the German inflator team called TAIC was established as Takata Aschaffenburg Inflator Center. Takata formed CPI, their own initiator company in Singapore. Then in 2002, operations were opened in China and by 2005, the Changxing inflator development center was running. Takata now had the three core regions of America, Europe, and Asia ready to meet their customers' airbag needs. The vision was almost complete.

TAIC reported to Paresh and ASL remained the global lead for inflator development. The core designs and propellants were decided there, and each regional applications team tailored them for their markets. Growth had been significant for the airbag industry and there was more to come as Federal mandates continued to evolve to include side-impact and dual-stage systems. Takata was growing and ASL was too – looking for more engineers to churn out inflators. In 2004, I became one of them.

4

An ASL Engineer

THAT SPRING, I interviewed for an engineering position in Armada. Soon to graduate from the University of Arizona with a mathematics degree, I had been apprenticing for three years with a pyrotechnic device company called Special Devices (SDI). There I learned about the pyrotechnic squibs that initiate the inflator sequence, along with micro gas-generators that tension seatbelts during accidents.

I flew to Michigan, spent time with family, and the next morning drove to Armada where I was given a small tour before my first interview with Bob Hardenburg. I liked him immediately and was applying for a position in his group. I met with Bill Martin after that, and then with Paresh. I liked Bill and thought Paresh a bit odd. He was somewhat aloof, didn't make eye contact, and our handshakes were awkward. Still, a few days later I was offered a position as an applications engineer. I accepted and in the summer of 2004, moved back to my birth state full of anticipation to work on inflators.

My first impressions were mixed. The computer I was given was a relic and barely turned on. The applications engineering team, our immediate managers, and the director, were all seated together in a former machine shop. Everyone had their computers raised off the floor with plastic-totes because the room could flood. It was spartan to say the least. There were no carpets or windows, and we were seated in old metal desks grouped around the room in threes. Talking on your phone was also talking at your two other desk-mates. As luck had it, I was grouped with my boss Bob Hardenburg and a loud and colorful engineer named Dave McCormick.

On my first day Hardenburg asked me to call a supplier. As a loud-phone talker, I was self-conscious, but I soon realized that McCormick was much louder than I could ever be, and Bob was hard of hearing. I got used to the place, including all the jokes and ribbing that came with the new team.

Engineers and technicians spent as much time in the prototype lab building inflators as we did at our desks. I fit in quickly and some became good friends.

I learned everything about inflators from Dave McCormick. He taught me the ropes and once we learned we both played golf, the friendship was sealed. Dave loved the game and was already taking swings before work with Hardenburg and others. Soon we were competing a few times a week, waging breakfast and temporary ownership of a trophy headcover. The loser's driver was shamed with the 'monkey-butt' cover. McCormick taught me how to properly hit a drive, get my head into the game, and how to design inflators. The new job was panning out well, with a close-knit group of younger engineers that I spent many after-hours within good Michigan pubs through the winter.

Hardenburg's applications engineers made up one of the two groups that comprised Armada. The other was the R&D engineers, who developed new chemistry and inflator designs. Their digs weren't much better than ours, but they had the status and were very secretive. A few would interact with us, but they mostly kept to themselves. They were Paresh's real team, the development chemists and engineers who had been with him the longest. It was their inflators I was busy updating drawings and making new customer variants for. We were the younger applications team, the runts, doing the same work as Kevin's group in LaGrange. With three years of initiator engineering, I was learning quickly and eager to raise the bar.

I met Hideo in my first month there when Hardenburg came over to my desk with him. They had an assignment for me to visit the LaGrange facility and supervise a build. I was elated. The plant had already built the inflators, a small batch of PSDI-4s for Honda, but no one from ASL was present, which made Hideo uncomfortable. He wanted to be sure they were right, so he was making them do it again with me there. I poured over the drawings, excitedly, coming up to speed on the dual-stage driver inflator. The trip went smoothly, and I met some great people, but the plant was eerily empty, having almost fully transferred to Monclova, Mexico.

I returned and was given my first real assignment working on Takata's newest dual-stage driver inflator, PSDI-5. It was recently developed and superseded PSDI-4, and I would responsible for Ford's design validation effort. The inflator build and baseline deployments were already complete, and the environmental testing was in process. My job was to see it through and finish the report. This was one of my key jobs as an intern, and I thought it would be easy, but soon I would find myself in crisis management mode.

My First Rodeo

Pouring over the PSDI-5 drawings and specifications, I learned it was a unique dual-stage inflator. PSDI and PSDI-4 were independent designs, where the primary and secondary chambers each had their own set of nozzles to control combustion and their own filter to cool exhaust gases. PSDI-5 was a dependent design, with the two chambers initially isolated, but connected internally by a one-way valve that let the secondary gases vent through the primary chamber for staged or full outputs. This greatly reduced design complexity with both gas streams exiting through the same filter and nozzles. Additionally, PSDI-5 used propellant tablets instead of wafers to improve variability.

Shortly after coming up to speed, however, I received a call from the test supervisor. He told me three of my parts had ruptured and urged me to come to the lab. I ran over and was directed to three totes on a table with the remnants of my inflators. The engineer who transferred the program to me, Hardenburg, the program manager Chris Adamini, and Paresh were already there. I looked at the parts quietly while they discussed the results.

They were startled by the failures but not surprised. It wasn't a first. Takata's PSAN had squeaked by Honda, but this was the USCAR specification and its heat-aging and thermal-cycling exposures were more difficult. Paresh was agitated, wanting to know how the prototype lab could have built them wrong and I ended up with all the action items. My first program went into failure and the investigation commenced.

Ford was notified which immediately spiked the intensity level. Chris and I set up a 'war-room' where we briefed the module engineers and PMs and kept all the materials. To say Ford was concerned would be an understatement. Production was imminent, and their design validation inflators were exploding. I worked late every night, plastering the room with the latest pictures, charts, and tables. Any critical measurements and trends I organized and presented. I was coached early to refer to the creeping number of inflators that were exploding, as instances of "energetic-disassembly", or EDs. Never was I to use or write the word 'explode.' While hectic, the madness afforded me the opportunity to interact with Paresh's chemists, who were brought in to help with the emergency, and I caught up quickly.

PSAN is extremely hygroscopic, meaning it will soak up all the moisture it can. This can become a severe problem if the propellant is subsequently exposed to temperature cycling, which drives the water in and out, slowly damaging it over time. Picture after picture of sectioned inflators showed discolored and degraded propellant with low density. Deteriorated PSAN like this would burn way too fast and the internal inflator pressures would rise too quickly. Moisture was the culprit, but where was it coming from? The data I was collecting showed that propellant was losing density in inflators that were perfectly hermetic. Sealed tight.

The final environmental test results were coming in and what a report this was going to make. The harshest environments were causing inflators to fail structurally. Some of these just split open at stress-risers and welds, the 'burps' we called them. But others were transformed into blasted-bits of shrapnel and mangled pieces of filter. These were the EDs. Even the lesser environments were causing the inflator's output to rise above its upper limits. It was insanity.

We cut apart inflator after inflator, took pictures, and kept digging until the missing piece of the puzzle became obvious. It was bad news. The moisture was not coming from outside the inflator, but from inside. We were so focused on the PSAN, that we hadn't paid much attention to the discolored auto-ignition (AI) tablets also evident in the teardowns. They would start out white but end up looking something between slightly-caramelized and completely-blackened. They were shriveled, melted, and discolored, a clear sign they were releasing moisture and other volatiles into the propellant. This became the new focus.

Pyrotechnic companies must pass stringent Department of Transportation (DOT) bonfire tests to ensure safe transport of their product. In case of a trucking accident that leads to a fire, airbag inflators need to function safely and self-dispose, so they don't become small bombs that injure people and rescue workers. The standard test is a few boxes of inflators cooked over a raging wood fire. The gas generators can't explode, eject fragments, or move too far from the fire's center. If they do, the government fails the design and it can't be sold.

Inflator engineers include pyrotechnics called auto-ignition materials to provide the self-disposal function. They act as a thermal switch to automatically ignite the inflator before fire's intense heat compromises the main propellant. PSAN has a notoriously low melting point which made this test very difficult to pass. Only a small offset between the auto-ignition function and propellant melt could be achieved and this forced the inclusion of multiple AI tablets within the same inflator.

The Ford PSDI-5 required two AI tablets, one in each booster tube in contact with the inflator cap, opposite the igniter. This was the proverbial

Trojan Horse, laden with moisture and slipped behind the inflator's impervious walls, and there was no way to eradicate it. If you took one or all of the AI tablets out, things would improve, but bonfire would fail. Time was ticking, and Ford was pressing for good news.

Fortunately, a chemist named Deb Hordos had a solution in the wings. She proposed putting desiccants, or scavengers of moisture, into the inflator to protect the propellant. The idea was that any moisture present or being released from the AI tablets, or making its way through the inflator's seals, would be trapped in the desiccant. We had to figure out how much and where, but we finally had root cause and a corrective action to test.

The chemists had calcium sulfate desiccant available and I started new builds with it immediately. The results improved. The AI tablets still looked discolored, but the propellant was in better shape, and the inflators started to pass their environments. I was relieved, Ford was relieved. Everyone was.

The delta-validation with the updated configuration was started. ASL chemists filed their patents on desiccating inflators. Paresh's team also updated the PSAN specification to lower the allowable moisture limits. Moisture was PSAN's kryptonite.

I was moved off the Ford effort after PSDI-5 seemed to be on course and transferred to work on Japanese programs. Our resident liaisons were complaining that their customers weren't getting the proper attention with the increased domestic business and I was selected to help remedy this. I considered it an honor.

I started working on passenger programs for Nissan and learned that being part of Team Japan came with some perks. We were often invited to big dinners with the Japanese leadership when they came through town and I enjoyed the exposure. Things on the new team were going well for me.

By the middle of 2005 and my first Takata anniversary, however, things had begun to sour. As I learned and worked with my Japanese colleagues, I found myself being confronted with ethical questions and conundrums. These were issues everyone who worked at ASL came to know. Until then, I was in training, but now I had my first sense things weren't right.

The young residents working alongside us, destined to become our future bosses in Japan, were frequently engaged in the 'prettying of data' that went to our customers. Sometimes they would manipulate inflator outputs that were just out of specification, so they appeared in, and other times they would make perfectly acceptable data just look better. I'd never seen anything like it, but then I found something far worse. I noticed a report of mine in an odd folder on the shared drive and when I opened it, I realized it had been modified with better data. The signature page was kept unchanged so it appeared that I had written and approved it. This was unforgivable and yet I didn't know what to do about it.

Already wary, I started hearing disturbing rumors from my former PSDI-5 Ford team. Apparently, someone had seen Paresh dumping desiccant into the trash. Why? Because there were more failures in the delta-DV with desiccant and he wanted to claim the inflators were mistakenly built without the drying agent. It was crazy, but in the back of my mind a seed was planted. Maybe it wasn't so crazy.

Never a dull moment at Takata and Nissan's PSDI-5 was up next. I thought I had escaped the beast, but now Team Japan had its hands full with it too. Nissan's design validation, using the same calcium-sulfate desiccant as Ford, was failing catastrophically and I was called in to help. The story was the same but magnified. The design needed three AI tablets to pass tougher German transportation requirements and even with desiccant there was just too much onboard moisture to combat. Making things even worse, Nissan had concocted the toughest specification to date, combining heat age and temperature cycling in a devastating sequence. I knew why the inflator was failing, but there was no solution I could offer. That would have to come from the chemists.

I went back to work on my passenger program, which was also finishing Nissan validations. The same issues emerged there too. The larger propellant wafers were degrading and being damaged by the harsh sequential environments. They weren't rupturing, but they were aggressive and failing output limits. Everywhere I turned, there were issues I found unsettling.

One day Hideki Mizuno approached me, a Japanese liaison stationed in Armada and responsible for Nissan. We had failed their passenger design validation, and he wanted me to run a different series of tests. Instead of the prescribed sequential environments in the specification, he wanted me to rearrange and remove certain ones. The request was reasonable, if he was seeking root cause, but I also knew a doctored report could be created with my name on it and that made me uncomfortable.

It was too much. I was just starting my career. I made a hard decision to start looking for greener pastures. As I reached out to former colleagues, some new developments arose that offered me a way out.

Meeting Kevin

LaGrange was finally closed. The production lines had all moved to Mexico and the ISI team was relocated to Armada. Just before their arrival, the new main building opened, and we finally moved out from the dungeon. On one end of the new building was Holloway's office, slightly smaller than Paresh's on the other end. In between the two was everyone else and I went over quickly to meet the newcomers.

I struck up a friendship with their accountant and started spending more time on the ISI side. They saw us ASL guys as the black-sheep of the organization and complained about Paresh and his designs incessantly. I was becoming aware of an interesting dynamic at work here, and since I had some of the same feelings, I thought I'd make a great fit.

I knew the ISI Director of Quality, Bob Phillion, from a family connection and explained my situation to him. Bob was sympathetic and offered me a job in his department as a quality engineer. This was great. I would get to travel to Mexico more and learn the operations. I applied immediately, was quickly tendered an offer, and gladly accepted.

I first heard of troubles with the transfer from my accountant friend. He was told by HR that Paresh learned of my transfer and was livid. When I was hit with that my heart sank. A battle was raging over my future that had less to do with me and more with a brewing power struggle. Paresh complained ISI was buying away his best guys with money he didn't have, and that Team Japan was happy with the critical role I was playing. I couldn't believe it. When I heard that the Japanese were siding with Paresh against my transfer, I knew it was over.

Still, I was given hope. I received a call from Pat Giampaolo, the Vice-President of HR for North America. An important call. He told me there was "some controversy" over the offer but not to worry, it would shake out in a few days. He noted that I was qualified for the position and assured me politics wouldn't get in the way. I was hanging on.

Then two days later he called again, this one less friendly. The transfer was being cancelled and he offered that I should be happy the Japanese and Paresh valued me so highly. I hung up the phone defeated.

A few hours later, Peter Holland, now Paresh's Director of Engineering, asked me to join him in Paresh's office. It was awkward. Paresh slid an envelope across the table to me. I read it and was crushed. The offer was only a fraction of ISI's but said they were happy I was staying on. The whole affair took thirty seconds, slamming shut my ASL escape and leaving me with some hard decisions to make.

My performance dropped, and I sulked while I thought about my next move. My boss could see I was upset and offered me a new assignment to try and cheer me up. Knowing I liked to travel to the plant, he asked if I would represent the team as the sole presenter for the upcoming Design Reviews in Monclova. It would save the company money to send just me, and he reasoned it could help soothe over any hard feelings. It worked.

I dove in again, sitting with each engineer to help ready their presentations, including my own. I knew it was an opportunity and was excited. I prepared well, bought two new shirts, got a haircut, and even had my shoes shined at the airport.

Design Reviews (DR) occurred periodically throughout the year. They were key milestones on the path to production readiness. Engineers presented status, validation results, plans, drawings, and key metrics. The executives from all departments and regions gathered to review and decide whether a program was ready to advance to the next tollgate.

I had experienced these gatherings before. They were always interesting but quite stressful for me. Normally, they would take place in Armada, on friendly turf, but ISI wanted more and more of the reviews to be held in Monclova and they were becoming more combative. I had no idea what was in store for me as I traveled to Monclova but was still excited. I arrived in the evening, had dinner with some friends, and stayed up too late.

The next morning, I arrived at the conference room early, to rehearse the slides and ready myself. When the time came, everybody that mattered filed in and found their place. There were two new gentlemen in the room I hadn't met before. They took seats in the very front and introduced themselves to me as Kevin Fitzgerald and Bob Schubert.

I began the first of the presentations and it didn't take long to discover the purpose of the two mystery guests. I was in for a long and difficult day. Kevin and Bob were clearly there to educate Paresh's guy, which was unfortunately me. ASL was not the best school of inflators, so when Bob started unloading technical questions on me and asking about interior ballistics, I knew I was in trouble. Nobody on the line from back home came to my rescue either. Here were two seasoned inflator experts gleefully peppering me with questions and demands for evidence.

I did my best, deferred what I didn't know and agreed to provide a long list of additional information at a later date. Suffice it to say, not all the reviews passed. More importantly, the plant realized they had engineering allies again – somebody to call out Paresh's team and stand up for them. They were happy to see me get schooled, even if they felt for me a little. It was part of the greater struggle and I was just learning.

I finished feeling defeated and stung. My hopes had been to impress, but this wasn't what I had in mind. I sent a quick e-mail back to Armada letting them know of the slaughter if they hadn't heard already, and also about the two gentlemen who showed up. I was certain they had an idea of what was in store for me and that's why I was picked. I have had rough moments presenting in my life, but this was the most memorable and painful.

I almost thought to stay in the hotel room that night and lick my wounds, but I convinced myself to join everyone else at dinner. I dressed and joined them on the patio of *Los Corrales*, just across the street. As luck would have it, Kevin and Bob were there, and the open seat was across from Kevin. The drinks started flowing and I cheered up.

At one point, Kevin leaned across the table and told me I had done a respectable job. Schubert chimed in too, agreeing and assuring me it wasn't personal. They were happy that I had kept my cool and hadn't made shit up. I thanked them and this brightened my spirits. More drinks came, and I started talking with Kevin. I liked him. People responded to him. He was smart and you could tell he had purpose. I wanted to work for him and now saw a sliver of an opportunity.

So, when the moment was right, I related my predicament and recent attempt to leave ASL. Phillion was sitting there too, and he vouched for me. I told Kevin that if he ever needed someone to please consider me. I wanted to learn what they knew.

Then after a few more drinks, Kevin lit up a cigarette. I thought that was a good opportunity to bond with him further, so I asked for one. He nodded, and slid the pack across the table with the matches in the sleeve. I thanked him and then struck a matchstick that decided to snap in two and light my shirt on fire! I quickly slapped at it with my hand, grabbed a glass of water and splashed it all over myself. Everyone at the table broke out laughing. I was mortified and when I looked down, I had a small burn-hole about the size of a quarter in my shirt.

A few moments later with everyone still chuckling, Kevin pointed at me again, laughing harder. The small hole had grown quite large due to something strange about the fabric and was now the size of a small plate. This meant my chest and upper belly were exposed – even a nipple was poking out. Nobody could contain their laughter at this point, and we agreed it was time to move to the next bar before we were asked to. The hotel was across the street and I asked everyone to please wait while I changed my shirt. They wouldn't have it. They were intent on parading me around this way all evening. Forced into a car, I proudly strutted into the next bar where more associates from work joined us. I had a blast that evening.

Even though I still worked for Paresh, I had found my tribe. It wouldn't be long until I was working for Kevin. Sometimes misfortune opens new doors and things are just meant to be.

Act Two

Part A: Kevin and Paresh

2005-2009

(KEVIN)

5

Fast and Furious

I RETURNED TO work for Takata in the summer of 2005. After joining Simula in 2001, things there hadn't gone quite to plan. They were never able to capitalize on their first-to-market, side-impact head protection system and were later bought by the French company Zodiac, which closed US operations in 2005. This left me without a job, so when a headhunter called for a Director of Inflator Operations position at Takata, I listened. I had spent most of my career in engineering management, but at Simula I made the conscious choice to go into operations. In my last years there, I served as the Vice-President of Operations, where I ran a plant in the United Kingdom and later opened one in Nogales, Mexico. I loved it and so the opportunity presented me a way to continue in operations.

Still, this was Takata calling, and we had a history to say the least. So that night I scoured the Internet for articles on field-events or recalls – anything to indicate issues. It had been almost five years since I left LaGrange and I found nothing. It seemed like Takata had it contained and without a job, I didn't have the luxury to be picky. There was one more consideration that pulled me that way. The position was in Armada, working for Chris Holloway in the same building as Paresh.

I won't deny that a part of me had a score to settle with Paresh, but more importantly the opportunity to be his counterpoint was a call to duty. I was not expecting to be hired when I gave the headhunter the green light to proceed. I just assumed he would get a polite, 'thanks, but no thanks,' when they saw my name. Why would a company that essentially pushed me out for my honesty have any interest in my return? Additionally, Chris had pressed me hard with the non-compete on my way out, so I considered it a longshot.

A week later, however, the phone rang. Chris wanted me to meet him in Destin, Florida, the following Monday where he was holding his annual inflator operations conference. He would squeeze in the interview between a few rounds of golf, sun-drenched beaches, and merciless hangovers. I accepted the invitation with both excitement and trepidation, but it turned out to be hardly an interview. I might have said two or three sentences to him the whole trip, which is exactly how he wanted it. It was more important to Chris that I spend time with the team, some of whom I'd worked with in LaGrange and hadn't seen in years. He knew exactly how to get to me. Camaraderie and booze. I was a goner.

Shortly after returning home, I got another call from the headhunter. It was time to fly to Michigan for further discussions. Getting the time off at Simula wasn't a problem. Everyone else there was doing the same. A week later I was in Detroit, this time expecting a full-fledged interview. It was more like a trophy march. Chris paraded me around the office, gave me a tour of the facility and enjoyed every jaw on Paresh's side of the building it dropped. After he was finished having fun, we returned to his office for a chat.

"It's a great job, Kevin. You're going to love it. You will be responsible for Monclova and Moses Lake. Luis and Thom, the plant managers you met in Florida, would report to you. We'll give you a 20% raise, company car, completely take care of the relocation. What do you think?" he said.

"Thom and Luis didn't seem so happy about having a third wheel," I answered. "Have they expressed their displeasure with you?"

"Yes, but they will be fine. They will appreciate having you around soon enough. That is, if you accept?" he pressed.

"What's the real reason you want me back Chris?' I asked finally.

He leaned back in his chair before proceeding, "It's Paresh. He has inflator R&D and applications engineering. He reports directly to Japan and refuses to listen to Frank or myself. He brought Bill back from LaGrange to run applications and made Peter his Director of Engineering. Neither one will challenge Paresh's authority."

Bingo. I was sold now.

"Peter is a Director?" I asked, trying to hide my surprise.

"Yeah, he went to Germany to help Kimmich set up their inflator engineering facility and apparently he did a pretty good job while there. Here, he just seems lost. Kimmich runs the group over there in Germany now. It's called TAIC," Chris answered.

"Stephen is still in Germany and running their inflator applications group? That is great!" I said proudly.

Chris brought the conversation back to the main point, "The relationship between Armada and Monclova is at a low, and we think you can help change that. Paresh is not known for developing a rapport with manufacturing, but you can work with Bill and Peter and get to their people. You are likeable and speak their lingo. Plus, I'm tired of doing all the heavy lifting around here," he ended with a smile.

"Okay, thanks for the honesty. I'm definitely interested. Of course, I need to talk it over with Sandy. She's back at the hotel, so I will do that now if we are wrapping up. We are still on for dinner tonight with your family, right?"

"Yes, 6 o'clock at the Lakeview Inn. Let me walk you out."

As we walked to my rental car, Chris shared a funny story with me.

"Armada HR reports to Paresh, which, now that I mention it, really pisses me off," he started. "Anyways, I was growing impatient with the progress being made filling this position and asked Diane, his HR specialist, why I hadn't seen any resumes in a while. Paresh happened to be in her office when I walked in."

"And?" I said smiling, knowing this was about to get better.

"Diane looks up at Paresh nervously and says, 'We haven't come across any good ones yet, Chris.' So, I'm thinking bullshit and pick the first one from the stack on her desk and it's yours. I turn to Paresh, hand it to him, and say, 'Bring him in,' and walk out. It was beautiful!"

"Sounds like Paresh hasn't changed at all," I said, sliding into the driver's seat.

"You'll see," he said closing the door firmly.

I drove straight back to the hotel and told Sandy of the day's events. As I did I could see both happiness and sadness in her face. She is so selfless. The last damn thing she wanted to do was move to Michigan, but she knew our backs were against the wall and that if I was working with inflators again, at least one of us would be happy. She got off the edge of the bed and gave me one of those 'everything is going to be alright' hugs, and that's all I needed to know.

Later at dinner, Chris talked more directly about why he and Frank were so frustrated with Armada.

"Paresh just tosses designs over the fence at us and they are riddled with issues. When we inevitably run into a manufacturing problem, it is always met with a 'your problem, not mine' mentality. He insists that everything works great when the parts are built in Armada, so something must be wrong with our process. Frank is tired of the nonsense and he wants someone who can fight back."

"You know, Chris, sending me right into a hornet's nest is not exactly a good selling point," I said playfully.

"That's exactly why you are sitting here." He smiled. "Frank and I both know you can't pass one by without taking a whack at it."

Truer words had never been spoken. I couldn't wait.

My return to Takata meant another big move for the family, this time from Arizona to Michigan, and it would prove the most difficult of them all. Arizona had been our home for nearly five years – the longest stability we had known. Our youngest two kids were born there. Our oldest son was starting his sophomore year of high school, a terrible time to be relocated, and they all had their friends. Michigan was green and beautiful when we visited that summer, a nice contrast to Arizona, but the kids, especially my oldest, Ryan, were hesitant. They knew they had no control and that their lives would be changing again.

We purchased a home in Lake Orion, a little north of Detroit, with access to the lake, and enrolled the kids in their schools just in time for fall classes. We did our best to enjoy before our first Michigan winter set in, still a few months away.

I began work almost immediately and being responsible for inflator and propellant operations in both Monclova and Moses Lake, I was busy. There were cost of quality meetings that took place every month at the Monclova plant and I began travelling there regularly as I integrated into the new role. Someone from Chris' staff was always in Mexico. He demanded it as the operations were still relatively new and continuous improvement a priority. He even rented us a home there because he believed it was less expensive than all the hotel rooms. The place was more like a fraternity house for middle-aged executives. It was infamous before it was eventually shut down.

There was an indoor pool in the middle of the living room, a fridge stocked full of beer, big TVs with satellite channels, and a maid that took care of cleaning and doing everyone's laundry. Chris had the master bedroom and we leased a white Suburban to drive around town and to work. The first time I made the trip down, the boss didn't come along, and being new, the guys let me have his bedroom. Unpacking, I had to laugh at the row of neatly pressed, horse-print button downs that occupied half of his walk-in closet. I was back.

Schubert Joins the Mission

I was involved in operations day to day, but Frank wanted me challenging Paresh's engineering group, too. Put yourself in Paresh's shoes regarding my return. ISI had been in Armada for months now, sharing the facility and getting into his business. The power struggle was well underway when I arrived, and it was obvious that Frank wanted more influence in engineering, like he had in the past. He was arming himself with the right people and increasingly prodding me to do the same. It was time to give the sidelined professor a call.

"Mr. Schubert, my friend. How the hell are you?" I said as soon as he picked up the phone.

"Kevin, I heard you were back. I am doing well and you?"

"Busier than shit, Bob. Things are crazy over here, which I am sure you can imagine, so I'll get right to it. Frank is on a mission to gain more control over inflator engineering and I'm calling to see if you are interested in taking up the fight. He all but mentioned you by name, Bob, so I am sure he has cleared it with Al."

"Oh, this is too good," Bob said. "For a time, I was given approval authority over Paresh's design reviews. I was told to attend each one and assess whether the program was ready to proceed through the tollgate. That ended the first time I turned one around."

"What do you mean?"

"My objection was overridden and when I went over to Armada for the next set of design reviews, Paresh had cut off my badge access! He refused to let me in the building and that was the end of it," he answered.

"So, I can take that as a yes then. You will be joining us?"

"You can take that as a hell yes," he roared.

"Great! Hey, before I let you go, Bob, one more question."

"Shoot."

"No one ever explained why you just disappeared from Lagrange like you did. What happened, if you don't mind me asking, why were you transferred under Al?"

Bob paused for a bit and said, "the Japanese asked me to misrepresent data and I refused. Let's just leave it there."

It's what I had suspected.

"Understood. Together we are formidable and can bring some long-overdue change to inflator engineering. It will be good to join forces again," I said.

"Yes, it will Kevin. I'm done languishing over here. Thanks."

A few days later Schubert took up permanent residence in Armada. Immediately we learned of an airbag test at Mazda where one of Paresh's newer designs, a PSPI-6 dual stage, passenger inflator, suffered a major burn-through in the ignition closure. This means a hole melted through it. In a real airbag deployment, this would dump hot gases directly into the passenger compartment of the car, endangering the occupant and resulting in an under-inflated airbag. It is never supposed to happen, especially not during a customer test. Structural compromise like this is the worst failure mode, resulting when internal pressures exceed the strength of the inflator. This was serious.

We walked straight over to the responsible ASL engineer and asked him to pull up the inflator's interior pressure data. It showed a maximum value well below the closure's failure pressure and the engineer argued he had adequate margin. He was baffled as to what could have caused the burn-through. Bob immediately noticed, however, that something was terribly wrong with his analysis.

"That data is filtered. We never filter an ignition event. It is too fast. What type of filter did you use?" Bob pressed the engineer.

"The same 60Hz filter that tank data is run through," he replied.

Bob and I looked at each other wincing. This time it was my turn.

"We smooth 60L tank data because the customer doesn't want to see noisy traces when evaluating performance. They ask us to, but only for tank pressure data. The ignition event, like Bob said, is too fast and was filtered out. You missed it."

"Missed what?" he said, confused.

"You missed the ignition peak pressure. Pull up the raw data please," Bob asked, putting a hand on the engineer's shoulder to let him know we weren't the enemy. A half-a-minute later we were looking at the data and it was not good.

"Holy shit! That thing is at 180MPa (26,000 psi) in what...10 microseconds!" I said turning to Bob. "It looks like it may be transitioning to detonation."

Bob never looked up from the screen. His eyes were fixed on the raw data and, his mouth was wide open. What does 'an ignition event transitioning to detonation' mean? In layman's terms, it means it was completely out of control – nearly running away to explosion. Takata was lucky that the closure failed and relieved the pressure, instead of ramping the main propellant up and causing a much more significant rupture. The reason why the inflator was failing at the customer was right here, clear as day, right under their noses, but ASL didn't have the understanding to interpret it. This was terrible.

Digging into the problem more, we soon discovered that inflator was having trouble meeting the customer's output rate and a second auto-ignition (AI) tablet was added to the ignition to speed things up. This was not the right approach, and it was aggravating the closure's internal pressure. We shared what we learned with Chris, along with a recommendation that ASL remove the second AI tablet and request a deviation from the customer for the slower timing. Our hands were tied – ASL had design authority. Days went by without any action or feedback. Then one evening, Chris sent an e-mail to myself and a few of the staff directing us to remove the second AI tablet, as we had recommended, but to 'tell no one.' ASL owned the design, but we built everything.

Amused, I picked up the phone and called my good friend Dennis Sharp, who oversaw logistics, and asked him if he had just read the same e-mail I did.

"What e-mail?" he said.

"Come on, Dennis, it's me, how are we going to change the design without telling anyone at the plant?"

This was a new one for me. Never had I witnessed operations make a unilateral change to a design without approved drawings from engineering. I am not sure if Chris even asked Paresh, but it was a direct order, it was the right thing to do, and we executed it. I had hoped that Takata had changed their ways, but this signaled they hadn't and explained why Paresh didn't want Schubert poking around his designs. Now he had the two of us to contend with.

Retaking Lost Ground

A structural failure of a production inflator at Mazda due to a fundamental design issue was all the leverage Frank needed to get Japan to agree with his push to re-take applications engineering. Two months after I was hired, the group they took away from me in LaGrange was mine again.

There was no chance it would be a smooth transition. Paresh would have to give up engineers and he was sour about the whole affair, especially considering it was me on the other side. He had first say and offered his 'B' team engineers, and not too many of them. This was no surprise. Negotiations were started. The 'B' team didn't mean they weren't good engineers, only that they were his newest and least-experienced. Arguments were had and at first I flatly refused, telling him if he sent certain people my way I would have them marched right back. He would have to offer more. I pushed for Dave Schumann, who impressed Bob and me in Mexico, to be included, and Paresh relented.

I had a motto I explained clearly to the group as soon as it formed: 'we will do everything right and win.' The goal was to gain the respect of the organization, especially the Japanese, with better designs and better engineering. I wanted to improve the technical know-how of our team and show Echigawa there was no need to cheat or wrestle with difficult decisions. Do it right and life gets easier for everyone. I also shared a radical idea to the new engineers used to life on the ASL side: the plant was the customer and our job was to make them happy.

Schubert and I formed two engineering groups, Applications and Core. Applications would perform the normal role of transitioning designs to the plant and supporting manufacturing. Core was new and would begin to develop improved inflators using off-the-shelf Takata propellants, along with better analysis tools and technical competence. From the very beginning, I wanted more. I wanted a group that was better than Paresh's. One that would deliver desperately needed USCAR-compliant inflators. With Paresh reporting to the Japanese, and their focus mostly on Asian business, he didn't have the priority to take care of US customers. Keeping the Japanese happy was all that mattered. If we could develop USCAR compliant inflators for The Big Three with the same basic technology and propellant, that would be a big win for Takata and our fledgling group.

To this end, Schubert began creating a ballistic model and teaching the team the fundamentals. This was their first exposure to the real science behind inflator design. He explained how it was wrong that they were focused on tank tests. That analyzing a tank result was like diagnosing a car by studying it from the outside. That you must open the engine and measure what's going on in the heart of the device to learn anything. He stressed how he would rather see one internal pressure trace than a slew of tank pressure results. The only time internal pressure was measured by ASL was to demonstrate safety factors, but this wasn't enough to understand.

The team began to model inflator performance, and from that moment on, there were no inflator tests that weren't simultaneously measuring internal pressure and tank pressure. It was a new world for the reassigned ASL engineers. They were no longer turning the inflator's tuning knobs without a real sense of the theory behind them. Before long, our 'B' team engineers were as knowledgeable, if not more, than the engineers Paresh refused to hand over.

The Core team needed a project to sink their teeth into. Something to get them up and running quickly, but with the potential to put them on the map. I pulled the new engineers together and asked them what they thought should be attacked first. The overwhelming response was the performance variability of our passenger inflators. It had Honda continuously frustrated and was closing business opportunities with U.S. car makers.

"Bob, you got a minute?" I asked as I plopped myself down in a seat in his cube.

"I guess I do," he smiled.

"We are never going to win more USCAR passenger business with SPI and PSPI. Their performance is all over the place."

"Not with those big wafers. Not unless you want a hundred deviations attached to the PV report," he said.

"I know. My team started to study it in LaGrange and published an initial report, but...."

"So, let's finish it! The new driver inflators, SDI and PSDI-5, have both migrated back to tablets for performance. It will be a much tougher case to make for passenger because of the cost, but we should do the study," Bob said.

"Agreed. That's exactly what I wanted to hear. Schumann, get in here!" I yelled through my office intercom.

Schumann worked closely with Bob and together they developed a new passenger inflator that replaced the propellant wafers with tablets. Compared to the random break-up of the wafers, the tablets stayed together during ignition, and that provided the consistency we were after. Dave ran the first test and then reported back to Bob with the results. They correlated it to the model, adjusted parameters, predicted the next performance, and then conducted more tests. We were hungry for results but couldn't get them fast enough. The sudden increase in workload created a bottleneck in the test department and that caught Paresh's attention. Rather than flexing his workforce, he sent Peter over to aggravate me.

"Kevin, Paresh does not have budget for all these tests you are conducting. He wants you to start writing Purchase Orders for them, at least for the remainder of this fiscal year. I am sure the accountants will sort it out next year," he said, nonchalantly.

"The end of the fiscal year, Peter? We're only halfway through, and you know that's a ton of unnecessary work for us," I shot back.

"Sorry, Kevin, Chris will have to take it up with Paresh. That's the way Paresh wants it."

"Does he want us to write a P.O. every time we need to take a shit in his building as well?" I said as he walked out. He didn't bother to answer, so I took that as a maybe.

Despite Paresh's roadblocks, in a matter of weeks, the ballistic model was accurately predicting performance and the new tablet passenger design was performing extremely well. Gone was the variability that had Armada's resident Japanese engineers building 'perfect' inflators, so they could show Honda the performance they expected. Their late-night follies involved sorting bags of wafers for identical sets, stacking them perfectly, measuring ignition mixes precisely, selecting filters with identical masses, and in some cases, simply omitting tests that didn't fit. Everyone knew this was happening. All of this was dishonest because manufacturing could never hold these tolerances or produce similar results, but this work continued because the SPI and PSPI inflators couldn't perform to standards. I made sure to document and broadcast what we were learning to the larger organization as we peeled the onion back. The ballistic model wasn't just predicting the variability wafers caused, it was also indicating that they were combusting poorly. In fact, calculations showed a large portion of them weren't even contributing to restraint performance.

"Look at this, Kevin," Bob said, pointing to his computer screen. "I would say only about 60%-70% of the passenger inflator wafers are being combusted when it counts. Can you have one of the guys take a real-time video of a PSPI deployment and let it roll for, let's say, 10 seconds?"

"Ten seconds. Are you serious? It's a 100ms event," I said.

"The model says those wafers will be pumping gas a lot longer than that. Trust me."

"I see it, Bob, but it's hard for me to believe that a combustion efficiency like that could make it all the way to production. I mean, it's a huge waste of money."

"Exactly, so let's get the video."

This resulted in the infamous 'hissing video,' that showed the inflator venting gas with a characteristic whistling sound that lasted for more than seven seconds. Why is this significant? An entire airbag deployment takes less than a quarter of a second from the time the sensors are triggered to the time the airbag has deployed. For inflator tests, the standard was to chart one-tenth of one second, or 100ms. An inflator that vents for five or more seconds is providing gas nearly 50 times longer than needed. Not only were these large wafers making variability worse, they were also wasting lots of Mr. Takada's money. The 'hissing video' was an embarrassment for Paresh and it was meant as a warning shot across his bow. We were not to be taken lightly. Demonstrating his incompetence was vital so that we could be allowed to improve things.

More of the Same

Frank, always an enthusiastic supporter, was paying close attention to our progress and invited me to speak at his annual Operations Summit in Greensboro, NC. I used it as an opportunity to share our vision. We didn't prove a tableted passenger inflator just to poke Paresh in the eye. Wafers had to go. They were causing too many inflator lot acceptance test (LAT) failures at the plant and too many late-night inflator builds in Armada. There was an obstacle, though. Moses Lake spread their expenses over pounds of propellant pressed in an hour and that put tablets at a big disadvantage. To compete, Monclova's LAT scrap dollars credited to poor wafer performance would have to be deducted from the tablet cost. I walked down to see Bob Phillion, ISI's Director of Quality, to check if he had the numbers. Bob and I had become good friends. We met during my interview on the first tee box in Destin, FL, where I proceeded to hit my first five drives into any body of water I could reach. Throughout the round, Bob demonstrated a killer foot wedge.

"Hey, Bob, do you have Monclova's scrap numbers for SPI and PSPI?" I asked. "I'm trying to make the cost argument for a tableted passenger inflator for a presentation I'm putting together for Frank. Our test results show that tablets would almost end Monclova's LAT problems and the dollars must be significant."

"They are buddy, but they should be even higher too," he said. "We flag many more SPI and PSPI lots for failing LATs than hit the books. PSDI too. All the inflators with wafers. Unfortunately, when the results are close, Chikaraishi's minions direct Carlos to test additional samples until he can replace the one that was out with one that is in. They would rather do that than hold up a customer shipment. You've met Carlos Iruegas; he is

Monclova's Quality Manager."

"Well, that's disturbing, Bob."

"You are preaching to the choir, Kevin. I've made everyone aware of the situation. Takata management knows it is going on," he said as he handed me the numbers.

"I'm sure you have Bob, but if these figures aren't all inclusive, they aren't going to help make my case. If Paresh and Japan continue to ignore the variability wafers introduce, we will be stuck with them forever and Carlos will be forced to continue the charade. That cannot be healthy for him or anyone else involved. I'll bring it up with Chris," I said.

"I'd appreciate it, Kevin. He's already heard it from me."

"Hey, while we are on the subject of Monclova passenger inflators, how are they doing on helium leak rejects?"

"No issues there. Why do you ask?"

"I noticed they are properly evacuating the inflator prior to backfilling it with helium now and was wondering if that increased the reject rate. Did anyone ever tell you how the first SPI and PSPI lines in LaGrange performed that operation?" I asked him.

"No, but I'm sure you are going to," he said with a smile.

"A pallet carrying the end closure/filter subassembly would come to a stop at the helium fill station which was essentially a nozzle that sprayed helium all over the outside of the filter. There was no evacuation step proceeding that, so the helium concentration levels must have been atrocious. We told Teramoto's manufacturing engineers, but they weren't interested. You know the pass/fail criteria need to be tightened as you come off 100% concentration?"

"Yes, I am fully aware of that and glad you brought it up," Bob said leaning back in his chair and clasping his hands behind his head. "Add it to the list of items to discuss with Chris. We approached him with that study too. I wanted to make sure we had the proper limits set. He came back a few days later and told us to stay clear. Something about management not wanting to open Pandora's box. It died right there."

"I will, Bob. I'll talk to him about both," I said shaking my head. The gap I needed to bridge was only widening.

I discussed both items with Chris, but the only thing that accomplished was to confirm that I was not to poke around helium concentration levels any further, or LAT failures, for that matter. More had to change. Schubert and I needed greater control of engineering and additional resources to scale up our successes. My team's sole mission was to deliver products to the plant that didn't require things to be hidden and that had not been happening for years. Still, we were making steady progress as we approached the end of 2005 and I was excited for what the new year held. I shouldn't have been.

Early 2006 stymied us with a pair of PV failures and when the launch process breaks down that late in the game, it's an immediate call to action. Everything else takes a back seat. The first issue involved an SPI inflator for General Motor's GMT-900 platform. Results from the sequential environments, that included mechanical tests like vibration, shock, and drop, were aggressive and failed to meet the customer's tank pressure requirements.

The design had already been through a DV test series conducted by ASL, so this seemed to indicate a problem with the production processes, and the way Monclova was building the inflators. At least that was my suspicion, but I was unsure as the teleconference with the plant ended. They had an entirely different take on things – 'We built them to the drawings; it has to be the design.' The DV report was where we needed to start. I pushed my chair back, stood up and yelled for Schumann to come over.

"Have a seat, Dave," I said. "I just got off the phone with Monclova and they are struggling with the PV for the GMT-900 SPI. The post-sequential tank deployments are extremely variable with some failing specification. Carlos' guys are busy collecting the build records to see if they can find anything, but there must be a passing DV report we can start digesting while that is going on."

"Say no more, boss. I'm on it," he said leaping out of his seat, and I sensed from his reaction that he suspected foul play.

The next morning, he was back in my cubicle, coffee in one hand, a stack of papers tucked under his other arm, and a look somewhere between satisfaction and disbelief written across his face. I cleared some space on my desk and said,

"Put those papers down, bud, and sit. You look like you have something important to share."

"I do, I do..." he said, situating himself. "I'll get right to it. The PV inflators with the greatest post-environmental variability, the ones that are failing, all came from the vibration and drop groups – the mechanical environments – so I looked there first. I figured all that shake, rattle and roll might be breaking up the wafers, maybe even damaging the tablets, all leading to variability."

"Good assumption," I said. "But what did you find that has you looking so concerned?"

"The pictures from the DV drop test, something is not right about them. Look at this sample that was cut open afterwards. The wafers are mostly intact, with only one or two slightly damaged. That never happens. Usually all ten of them break to a certain degree and some pretty badly."

"What do the pictures from Monclova's PV look like?" I asked.

"Nothing like this," he said shaking his head. "They show much more damage, like we would expect."

"How is that possible, Dave?" I asked. "It's a pretty straight forward test. You drop the inflator onto a steel plate from about three feet in each of three different orientations, or something like that. Right?"

"Close enough, but stay with me," he said. "Monclova is saying there is nothing out of the ordinary on their end. All component certifications are good and all finished inflator inspections check out. That tells me the force the spring was applying to the wafer stack was design intent."

"OK, I'm with you so far, but the results should be independent of the test location." I said, pushing back.

"Exactly," he said, moving to the edge of his seat and taking the volume down a notch. "Nothing was adding up, so I went and talked to the test technician and the ASL engineer responsible for the DV report, and they both told me about a 'special' drop test that Paresh asked them to concoct.

"Special drop test?" I asked incredulously. "Really?"

"Oh, it's 'special' alright. He told test to put a thick foam cushion under the steel plate to soften the impact. Then he told them to make sure the inflator only bounced once, absolutely no rebounding. Somebody had to stay crouched next to the plate, ready to pounce on the inflator after the first impact, lest it make landfall again. He told them neither was explicitly forbidden by the specification."

"But it's clearly against the specification's intent," I said. "So, they cheated the test, weren't expecting oversight during the PV and got caught out. These are the kind of pranks I used to play on my sister when we were kids. Break something, barely put it back together again, then let her finish it off and take the blame. We're dealing with children."

"Yep," Dave said shaking his head up and down in affirmation. Then he looked up with a smile and said, "You did that to your sister too. That's funny."

I immediately broadcast Dave's findings to management, but that didn't change the fact that we were in trouble. The customer was expecting an inflator that year and the current design couldn't pass. We were thrown into emergency mode and began to study how it could be fixed. Dave learned quickly that the spring was good at protecting the wafers from vibration but did little when it came to drop. Basic calculations showed the forces were too great. Cushions provided the required shock absorption but the continual cycling during vibration left them shredded and useless when the drop sequence came. We needed both and by inserting a cushion inside the spring, Dave had the solution. The spring took the load during vibration, protecting the cushion in the process, and the cushion absorbed the shock of the drop when the spring compressed too far. We had to add one of the sub-assemblies on each side of the wafer stack, but we squeaked by the PV and met the customer deadline – and we did it with a design that truly met the specification intent.

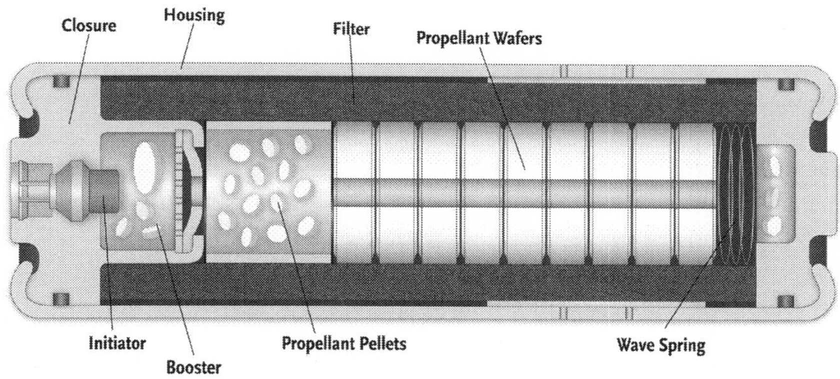

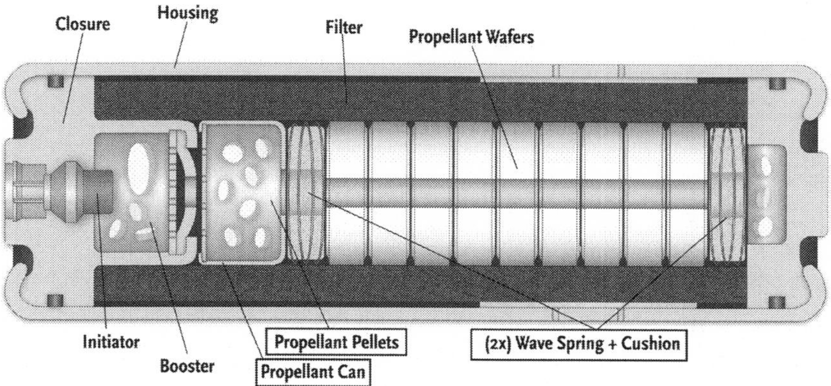

FIGURE FIVE: SPI GMT-900 GEN 1 (TOP) VS GEN 2

The amount of work to correct the GM inflator only took a month, so one had to wonder: Did ASL even try? In the end, it wasn't a difficult solution, so why hadn't they taken the time to do it right? The answer was Paresh. Evidence of his incompetence and willingness to bend the rules was mounting. We could stop his poor designs with a concerted, sustained push-back, and that process had already begun, but we also had to destroy the culture of deceit he had erected to hide behind. If we didn't, pushing-back is all we would ever be doing, and that didn't appeal to me. My hope was that by exposing the foul-play Armada was up to, management would be forced to act. You think I would have learned my lesson, but since I hadn't, we continued undaunted into the minefield, and around February of 2006, were hit with our second PV failure.

This time, the inflator was the SPI-2 for Nissan, a slightly different single-stage passenger design, but essentially the same as SPI. I called on Dave again. One thing I had learned about him in our short time together was that he loved a good conspiracy, and this smelled like one. A few days after I set him loose, he was circling outside my cubicle waiting for me to finish up a call.

"Hey, Kevin, I found something that you are not going to believe. Can I come in?"

"What am I supposed to say with that kind of opening, No? Sit down. It can't be any worse than putting pillows under the drop test plate," I said jokingly.

"I'm afraid it is," he said in no mood to joke. "I always knew Paresh fostered a culture of dishonesty, Kevin, but this takes it to a whole new level."

"What is it Dave? Spill."

"The DV report looks good and the inflator passed easily, but I found the same issue in the post drop live-dissections as I did in the GMT-900 report," he said, exhaling. "The wafers are unscathed."

"No way! They cheated the drop test again? Did you check with the test technicians?" I interrupted.

"No. Let me finish and you'll understand why I didn't bother them. There's more in this report that is troubling. The post environmental tank performance is too perfect. There is no shift in slope or peak pressure – at all – after aging, and you and I both know that's just not possible with our system."

"Please don't tell me you found more fraud, Dave," I said, resting my elbows on the desk and clasping my hands in front of my mouth. There was that 'too perfect' again, I thought to myself. I shook the image of Sheridan sitting across from me.

"Yes sir, I did," he said sitting up in his chair. "I started pouring through the build and test paperwork to make sure everything there was in order and that's where I discovered a problem, a big problem."

"Go on."

"You know how we inspect for weight, electrical resistance and helium leak before we send the inflators out to the environmental test-house," he continued as I nodded affirmatively. "Those inspections are date stamped, and when the inflators return from the test lab the same characteristics are inspected again and date stamped. There's only a 20-day delta between when the inflators left and when they came back."

He let his words hang in the air until it clicked, watching me realize, "The Nissan environments take at least two months..." I said. "And that's if you have the lab to yourself. Did Chikaraishi or Nissan approve an abbreviated test-series? If so, it has to be documented somewhere."

"You're getting ahead of me boss and giving Paresh way too much credit," he said smiling for the first time. "Once I found the discrepancy, I went and dug up the purchase order (PO) for the outside lab. I was also looking for a shortened test sequence, which would have been bad enough, but what I found is much more serious."

"So, we are not just dealing with children, are we?"

"No, sir. These are full grown deviants," he said, smile gone. "I couldn't make heads or tails of the PO. It was a mess with scratch marks all over it, so I decided to call the test house myself. They told me the parts had arrived, but the PO was never successfully negotiated, so they just sat there. Three weeks later he said he got a call from ASL canceling the tests and asking for the parts back. They never were tested to any environments! They just sat there for 20 days, were returned, inspected, deployed and reported on as a successful DV by ASL. There was no performance shift after environments because they were baseline units! Seriously, I'm appalled..."

"I'll go see Schubert right after we're done and make sure we document this and send it over to Al Bernat. He's responsible for the Design Review (DR) process. Meanwhile, we need to scrutinize everything ASL does. We take nothing for granted. Understood." I said.

"Yes, I understand, but think about it, Kevin. Some ASL engineer stood up in front of everyone at a DR, showed those results, and with a straight-face, told the audience the inflator was good to go into production."

"Not on our watch, Dave. Not anymore," I said as I stood to go see

Schubert.

The force of evil was strong with this one. Paresh had Armada's technical competency in a stall, and their ethics in nosedive. These surprises, as he liked to call them, were occurring between January and March of 2006. We documented clearly in the SPI-2 PV report that the inflator did not meet customer specifications, and that the root cause was not poor processing. I made everyone aware of it, but nothing happened. Chikaraishi ordered production to proceed and I had our PV report filed in Armada Document Control, with the uneasy feeling that another Echigawa report telling a different story was already on its way to Nissan.

While we were busy contending with Paresh's nonsense, Chris Holloway started to implode. Great, just what we needed. To those around him, Chris seemed inflated with power and a sense of invincibility. ISI was raking in money after moving operations to Mexico and Chris had a great staff that took care of business. With too much time on his hands, he began to disengage, started working out, lost weight, put the horsey shirts away, and began an ill-fated relationship with a Human Resources executive based at Takata headquarters, in Greensboro. It didn't take long for people to catch on to what was happening. While in Singapore, he ran up a huge bill texting her on his company phone. They were called in front of Frank and confessed. Both were fired, and I was re-assigned to Bruce Thames, who ran the module side of Frank's business and was now adding inflators to his responsibilities. Chris would get two years of severance and keep his company furnished Cadillac STS.

The first thing Bruce did was close the ISI house in Monclova, which by this time, truly had become infamous. That was a good move. The second thing he did was summon me to Greensboro for the annual 'Let's Get Frank Ready to Brief Jim Takada' week. Operations folks from all over North America descended on Takata's headquarters for a required week of PowerPoint and debauchery.

It was during this trip that I first met Scott Caudill. Scott managed Mr. Takada's seat belt operations, which had people wondering what he was doing there in the first place. It was widely known that he and Frank were not the best of friends, and Scott, like Frank, reported directly to Mr. Takada. But, rumor had it that weeks earlier, Jim had combined seatbelts and modules under Frank to reduce direct reports and that Scott was not pleased. I didn't ask when I realized it was him I ran into outside having a cigarette.

“Hi, I don’t think we have ever met. My name is Kevin Fitzgerald,” I said. “I run the inflator applications group up in Armada. I work for Bruce now, but was working for Chris Holloway until...”

“I’m Scott Caudill and I manage Mr. Takada’s seatbelt operations out of San Antonio,” he said shaking my hand. “Yeah, I heard that story and I’ve also heard of you.”

“Only good things, I hope?” I said somewhat curiously and lit my cigarette.

“Yes, of course, only good things!” he said laughing and patting me on the shoulder. “It’s cold as shit here.”

I almost burst out laughing. I had just moved from Arizona to Michigan and it was winter back home.

“Oh my God, this is heaven,” I said, as he put his cigarette out.

“They need me back inside. It was good to meet you, Kevin.”

“It was good to meet you, Mr. Caudill.”

I liked Scott straightaway and as the week progressed it was easy to understand why. He didn’t rule with an iron fist like Frank. He had a charisma that tugged at you and a swagger that radiated confidence. He was smart, energetic, and a fierce supporter of the Mexicans. You wanted to succeed for both, but you wanted to work for Scott. I made several of those trips to Greensboro, but that first one was the most memorable. It was also the last one Scott would have to attend. He was never going to work for Frank and as soon as Mr. Takada realized this, things quickly returned to status quo.

Brent Streeter, our inflator controller, made the trip from Armada with me, and when we arrived, Bruce scurried us into a conference room and gave us our assignment. We were asked to prepare three slides detailing inflator design changes that could be immediately incorporated into current production to reduce cost. No advance instructions. No heads up at all, and they send a bean-counter with me.

“Bruce, with all due respect, we haven’t been asked to evaluate any cost saving ideas yet.” I said. “We’ve begun work on USCAR compliance, and I can put a few slides together on that, but that progress was slowed by some recent PV failures.”

Bruce didn’t like that answer, “Three slides on cost down ideas, and don’t come out of this room until you have them finished.” After the door slammed, I looked over at Brent and said,

“OK, what you got?”

Sadly, Brent didn’t have anything and looked quite concerned. I told him not to sweat it. I downloaded some images of inflator design features from our competitor's websites, photoshopped them into Takata inflators, and then asked Brent to help me put some numbers against them. The presentation had absolutely no substance, but I knew how to make pretty slides, and Frank and Bruce loved them. Thankfully, nobody bothered to follow up on our implementation progress which was a pretty good indicator of how to handle these requests going forward. I did get to meet Scott and quite a few of Greensboro's bars, so the trip wasn't a complete loss.

Back in Armada, the group continued to be inundated. We didn't have the resources to deal with everything we were being hit with, so work on the USCAR compliant inflators and other side-projects had to be pushed back even further. All hands were on deck to fight a raging fire that Paresh lit, but was our job to extinguish. As if all of this weren't enough, the last day of March 2006 would change the company forever and put even more strain on our small group when the Monclova facility was nearly destroyed by an event that would shake the entire automotive industry.

6

Fireworks

ONE NIGHT, I was sitting in our kitchen letting the first wave of whiskey pour over me and catching up with e-mails when I received a call from Dal Luke, Vice President of Airbag Operations. I'd only met Dal once or twice before on my visits to Monclova, but we had clicked. There was a sense of urgency in his voice.

"Kevin, thank God I got you!" he shouted into the phone. It was obvious that he was outside and in a chaotic environment.

"What is it, Dal? Where are you? I can barely hear you," I said, rising off my barstool and heading into the garage.

"I am at the Monclova plant. Listen to me, Kevin, the propellant containers are on fire and the fire department wants to go in and fight it. What should I do?" he shouted even louder.

"Say again. The propellant bunkers are on fire?" I asked in disbelief.

"Yes! What should we do?"

"Nobody goes in to fight that fire, Dal. Do you understand me? Nobody! Get everybody out of the building and as far away as possible. Now, Dal. Do it now!"

"Okay, got it, Kevin. Don't stray from your phone!" he said hanging up.

There were six large propellant containers all lined up in a row off the warehouse in the rear of the facility. They were purportedly located at the required safe-distance (QD) from the plant, but one could easily throw a rock from the shipping dock and hit them.

The fire started in the first container, which stored mostly scrap propellant, and from there it spread from one metal container to the next until it reached the last two, which housed bulk PSAN propellant. There were massive quantities of the material on site. By the time the fire reached the last containers, the heat was so intense it had reduced the propellant to a sea of liquid fuel and oxidizer. What once were bags of pressed pellets and wafers were now melted and far more dangerous. A spark and confinement were all that was needed for the unthinkable to happen. Thousands of pounds of propellant were confined in the large metal containers and there was no stopping that spark now.

Dal instructed his crew to pull everyone out and let it burn. Not much later, the final bunkers exploded, delivering a massive shock-wave that decimated the plant and rang out across the city. I was on the phone with him at that moment. He had called back to tell me that everyone was out of the plant and at a safe distance away.

"Wow, that was a big one! Did you hear that?" he asked.

"I heard it, Dal, but more importantly, did you feel it? Did you feel it in your chest?" I asked, afraid of the answer.

"Yes. That was a shock wave, wasn't it?"

"Yes, but thank God you got everyone out first. I'll let you go. You have your hands full, but you won't be able to get close to the facility until morning, by which time I'll be on an airplane heading your way. Stay safe and see you soon."

"See you tomorrow, Kevin and thank you," he said as he hung up the phone.

Had any attempt been made to fight the fires and not heed the warnings to pull out, the shock wave that gently rolled over Dal and the Monclova associates would have undoubtedly ended many lives. Instead, everybody was safe and Takata would get the chance to try and rebuild the crippled facility. It had to happen in a matter of weeks or the crisis would expand to an industry-wide one.

I sat in the chartered plane with Al Bernat and Bob Schubert. There was little conversation, and we had no idea what to expect when we landed. As we started our final approach, I saw a familiar sight, the city of Monclova stretching out and then disappearing into brown, dry desert.

As luck would have it, the plane flew directly over the facility, providing a bird's eye view of the conditions. Half the plant was demolished. Landing at the airport I was stunned to see that all the windows were blown out in the terminal. This was the first real sense of the devastation. Walking from the jet to the terminal, I turned to Bob and said,

"The shock wave rolled right through here. Look at all the windows!"

"I see. I can only imagine what ground zero looks like," he said ominously.

We were at the plant in less than ten minutes. From the front it didn't seem too bad. Schubert and I donned hard hats and headed deeper into the facility while Al split off to meet up with Frank. As we neared the back, however, the scope of the damage set in. There were literally no walls. The roof was torn off. Plumbing and ventilation ducts were strewn everywhere. The ground was still hot from the explosion, a testament to the incredible amount of energy that blasted through the facility. Initiators could be heard popping among the rubble as the lingering heat set them off. A day after the explosion the plant was still not safe, but we continued into the ruined areas. Smoke was still coming off the ground. Boxes and inflator parts were littered across the floor. Pools of water were everywhere from the sprinkler system that had partially failed during the explosion. The production lines were covered in debris and knocked around with their electrical cords dropped from the ceiling twisted, severed, or simply missing. The only good news as we studied the inflator lines was that by a stroke of luck, the main deluge line was severed by the blast, preventing the emergency sprinkler system from soaking and destroying the equipment. The building was probably unsalvageable, but the production lines were not ruined. They could be repaired.

We looped around to the front of the facility, where Frank and Al were waiting for us.

"Well, what do you think?" Frank asked me.

"Holy shit..." is all I could muster.

"Well, no shit, Kevin!" Frank exclaimed. "The best you can come up with is 'holy shit'? Thanks for your engineering opinion! I know it's holy shit!".

I knew Frank wasn't mad at me, even though Al and Bob winced as he turned and walked away. What Frank wanted to hear was that we could get the facility back up – and soon. The very life of the business hinged on it. This was a big deal. Everybody in the automotive industry knew what happened almost as soon as it did. Dozens of executives from major automotive companies booked flights to Mexico that morning and were en route to see how bad it was and what needed to happen. This was an emergency.

The automotive industry operates in what is termed a 'just-in-time' supply chain. Parts are produced and shipped to final assembly lines in a matter of weeks. Serious delays in delivering parts cause big problems in the supply chain with automakers having essentially less than a month of inventory. There were no large reserves of Takata airbag inflators or modules stored in a warehouse somewhere. No airbags meant the automotive lines would come to a standstill because you can't roll a car off the line without one. Every one of us standing there knew this. The Monclova plant was the main production center for Takata inflators and it was still smoldering. The U.S. plants were mostly shut down and didn't have the infrastructure to build the volume needed. It went unsaid, but we needed to make a miracle happen.

Getting the facility up and running was going to be a challenge, not just technically and logistically, but the city of Monclova, the state of Coahuila, and ultimately the country of Mexico, would have to cooperate and approve the restart, considering the incredible nature of the explosion. This would be made easier because nobody had died, incredibly, although thousands of windows across the city had been blown out from the massive explosion. Everybody in Monclova knew what happened. People were scared, and they had every right to be. Homes had cracked walls and ceilings. Debris and flaming objects had been strewn into residential areas in proximity to the plant. The massive explosion was accompanied by a shock-wave, impossible to ignore. No doubt, this was the most frightening occurrence this city had ever witnessed. Some associates would not even return to work for Takata, terrified of a similar incident.

The Recovery

Schubert and I immediately went into action, the first day ordering more than $2 million in laser-weld generators, the engine and most fragile part of a weld station. All the driver inflators were joined with welds and many of these stations had been heavily damaged in the explosion. Laser weld equipment is extremely sensitive under normal operations – the slightest misalignment, nick, or wear can cause trouble. An explosion meant there was little chance of recovering them. The production stations themselves were more resilient. Each inflator line, whether driver or passenger, was comprised of a dozen or so individual stations responsible for one or a few of the various assembly steps. They were modular and able to move from line to line. The explosion left them dirty, with only minor damage that could be repaired. The greatest need was a safe and secure place to put them.

While Takata's issues and problems may have been more than the average company, there is no doubt the people could shine when called upon. In some sense, the automotive industry and the difficulty of keeping up with cost, technology, and time-to-market pressures had honed a culture that could move when needed, and this was an all hands-on deck moment.

The Mexicans rallied first and led the charge while Americans received their marching orders and booked charter flights down. I had Schumann come down first with two of Paresh's engineers, including Dave McCormick. Plant personnel were organized extremely quickly into an army that began work on restoring the plant in haste. A battalion of workers armed with squeegees began clearing out the water pooled everywhere. Another battalion began bolstering up the dangerous parts of the plant, reinforcing and repairing the structure, so the lines could be moved in. Mops, brooms, buckets, shovels, bins, and arms cleaned and removed mountains of debris and mangled scraps of metal.

The Plant Manager, Luis Rodriguez, disobeyed my orders and began moving production lines at night before the structure could be safely secured. It was a risk, but it saved precious time. He became a hero to the workers and me. Everywhere there was activity, like a nest of ants, slowly putting the pieces together, cleaning, repairing, and reassembling the production lines in safe spaces.

Logistically, hundreds of Takata employees, including members of my staff, were flying in from across the U.S. and Japan. An entire support organization was relocated and formed, including dedicated travel agents, nurses, doctors, cooks, and drivers. Large tents were erected. Contract laborers were hired in droves. Massive amounts of food were prepared constantly every day: mashed potatoes, pizza, rice, meat, tortillas, and large trays of red, liquid salsa served on Styrofoam plates next to jugs of water and Gatorade. From the outside looking in, one might have confused the scene for a festival or party.

I ran into Dave a few days after he arrived. It was that crazy. He was standing in line to get some grub with a highly dissatisfied look on his face. What was a vegetarian to do with this menu? I walked up behind him, putting my hand on his back. He spun around startled, and a big smile broke out across his face.

"Kevin, it's good to see you," he said. "What a couple of days we've had!"

"Tell me about it. The plant took quite a hit, didn't it?" It was good to see him.

"My God, it did. I never imagined it would be this bad," he said with a hint of despair.

"We'll put it straight, Dave. What do they have you doing?" I asked.

"McCormick and I have been assigned to the warehouse. It's a mess. Looks like it took the brunt of the blast. Parts were tossed around everywhere, and they have us trying to bring some order to the chaos," he replied.

"Now that is a shit job," I said with a smile. "But an important one.

Without those parts we have nothing."

"Shit job is right! Everything is covered with a grimy, black residue. Look at my clothes, my hands," he said extending them forward for inspection.

"You really should wash those before you eat, David," I said as we both broke out laughing. "Where do they have you staying? All the hotels filled up pretty quickly."

"I know!" he exclaimed, now animated. "They found us a motel downtown but warned us it would not be very comfortable."

"Oh, that can't be good," I interrupted.

"Not good is an understatement, Kevin. Thank God we were only there two nights. It's called the Hotel Noriega and it was like a scene from a bad movie. The windows were cracked and had bars on them and you could hear people milling around just outside. It was all pretty scary. They had us two per room and that was just a pair of beds with a plastic *Tecaté* beer table in between. The bathroom was disgusting, and the shower was nothing more than a pipe coming out of the wall."

"I'm sorry, Dave. Where did you finally end up?"

"It's okay, Kevin. One of the associates invited us to stay at his house after hearing of our plight. We're sleeping on his floor and couches now, but it's far better than that motel and they told us rooms will be opening soon where you are."

"That's good," I said. "Make you way over to Los Corrales tonight. We're there every night after work, and after a few tequilas, you won't care where you lay your head down."

That brought another smile to his face just as my walkie talkie came to life. "Gotta run, see you later."

In the days after the explosion the main issue was convincing Mexican authorities that Takata could operate safely and should be allowed to restart operations in the same facility they just blew up! This turned out to be easier than it might have first appeared. Jim Takada himself flew to Monclova, along with his support staff, and began to make assurances and work personally with the governments. He bought the city brand new fire engines. He made sure Takata repaired windows, fixed people's houses, and he repaired the schools while also pouring new money into them.

A few days later, we rolled the first inflator off a repaired production line and, along with Hideo, I raced it up to the conference room serving as Mr. Takada's office. He was elated, and later that evening at Los Corrales, he returned the favor with a big smile and an outstretched arm with an ice-cold beer at the end of it. We all felt a deep sense of accomplishment and pride. The Monclova facility had suffered one of the worst explosions in the industry's history and just days later was producing inflators again. It gave us all hope, but this simple achievement was an especially important milestone for Takata's customers. It was a sign of incredible progress, and their worry about lines shutting down and needing to find alternate solutions was significantly allayed.

Now the focus shifted back to finding places to locate the lines that were being refurbished and needed to be running. There were cleared spaces on the facility floor, but still a battered roof and missing walls! This didn't matter. The first lines were put back together, and inflators began to roll off them, essentially out in the open. Schubert was standing at the end of one reviewing some LAT results when I wandered upon him.

"Did you ever think you would see such a beautiful sunset over the production lines, Bob?" I asked him with a smile.

"It is a pretty evening, that's for sure," he answered, glancing up from the data.

"How's it going? Everything seems to be humming right along."

"Pretty good. I'm not too thrilled about these conditions, though," he answered.

I nodded in agreement. He was right. The environment was far from ideal, but the rush to prevent customer shutdowns was trumping everything. Fortunately, April is a dry month in the Monclova desert and there was no rain, but the relative humidity still averaged 40-60% each day. We needed to get these lines under cover as quickly as possible.

Politics and Sushi Wind It Down

What would a crisis of this scale be without corporate infighting? Behind the visible chaos of a plant in recovery was a similar struggle. Frank wanted all of inflator engineering and was pinning the disaster on Paresh. It was Paresh's propellant that took out the facility and this seemed an opportune time to press for control of his organization. North American operations wanted the flood of bad designs and problems stopped. They wanted USCAR compliant inflators that Paresh was dragging his feet on.

Our discoveries in the beginning of 2006 began this momentum, but the tidal wave against Paresh kept rising. Issues were rampant, had been pasted over, covered up, and inflators had been pushed on the plant prematurely that were failing PV tests regularly. When the explosion occurred, the moment was ripe for Frank to launch a new salvo and push for more control. To make matters worse, at first Paresh didn't want to send any of his people to help in the recovery until Frank shamed him into it. Not only did they eventually arrive, but later Paresh came himself. It was his first visit to the Mexico plant ever. Incredible. He was mocked and chided for this. The first time he had been to the plant it was blown up by his propellant and was in total crisis mode. It was not his finest hour.

Paresh was not a confrontational man in person. Talking with him it became quickly obvious he disliked direct or pointed conversations. Frank was all about confrontation, famous for his outbursts at people who had done something wrong. I witnessed one memorable scene with Frank and Paresh in front of the damaged plant where Frank was screaming at Paresh, who had just arrived. He had him in front of the facility, waving his hands and pointing at him. Here was this imposing man towering over a stoic and clearly rattled Paresh. Certainly, it had elements of grandstanding, but the push was being made and a demoralized Paresh would be less apt to fight back. Frank knew what he was doing.

The work continued day and night. Engineers from the states took twelve-hour shifts standing at the end of the inflator lines, making sure everything was going together correctly. The sounds of power tools and equipment was almost deafening at times. The army of workers began to build plywood structures around the lines in the open, even fitting them with air conditioning. These would be called the 'boxes within the box.' The walls and roof of the facility were slowly but surely patched up and replaced. Damaged metal was cut out and new sheets fastened in place. At the end of each grueling day, I would report our progress back to Executive Management in Auburn Hills. You could feel everyone on the other end of the phone pulling for us as a great sense of camaraderie was settling in across Takata. Tim Healy, then President of Takata North America, would always lift our spirits as we ended those calls and I made a mental note to make sure to meet him in person. It truly was a remarkable time.

But not for all of us. We were about four weeks into the recovery when Dave became very ill. I had no idea until McCormick ran me down at the plant.

"Hey, Kevin. Listen, Schumann is not in good shape."

"What do you mean he's not in good shape?" I asked.

"He's sicker than shit. At dinner a couple of nights ago, the vegetarian thought it would be a good idea to order up a few rows of sushi and I think he has food poisoning."

"Sushi? In the Monclova desert?" I asked in disbelief.

"Yeah, I know, Kevin, but focus. This isn't your average Montezuma's revenge. For three days now, he's been crawling between his bed and the toilet and it hasn't been pleasant. Trust me, I know. I have the room next to him and the walls aren't very thick."

"Okay, I get it, Dave. How is he now?"

"I think he's coming out of it. The plant doctor recommended I bring him bananas, water, and *Pedialyte* and he's starting to keep those down now."

"Okay, well that's good. Do we need to send the doctor over to the hotel?" I asked, concerned for my friend.

"No, let's see how he is tomorrow. If he is still keeping food down, I think he'll be alright."

"Damn, we're all so caught up in what's going on around here, I didn't even realize he was missing. I'll go see him tonight," I said.

"No, don't. He doesn't want any company. I'll tell him you asked about him. If he doesn't continue to improve, I'll let you know, and we can make arrangements to get him out of here."

"Alright, but keep me posted," I said.

The next day, I bumped into Dave staggering around the plant looking like a different person. He must have lost 20 lbs.

"Hey, you're up and about!" I said, happy to see him. "McCormick just filled me in on your weight loss plan yesterday. How much have you dropped? Your pants look like a crap sack."

That got a small chuckle out of his frail body, but it was clear his time in Monclova was over and that he needed to go home. He would resist, attached to the work and camaraderie, and as I readied to have that conversation with him, Frank Roe, who was passing by, stopped at the sight of him and said,

"You look like shit, boy. Go home." Conversation over. Dave was on the next flight back to Michigan. He had his own mending to tend to.

The recovery was coming to an end. One by one, lines turned back on and inflators began to be churned out with numerous additional controls in place and among continual facility repairs. The propellant couldn't be stored on-site anymore, of course, since all the containers were blown to pieces and the governments were still wary. So, it was housed many miles away and the plant was fed by truck after truck carrying small loads of propellant a growing number of times a day. Minus the obviously damaged facility patched up here and there with plywood-housed production lines churning out inflators, things were back to normal. There were walls and a roof, and it was now time for me to return home. The patient was patched up and blood was flowing again. A construction site had been identified for a new facility and none of our customer's production lines were facing disruption. I was ready to go home and was looking forward to spending time with Sandy and the kids.

Just before I left, Frank Roe asked to speak to me in private.

"Kevin, Takata has decided to put inflator R&D and applications engineering under one umbrella again," he said, taking me aback. Management had kept a tight lid on the behind-the-scenes politicking.

"What are you telling me, Frank? Do I still work for you and Bruce in operations or do I work for Paresh now?"

"Neither. Paresh is not part of the equation."

"I'm not following."

"You will run Armada. Inflator R&D and applications," he finally said.

I was in shock. "Get out of here," was all I could blurt out.

After he stopped laughing he continued, "There is more I have to say. I recently learned that it was you that Dal called the night the plant exploded. I know the Mexican fire department wanted to go in and fight the fire, and you told him no and to pull everyone out. You are a hero, Kevin. Nobody died that night because of you, and I wanted you to hear that directly from me."

"I was just doing my job, Frank, but thank you. I really appreciate that."

The gravity of the situation sank in. Frank had won his political struggle – and we were going to begin the process of fixing inflator engineering. I could finally right the ship.

"And don't for a minute think that is why you got the position," he said, as he patted me on the back. "You earned that. We have a charter going back to Michigan tomorrow. You'll fly back on that. There will be a limo waiting for you when you arrive, and I'll talk to you after you get some rest. Thanks again, Kevin."

I was returning to Armada triumphantly and in style, or so I thought. The next day, it all fell apart. Al Bernat was en route to Armada to deliver the news to Paresh, when he was turned around by a last-minute call from Japan, who suddenly got cold feet. It could have been because of my previous reporting of falsified reports and confronting of key management figures, or it could have been because they felt they had no control over me. Either way, my promotion was cancelled just moments before Paresh was to be informed. Instead of taking Paresh's role, I fell back to reporting to Bruce as Director of Inflator Operations with my same, small engineering group.

A few weeks later that changed again. I was out with the team at a local Buffalo Wild Wings' happy hour when Bruce called.

"Hi Bruce, how are you? Is there an emergency?" It was odd for Bruce to call me at all, let alone after hours.

"No, not an emergency, Kevin, but there is something we need to discuss, so I'll get right to it," he answered curtly. "Applications engineering and operations are too much for one person. Dal and I think it best that you focus your energies on engineering...and we'll take care of operations. We want you to stop the bad inflator designs from ever reaching us."

I pushed back immediately, "Bruce, that is not what I signed up for. I was hired on as Director of Inflator Operations, not manager of a small inflator applications group. That's the responsibility level I had when I left Takata six years ago." I was angry.

"Relax, Kevin. This is best for the company and the decision has already been made," he said coldly.

"Did you ever think to ask if I'd prefer one position over the other? Was that even a consideration?" I asked rhetorically, exasperated with Takata again.

"Focus on engineering, Kevin. We've got the plant. Have a good night."

Conversation over. I walked back into the bar, finished my beer quietly, said my goodbyes, and drove straight home. I went from being the most important inflator person with influence over operations and engineering to a role with even less responsibility than I had before the Monclova ordeal. It was back to me and my small band of resistance fighters keeping Paresh in line.

7

The Second Damning Report

A SKELETON CREW at Armada had done their best to slog through the issues while most of us were in Monclova, but despite their valiant efforts the work had piled up. We circled the wagons and in a few short weeks were caught up – an amazing job by all and the reason we were out at Buffalo Wild Wings the night Bruce called and told me to let go of operations. There was motive to clearing the backlog so quickly. The team was eager to get back to where we were before the PV failures and the Monclova explosion. They wanted to have fun again, and they were not about to let me sulk over my perceived demotion. There was still plenty of important work to do, and without operations to worry about, I listened to them, and focused like a laser on Paresh. He absolutely hated that we were right down the hall from him and he could no longer use the plant as his scapegoat. Those days were over, and he knew it. Peter Holland became his messenger. Paresh would never make the trip down the hall, and when I looked up and saw Peter leaning against the entrance to my cubicle one afternoon days after I got home, I knew the news wasn't going to be good.

"Kevin, do you have a minute?" he asked.

"Sure, Peter, what is it?"

"We can't get the PSDI-5 inflator to pass Nissan's specification. It keeps rupturing after sequentials. We threw the kitchen sink at it and nothing has worked, and that includes desiccant. We added calcium sulfate to both chambers and the inflator is still coming apart after environments."

"You have got to be kidding, Peter!? I was just looking at the list of our upcoming PVs and the Nissan PSDI-5 is right at the top. I just assumed the DV was already in the books."

"Well, you know what happens when you assume, Kevin," he said with a smile, trying to lighten the moment.

“Have you told Nissan? If you haven’t even passed DV yet, there is no way we are going to hold their production schedule. Please tell me someone has notified Nissan,” I begged him.

“You’ll have to ask Paresh that, Kevin.” That was a no.

“Get me everything you have, Peter. Drawings, reports, lessons learned – everything. We have no time to waste. I’ll let Frank and Bruce know what’s going on. You guys are unbelievable,” I said as I got up and walked around him to find Schubert.

They couldn’t hide from us anymore, so now Paresh just dumped his problem over the wall for us to deal with. It was widely known that he struggled with the PSDI-5 launch for Ford that preceded Nissan. Schumann had lived through it. Calcium sulfate desiccant was added to that inflator to absorb what was eating it alive from the inside out, but now, far too late into the game, Peter was telling me the same solution was coming up short for Nissan.

The Nissan specification is the most difficult, bar none. It combines long-term heat aging and thermal shock in a sequence, the only customer specification that does. USCAR and others separate the heat aging portion out, making their requirements easier to pass. The sequence packs a one-two punch that is brutal to any propellant system, but even more so to a moisture-sensitive one like PSAN. The sustained and elevated temperature of the heat aging liberates any pre-assembled moisture that might exist in inflator components, like the cushions or filter, and that free-to-roam moisture seeks out and finds a new home in better desiccating materials, especially the propellant. Follow that with endless hot to cold temperature cycles that pump that moisture in and out of the propellant and bad things start to happen.

When Peter came to us, ASL had already failed multiple attempts to pass the Nissan specification, all with the same results – aggressive and rupturing inflators. Paresh had emptied his bag of tricks. Desiccant in both chambers didn’t work. Their last foolish attempt was to wrap the AI-1 tablets in aluminum foil, but there was no science behind this kluge. Moisture was still free to migrate wherever it wanted. The proverbial kitchen-sink never had a chance, and when Peter unloaded all the reports and drawings on us, the only thing we could do was to reduce as much of the inflator’s pre-assembled moisture as possible. There was a layer of paint on the cushions that allowed cameras to detect their presence during assembly, which was the only thing left to remove. We used a more elegant solution to do the same, gave it one last try, and BOOM! There was no fixing Paresh's propellant weakness in the face of Nissan's environments.

I had been communicating the Nissan situation in my weekly Good News/Bad News reports, which I was responsible for circulating to Takata executive management. The distribution included Frank Roe, Bruce Thames, Chikaraishi, Al Bernat – everybody that needed to know – and as our last grasp at straws progressed in Monclova validations, I made sure they all knew we were headed for trouble. I drafted another Good/Bad News report to the group with the final PV results, making it clear the inflator would never meet Nissan specifications. Just before I hit the send button, I thought it best to give Bruce a call first,

"Bruce, this is Kevin. Do you have a minute?"

"Yes, what is it, Kevin?" he said curtly. Bruce was never happy.

"You are aware of the issues we've been having with the Nissan PSDI-5," I started. "Well, it failed PV in Monclova, like we feared. Another rupture. We are out of options and we need to tell Nissan that we can't pass their sequential environments, specifically their combination of heat age and thermal shock. See what they recommend. Sorry Bruce, but someone should have approached them much earlier."

"Did the module PV pass with the same inflator?" he asked, catching me off guard.

"Yes...it did, but the module PV doesn't include the sequence of environments that is causing the inflators to..."

He cut me off, "I only asked if the module passed its PV, nothing more. Thank you. We are going to release the inflator for production based on those results."

"You can't do that, Bruce. This is not some small failure! The inflator is rupturing after environments. My group will not release a PV report that supports your decision, and I can guarantee you that Chikaraishi will. He will make sure one will go to Nissan that says it passed."

"Good-bye Kevin."

I put the phone back in its cradle, sat there staring at my computer screen for a minute, and then hit the send button on my report.

Bruce may have moved on, but there was no way I could. I instructed the group to do what engineers are supposed to: dig into it, verify root cause, and seek corrective actions. Schubert and I put the test matrix together and gave the assignment to one our newer engineers to shepherd. We had him evaluate PSDI-5 inflators alongside just the propellant, sealed in vials with varying amounts of desiccant and AI tablets. We constructed a series of controlled experiments to understand this relationship. AI-tablets were one big inherent source of moisture and the Nissan design required three of them. And the tests confirmed they were the culprit; what Paresh's team already knew. The vials had 'marsh-mellowed' tablets that couldn't even have a basic measurement taken from them to calculate density. The very first inflator tested after environments exploded.

It was indisputable evidence the design would never pass. The more auto-ignition material added, the worse things got. One hit from the ignition system and the weakened tablets would crumble and generate gas far faster than any inflator could expel it. It was game over. Calcium sulfate desiccant did little to help, only marginally improving the situation, but no matter how much of it was added, a PSDI-5 with three AI-1 tablets exploded after Nissan's environments. Every time.

I filed our report with configuration management. Kelli Kirkum, or KK as we called her, managed that department for me. I was serious about documentation and she was serious about recording, sorting, retrieving, and presenting it. She joined Takata as Bob Phillion's assistant coincident with my return in 2005, and it was clear early on that she was being underutilized. A few months after meeting her, she was part of the team.

"I know you are new here, KK. Hell, you are new to working in general, and for you to have to see this kind of behavior is sickening. In the twenty years I've been at this, I've only seen it at Takata, and this is the second time now," I said to her.

"The second time now! What was the first?" she asked, visibly upset. "It couldn't have been worse than this, could it?"

"Yes, it could have, KK, but that's a story for another time," I said, ready to call it a day. "Let's get this thing filed. We document everything, just the way it happened and then we fight. That you will learn about me."

The string of failures was impressive. Honda's tragic PSDI PV in LaGrange, then Mazda's PSPI-6, GM's SPI, Nissan's SPI-2 and now everyone's PSDI-5. The coverup of Paresh's incompetence was in full bloom, and with North American executives now actively participating, it was starting to get lonely on our island. My whole assertion that Frank brought me back to end this type of behavior was crumbling right before me like a PSAN propellant tablet withering in the hot, Florida sun. What was so baffling to me was that they didn't seem to mind that I was documenting every step of it along the way.

The Deck Chairs Are Rearranged

Working for Bruce was really starting to suck. He never had a nice thing to say, never smiled, and had no understanding of what we did in Armada. We were a distraction. His decision to look the other way on Nissan PSDI-5 was reprehensible, and our relationship only soured from there. I was in my office when he called next. It didn't happen often, and it was never good.

"Kevin, Frank and I have important meetings in Auburn Hills tomorrow. We will be taking a charter out of Greensboro in the morning and will be landing in Pontiac around 9:00 am. Rent a nice car and be there when we arrive. Block out your whole day."

"Do I need to prepare anything for the meetings, Bruce?"

"No, you are not participating," he said half-laughing. "But you need to stay in Auburn Hills in case Frank makes any change in plans. We'll find you when we need you."

"Okay, then. Will you e-mail your itineraries please?"

"Yes, I will." He hung up.

It was a snowy winter morning when they landed, and as I pulled up to the small terminal, I was muttering at myself for having had the rental car freshly cleaned before picking it up. Snowplow after snowplow had made that effort meaningless. Frank said hello as he piled his bags into the trunk while Bruce shivered, waited his turn, and grumbled something about the car not being very clean. Great. Later in the afternoon when their meetings finished, I took them over to the hotel, so they could drop their bags off and freshen up before dinner. It was a quiet ride, and when I pulled the car up in front of the lobby, Frank jumped out and went straight in out of the cold. I walked to the back of the car where Bruce was waiting and popped the trunk. Leaning in to get his briefcase he barked at me,

"Bring Frank's bags to him." It wasn't an ask. He didn't even give me a chance to offer.

"Excuse me?" I said.

"You heard me. Carry Frank's bags."

I stood there dumbfounded, not quite sure what to do as he walked into the lobby. After a moment, I reached in, grabbed Frank's bags, slammed the truck closed, cursing under my breath, and wheeled them up to where they were waiting to check in.

"Meet us back here in an hour for dinner," Bruce said, dismissing me.

"Thanks, Kevin," Frank offered as I fled to find a cup of coffee and an hour of normalcy.

Years in the defense industry exposed me to leaders like Bruce. They weaponize intimidation. We used to call them the 'Vikings' at Martin Marietta. Hell, I worked for some and even grew to respect a few. Tough is okay, if it is balanced by fairness, but I wasn't seeing much fairness from Bruce. In fact, every time he called, it took a back seat. It wasn't long after he rang again.

"Kevin, this is Bruce. Can you talk privately?"

"I'm alone. What is it, Bruce?"

"I've made the decision to let Ed McGuigan go," he told me. "I know when we talked last I had pulled back from that, but I've had further discussions with Japan and they want him terminated. They feel he is too confrontational."

"No way, Bruce. You and I both know that Ed is just doing his job as head of Program Management. If he didn't push back, we would have even more redundant inflator configurations. He is doing exactly what you need him to be doing!" I was hot, and Bruce knew it.

"I will send Pat Giampaolo (the VP of HR) over to assist you..."

I cut him off. "What?! You want me to fire him? You can't be serious. He works for you!"

"I know that, Kevin, but I am not flying up there just to fire someone..."

I cut him off again. "Bruce, Ed is a retired Naval aviator. He put fighter jets down on dark, aircraft carrier tarmacs. I have nothing but respect for him, he has done nothing wrong, and I am not doing your dirty work for you."

"Pat will be there at 4:00 tomorrow. Have a good night, Kevin."

I was so angry – angry at Bruce again, at Takata again. This was bullshit. Everyone knew Bruce tried to fire Ed once before over some ridiculous argument the two had had years earlier in Greensboro that had almost come to blows. Now with Holloway gone, and Bruce securing the backing he needed in Japan, Ed was hopelessly exposed. It was one of the worst things I ever had to sit through. Pat set the meeting in Chris' old office and when he arrived, he asked me to join. I still have no idea why. Pat did all the talking, and Ed was rightfully outraged. It was awful. The next week, I had the office ripped apart, and moved some of my engineers in to rid ourselves of the stench.

Ed's abrupt termination was not the only chatter trending at Armada's water coolers. Talk was beginning to circulate that the operations group would be moving closer to Bruce in Greensboro. Most had just relocated to Michigan two years earlier, and I was only coming up on a year, so we were all rightfully concerned. It didn't end the same for all of us. Arguments could be made for moving functions like quality, purchasing, and logistics to Greensboro, but not inflator applications engineering. Since it wasn't practical to be at the factory in Mexico, where it should have been, the next best place was to be in Paresh's grill, and that's where we stayed. Everyone else went to Greensboro. That was a huge relief, but it was still unclear who I would be reporting to. There was talk that was changing too.

When I came into work the morning after learning we were staying put, I noticed Al Bernat sitting in Paresh's office with the door closed. Half an hour later, he was standing at the entrance to my cubicle asking if I had a moment to speak to him alone.

"What is it, Al?" I said, closing the door to a small conference room. I didn't trust him. I could rationalize why Chris put the screws to me back in 2001 when I was exiting. He needed my help. But I could never understand why Al called me. His threats seemed more directed at keeping me quiet.

"Good news that the team is not moving to Greensboro, isn't it?" He offered first.

"Yes, it is, but did it ever really make sense, Al? I mean, everything is here."

"No, I suppose not. Let's talk about the inflator organization because it is changing again," he continued. "Takata is putting the inflator R&D and applications groups back under one umbrella again, this time reporting to me."

"So, Paresh and I will both report to you, and I am no longer part of operations?" I said, asking for clarification.

"Yes, your thoughts?"

I let out an obvious sigh. The only thing that could have been worse was reporting to Paresh. When would this company learn? Al knew nothing about inflators. Zilch. In reply to my obvious displeasure, he said,

"I was hoping for a more welcoming reception. Maybe even some congratulations."

"I'm sorry, Al," I said halfheartedly. "I got distracted. There is a lot we need to talk about."

Al and I were not off to a great start, but not all the news was bad. Several other big organizational changes took place at the same time. Jim finally made the move to combine airbag and seatbelt operations, this time correctly putting Scott Caudill at the helm. He also realized it was time for a new guard, and that included handing over more responsibility himself. He promoted his son, Shigehisa, to President, Frank moved on to non-automotive initiatives, and Bruce retired. Even though I was reporting to Al Bernat, and deeply disappointed by that reality, I was eager to begin working with Scott. He was the antithesis of Bruce, and a much-needed breath of fresh air.

8

Improvements and Wins

I ALWAYS TRIED my best to look on the bright side of life. Scott was a major trade up, and Al was adamant about not moving his office to Armada, two positives, but still nothing was working. We couldn't hide from Nissan's requirements. I had to push back against this happening in the future, and the only way to do that was to add heat-age and thermal-shock to the DV check-list, regardless of the customer. Nobody could deny me this and I hoped that would improve things going forward. Paresh had to be feeling the heat. Chikaraishi and Echigawa too. They had to be tired of falsifying customer reports, and with me in the mix pushing back, their workload was only increasing. Paresh had Europe to contend with as well, and they weren't happy with him either. The man was fighting a war on three continents. My good friend Stephen Kimmich filled me on the European theater.

In his role as TAIC's Chief, Stephen was fairly independent, but he reported to Paresh on paper and always visited Armada when back in the states.

"Stephen, my God, look at you!" I said giving him a big hug, "how many years has it been?"

"I'm not sure. Six or seven, I think, but you look like you've aged much more than that," he said as we burst out laughing.

"Did you see Hardenburg?" I asked, "you want to talk about aging!"

"Yes, I did. You guys look great. It's good to see you, Kevin."

"You, too, Stephen. Hardenburg is running our driver inflator group now. Don't let his cranky old demeanor fool you. He's a Michigander and loves it up here. So, what's new, bud?" I asked my old friend.

"Too much," he bemoaned. "You know I run TAIC now and report to Paresh, so it would take a few beers. Have you met Christophe Dervyn yet?

He runs our Europe inflator operations."

"Yeah, I met him briefly in Singapore. He jumped into the same cab as me on the way from the hotel. After I introduced myself, he says, 'Oh, you are Kevin Fitzgerald, you work in Armada with Paresh. I hate that man.'" We burst out laughing again.

"Christophe doesn't hate Paresh as much as he hates PSAN," Stephen continued. "You remember that massive explosion in Toulouse, France. That was ammonium nitrate and it's not just Christophe that doesn't want anything to do with it. Neither does Renault and they are 30% of Europe's business."

"Ouch. What's Paresh doing about that?"

Stephen sighed, "nothing – and that's the problem. Christophe will not lose that business and he doesn't believe we should be using PSAN anyway. He convinced someone in Japan to license an old TRW GuNi propellant and I'm using it right now to develop a driver inflator for Renault."

"Really? Well, you know I'm always up for a little anarchy, Stephen. And Paresh knows about this?"

"Yes, he does, and he is not happy. That puts me in an awkward position. I am not against PSAN like Christophe is. I know Paresh is working on his next generation of inflators and is on the hook to pass all customer specifications, including USCAR and Nissan. So, the jury is still out."

"Yes, I've heard the X-Series will fix everything too," I said. "It had better, Stephen, because right now, nothing is working."

"Well, we'll know soon enough. I have to run, Kevin. Paresh wants to have lunch and I have to head to the airport after that. I'm glad you're back, and I am sure we will be seeing much more of each other. We are counterparts now," he said, shaking my hand.

"Yes, we are, my friend. Travel safe," I said as he turned to leave.

Paresh was under a lot more pressure than I realized. I'd heard the rumors about Christophe: that he was a political dynamo hellbent on getting whatever he wanted. I always wondered what he meant when he told me he hated Paresh. Did the two have a past, or was it simply Paresh's decision to go forward with PSAN in the face of all the warnings? The devastating accident in Toulouse took the lives of many of Christophe's countryman. Either way, it was more trouble for Paresh who was betting his redemption on the X-Series and staying deeply immersed in its development. If he could show that his new inflator lineup solved all the problems of the past, he could stop the walls from closing in on him.

All we heard about the new line-up, however, was that his team was struggling and already late to key milestones. The pressure of this must have been too much for Chikaraishi because suddenly, I received news that the new lineup was being handed to us early, before design validation had even started. All the failures that Chikaraishi had to cover-up and lie for over the years must have eroded his trust in Paresh. We had only a year before production was to start. A major challenge, but one I took as a clear signal my team was starting to gain the respect we deserved.

Now this was exciting because with the X-Series transfer came more of Paresh's people, and our group nearly doubled in size. We landed Dave McCormick, who Paresh was likely happy to give over. Dave was more like us. Schumann was elated. The two were very close and he was a major pick-up. Schumann was promoted to supervise the passenger launches, and McCormick would lead the driver efforts. Schubert fit seamlessly into the role of sweeper, providing guidance and support. It was the perfect team and it needed to be. Paresh left us with half-completed designs and little time to pull off a miracle.

Knowing this, Japan also moved the test and prototype departments under us. They wanted no excuses since I had already made loud and clear the road-blocks Paresh had thrown up that would make it difficult to get our testing completed. I promoted Hardenburg to manage those departments and clear the way for us. Even bigger, Armada's Japanese engineers also joined the team – a must since the first X-Series launches were for Honda and Nissan, and they had been involved from the start. Adjusting to our way of doing things would be a sobering experience for them, but it was all good.

For too long, Paresh had given the young, Japanese residents too much freedom, and many were still up to the same antics Hideo was famous for in LaGrange. Calls would come in at night. Prototype hardware would show up at their desks, and overnight clandestine builds would produce data that was in Japan before people arrived for work the next morning. It was dishonest, unsafe, and never should have been tolerated by Paresh.

We went on full lockdown, instituted sweeping procedural changes and enforced them vigorously. We conducted a full physical inventory and floor sweep and threw out all the rogue hardware we could find. And yet the shenanigans continued. We checked everyone's lockers next and found parts there, some of them live! As a last resort, we removed the lockers and fenced in all the prototype hardware. When this last line of defense was breeched, I blew a gasket.

"Kevin, you are not going to believe this," Hardenburg said.

"Oh, I bet I am, Bob. What is it?" I asked.

"Well, we were doing our routine checks this morning in prototype and we came across some footprints on top of the file cabinet next to the parts cage. Looks like someone used it to jump the fence, now that you locked up all the hardware," he said covering his head in anticipation of my reaction. I took a couple of deep breaths, collected my thoughts, and said,

"Raise the fence to the ceiling, Bob, and find out who it was."

"I'll take care of the fence today boss and get back to you on the other. It's hard to believe we have to go to these extents."

"Whoever jumped that fence is going home, Bob. This is not a game. The only way we are going to be successful is if we are all pulling in the same direction."

Paresh and Al knew I was serious and after a thorough investigation, the offender was removed. That ended the practice once and for all, and although our Japanese associates never admitted it, they were relieved. They didn't appreciate being forced to deceive us. From that point forward, we pulled in one direction. All of us.

Second Class Citizens

Paresh was not at all pleased with the new arrangement in Armada and, of course, Schubert and I didn't think it went far enough. When Japan handed us the X-Series and two of Paresh's key departments, we pushed hard to include inflator R&D, arguing that Paresh was a chemist, and needed to focus on propellant. We almost had Al convinced, but Paresh claimed he needed devices to develop his propellant. A Catch-22. Eventually, Paresh won Al over and kept his small group, but the process left him feeling marginalized and when he found an opening for payback he took it.

The opportunity presented itself at a meeting Al called to introduce Tim Healy to all the personalities in Armada. It was an informal gathering that we used to outline the new organization and update Tim on the status of our projects. As we were wrapping things up, Paresh asked if we could spend a few minutes on a separate topic. There were no objections.

"Tim, the conditions of the R&D offices out back are atrocious," Paresh started. "The building is old, poorly insulated, and the roof is in desperate need of repair. I can take you out there right now and show you, but I am losing people over it and we need to act now."

"Well, we can't have that," Tim answered. "Why can't we move everyone into this building? There seems to be plenty of room."

"No, no, we can't all fit in here," Paresh exclaimed! "The old office space can be converted into an R&D lab. I need a small build area now that I don't have prototype anymore and that will only require a new roof. For more office space Tim, we need to build a new structure."

Schubert and I glanced at each other. Was he serious? Yes, the building out back was old and in need of repair, but it was not why his people were leaving. They were leaving because he was constantly asking them to lie and taking all their credit.

"I can't put them through another winter out there, Tim," he persisted. "They need to be out by the end of September, even if it means renting a couple of trailers and relocating people there until a new building is ready. And they shouldn't be the ones to move into the trailers, either. They've suffered enough."

"Why are you just bringing this up now, Paresh?" Al interrupted, somewhat irritated.

"I'm sorry, Al, but the R&D guys have become more vocal recently and I thought it would be a good idea to discuss it while Tim was here," he replied sheepishly.

Crickets. More crickets. Way too many crickets. I couldn't take it any longer.

"We'll move into temporary trailers," I finally said. "I think we can all fit in this building, but if we really think more office space is...."

"Yes, yes, I think that's best," Paresh exclaimed, his pitch rising. "And your folks can have the new building when it's finished."

That sneaky little man, I thought. "One promise," I said looking directly at him. "Do not build us a pole barn. It needs to be a decent building with the same facade as the rest of the campus. I'm volunteering to move my people to trailers because I agree that where you work does matter."

Al and Tim nodded to me in appreciation, while Paresh grinned. He got exactly what he wanted, which was the main building to himself. His concern was not for his people's welfare. That was feigned. What he was after was tighter control of the information flow, and my guys were too close, and picking up on too much real-time intelligence for his liking. I wasn't going to be bothered by the separation. People tended to gravitate to us.

So, we crammed into two, spartan single-wide trailers with our heads held high and the X-Series ours to deliver. They were rough, but far worse for the women who understandably refused to use their bathrooms. That meant schlepping over to the main building several times a day during the nasty Michigan winter we spent out there. When the team felt like second-class citizens, I reminded them that we were the ones called on to perform a miracle, and not the folks across the parking lot in the cozy main building.

I reminded them of that every morning as we piled into the small conference room at the end of my trailer to run through the day's hot-ticket items. My job was to keep their spirits up, keep them focused, and not let anything get in their way. We had the full support of Auburn Hills, Japan and Scott Caudill, and for once Paresh wasn't a problem. He was too busy arranging the main building to look fuller than it was after moving all his people in.

I loved those morning meetings in the trailers. The fate of Takata's inflator business was in our hands now and they were a great way to kick-start each day. Even though intense at times, they were always good for a laugh too. Schumann had this habit of answering every scheduling question I'd ask him with 'soon, boss', but these were different times now.

"Dave, how are you coming with the PSPI-X initiator tolerance study? Are we going to keep the current press fit or are we switching to a standard o-ring?" I asked him one morning.

"Yes, I am working on that," he answered.

"I know you are working on it, Dave, that's why I asked. You all know we have to freeze these designs and get into DV. The schedules are right there on the wall behind you and if you look closely you will see we are already releasing production equipment on redlined drawings. When will you know, Dave?"

"Soon is not going to work this time, is it boss?" he said, smiling and twirling his pen in his hand. "I understand, Kevin. I'll have that date tomorrow when we meet again, and it will meet schedule. I understand the urgency..." he said trailing off and pointing out the window. "I thought you told Peter not to empty the toilets while we were in here. That sure looks like the septic truck pulling up to the trailer again."

"Don' try to change the subject, Dave. This is serious."

"I'm not, Kevin. I swear. Look for yourself."

"Son of a ....," I said reaching for my coat to go raise some hell. Schumann was right. I had warned Peter twice about this already. Paresh must have finished all the three-foot extensions to the cubicles in the main building and in his boredom called in a septic strike. It was disgusting. They would pull this pink, fuming truck up alongside the trailers and drain our bathrooms while we were working – exhaust and stink wafting around us.

I swear that Paresh, Peter, and Jeff Douma, Armada's local HR manager, invented ways to drive me batshit crazy. Jeff did nothing to improve my opinion of Takata's HR department. To give you an idea of his decision-making prowess, he actually showed up at a company Christmas party dressed head to toe in form-fitting black leather. He sided with Paresh early on and was a constant thorn in my side. Whenever they could, the trio made life for my team more difficult than it needed to be. It only strengthened our resolve. We finally bought our own locks and put them on all the trailer's septic drains and kept the keys to ourselves.

The 13X-Factor

The X-series inflators were developed around Paresh's next generation PSAN propellant. It used a more widely available fuel and advertised a 5% higher gas efficiency. He coupled the chemistry with new inflator designs to produce a portfolio of even smaller devices. The driver side inflators, SDI-X and PSDI-X, and small passenger SDI-X 1.7, were all disk shaped and would be market leaders. The cylindrical passenger inflators SPI-X and PSPI-X, however, would not be. The industry was moving to full-size, disk passenger inflators, but Paresh instead chose to use more wafers to develop smaller diameter cylinders. Yes, wafers, and after all our prior demonstrations highlighting their variability and inefficiency.

Still, it was our job to push them all into production, and fast. The underlying designs of the disk inflators were sound, save their auto-ignition mechanisms. With a sustained, focused effort and a lot of luck, they could be readied in time. The passenger-side inflators were Xerox copies of the previous generation, set at a 25% size reduction, and were of lesser concern. Everything hinged on getting through Nissan's nasty environmental sequence and keeping everything together on the bonfire grate.

What was it that enabled the substantial reduction in the size and weight of the X-Series disk inflators? One might think the new propellant's higher gas efficiency played a role, but that was merely a marketing ploy. Its density was lower than the previous generation, which meant more was needed to deliver the same amount of gas. A swap. The real size reductions came from the new mechanical designs. Paresh finally dropped his self-imposed requirement prohibiting the inflator from growing, or 'baseballing,' during deployment. That took the handcuffs off his engineers. The booster tube no longer had to be welded to both the cap and the base and that's where the real breakthroughs sprang from. The PSDI-X dual stage inflator made the greatest gains by moving the second chamber inside the first, slashing part count, and enabling a package size that rivaled most competitor's single stage devices.

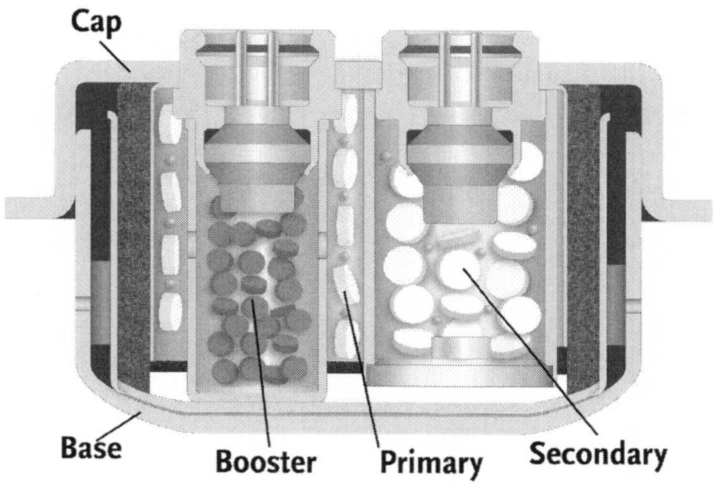

FIGURE SIX: CROSS-SECTION OF 'PSDI-X' INFLATOR

But the new propellant was still ammonium nitrate and nearly identical to last. Why would it behave any differently? The short answer is, it didn't. Put three AI tablets and calcium sulfate desiccant in an X-Series inflator, subject it to Nissan's environments, and it would explode every time, just like PSDI-5. Paresh knew this and had his chemists scrambling to find a solution. This time they delivered.

Their answer was Zeolite, or 13X, a new desiccant discovered by Deb Hordos. It came in small beads that nestled nicely between tablets and was a dream to handle. Deb worked for Sean Burns, Paresh's chief chemist, and it was their work that many accused Paresh of either taking credit for or burying. The new inflators also included a better auto-ignition material aimed at reducing the amount of on-board moisture the thermal switches carried. We asked Deb to run studies to determine the smallest tablet that would work, independent of the number of locations it was needed. While they focused on this, we made improvements to the inflator's manufacturability and safety margins. With a new killer desiccant and as little auto-ignition material possible, maybe we had a shot at this.

Bonfire was the other half of our challenge, specifically the disk style bonfires. The new passenger side inflators used a proven, carry-over auto-ignition design that posed no issues, but the driver side mechanism looked more like an after-thought, falling far short of Sean and Deb's efforts. McCormick, Schumann and I were in the trailer conference room with parts and drawings strewn across the table, searching for options. McCormick had the PSDI-X's small booster tube in his bear claw and was trying to point out some design features. It was almost as funny as watching him type out an e-mail on his Blackberry.

"You see this pocket at the top of the booster tube with the hole in it," he said. "That's where the AI tablet goes."

"I could see it, if you moved your big thumb out of the way," I said laughing.

"Very funny, Kevin. Listen, we can change the diameter of the pocket easily, once Deb tells us the final size of the tablet. A piece of tape holds it in place and that won't change. The issue is the contact between that tablet and the cap once the final assembly is pressed together and welded."

"I understand it's not like PSDI-5 where the AI-tablet is forced into contact with the cap when the igniter assembly is crimped in place," I said. "It's almost the opposite now. The cap is brought to the AI-tablet when it's pressed into the base and welded. Is there an interference, that pulls everything together to make sure rebounding doesn't result in a loss of contact?"

"No there isn't, boss, and that's the issue," Dave answered. "Maybe they were afraid of cracking the tablet, but instead the booster tube is pressed to a specific height on the initiator holder, so that when the cap is installed, it engages it and presses it further. That is how contact is created, but the booster tube never bottoms to create an interference and lock everything in place."

"The parts will rebound," I said. "We will we never be able to guarantee airgaps don't exist between the tablet and the cap. An air gap will kill us in bonfire."

"Yes, it will, but there is not much we can do at this point," Dave continued. "The mechanism is hard coded into multiple parts. To change it would ripple across the whole design and we don't have time for that. We are going to have to control it in Monclova, as much as I know you hate that."

"It will still be a crapshoot, Dave. There is going to be a lot of puckering going on when we light that fire in front of the Government regulator," I said.

"I agree, Kevin. We may need some of your Irish luck," he finished.

"I'm not going to have any left after this. Let's push Deb for the final tablet dimensions and I'll give Scott and Phillion a heads up about the potential rebounding issue. They will not be happy, but it is what it is. Thanks, guys. Let's get back at it."

It was time to start the DV. Time to face our demons. Deb delivered on her promise with an AI micro-tablet and we froze the design. Every day we were not in validation testing was a day lost to fixing things on the back end, before the PV had to start. The time allotted for that had already shrunk to nothing and the customer launch dates were not moving. Following a massive prototype build in Armada, we initiated the Honda and Nissan test sequences for the five new inflators. A whopping 10 validations.

Three months later we had the results and they were near perfect. It wasn't just that the ruptures were gone. Amazingly, so were the performance shifts we'd grown accustomed to after environments. This was game changing, and as the data began to roll in, I could see the team's excitement starting to build.

"Kevin, you've got to see this!" Schumann exclaimed. McCormick was close behind him.

"Okay, let's go to the conference room," I said. "More good news?"

"Yes, it is," McCormick said. "We just got the SDI-X and PSDI-X full sequential results for Nissan and they are unbelievable. I can't tell the difference between baseline and those that took the environmental drubbing. They are nearly identical. That 13X is amazing stuff."

"That is great news, Dave!" I exclaimed. "How about SPI-X and PSPI-X? How are they coming along, Schumann?"

Now it was the other Dave's turn. "My news is why McCormick is so certain 13X is the silver bullet. If you remember Kevin, we ran two passenger groups through Nissan. One with 13X and one without. You asked for the latter as a control group because we couldn't find any data for the new propellant wafers and Nissan environments."

"That's right," I said. "We found data where the Nissan SDI-X ruptured without 13X, but we couldn't find the same for the passenger inflators. I remember now."

"Well, PSPI-X just went from rupturing violently without 13X to passing everything comfortably with it. And that's with four AI micro-tablets," Schumann said. "The performance is not as tight as driver, but I have to agree with Dave. 13X is the silver bullet."

"So, it turns the switch on and off. Perfect," I said. "We are not launching anything now or in the future without it, and as soon as we come up for air, we need to make a push to add it to everything already in production."

"Good luck with that," they said in unison. "You will never convince Japan to go along. What we see as continuous improvement, they see as a sign of weakness. An admission of guilt."

"Well, we have to try," I said. "Great job, guys. You rock!"

"Hey, one more thing for you to chew on," McCormick said. "I checked, and we can fit one mole of the original PSAN propellant tablets in an X-Series driver inflator. They are denser, so you need less of them. I would argue Paresh could have designed the entire X-Series lineup with his first PSAN. What a waste of time."

"Nice, Dave. Thanks. Now get out of here, both of you, and get back to work," I said shaking my head. The big grin on McCormick's face was because he knew he was right. Paresh's new formulation added nothing. It was just a gimmick. Finally passing Nissan's environments had everything to do with 13X.

We did not sit idly while the Nissan and Honda's environments churned away. We had our other demon to stare down, bonfire testing. If those tests weren't successful, everything else was moot. Nothing could ship. The disk inflators still lacked a sure fire method for closing the thermal circuit and that meant even with our finest effort, there would be risk. The inflators that would be built for score, the ones the DOT regulators would witness, would be assembled in Armada under a microscope. Each one would be X-rayed to verify contact between the cap and the AI tablet before it ever found its way into a box and atop a fire; a luxury Monclova would never have. We would install what controls we could at the plant to improve their odds come production, but it would be impossible to inspect for after the fact. The very reason it needed to be designed in. I called the team together to discuss how we would prepare for the DOT approvals.

"I'm not worried about the passenger side," Schumann said. "Our preliminary tests suggest we should have no problem."

"Agreed, Dave. McCormick's the problem."

"I'm not the problem you idiots," Big Mac said. "It's Paresh's half-ass attempt at a thermal circuit. There is going to be risk."

"We've already been through that Dave, we're just yanking your chain," I told him.

Schubert spoke up, "I don't think we should schedule the DOT regulators until we have three passing tests for each inflator configuration. One full box per test."

"Nobody's going to argue with that Bob," I said. "Hardenburg, you know the drill. Build them with care and X-ray each one. There is going to be a ton of them coming at you. Every test we run will be a full box quantity of thirty."

"Got it, Kevin," Hardenburg said. "We need to add the full box requirement to the concept validation checklist. Right now, the R&D guys just test a couple in a box, so they can get their new ideas out to the module engineers quickly and then we are left holding the bag when it is time to go live."

"Good point," I said. "It's a major hole in our tollgate system that needs to get plugged. Thanks guys. Let's go burn some fires."

Three passing boxes of each inflator would certainly raise our confidence level, but with pyrotechnics and fire, that's all it would do. The only thing I held certain about a bonfire was that once it was started, there was no stopping it and we were either going to pass without incident or fail spectacularly. Armada's bonfire pit was located a mere hundred yards from our trailers. It was way too close to the office buildings, prompting Paresh to build a ridiculous, thirty-foot-high chain link fence around it, presumably for safety. It looked like a giant death match cage, except it was littered with cannon ball size holes where inflator fragments had sailed through over the years. Genius.

We started with SPI-X and PSPI-X and they passed easily, all three boxes. We followed with SDI-X and SDI-X 1.7, and they also passed without incident. This was going far better than expected and left only PSDI-X to screen before we could schedule final approvals and that's where we got stuck.

PSDI-X was a chamber within a chamber, dual-stage inflator with the same autoignition scheme as SDI-X. The second chamber was a small cylinder filled with propellant and closed off with a cap the size of a quarter, buried inside the primary chamber propellant bed. It was direct ignited without the aid of a booster material and did not have its own AI tablet. The chamber stayed closed in a primary stage, only firing preventing sympathetic ignition of its propellant but was opened in a delayed firing or full output as the cap was pushed off by the rapidly mounting pressure inside the small chamber.

But the closed off cylinder also acted like a little oven, heating the propellant inside it at a rate very close to, if not faster, than the AI tablet and that was a big problem. That meant the second charge was already compromised when the thermal switch closed and that's what puts big, giant, Swiss cheese holes through Paresh's death match cage. We were already in validation testing. Any major change to the design would sink the launch. We tried what we could, even placing small ceramic insulators in the second chamber, but nothing worked. During one of these iterations, Tim Healy and I were outside having a cigarette. He happened to be in Armada that day to see Paresh.

"What are they doing over there in that big cage?" Tim asked me.

"They are gearing up for a PSDI-X bonfire test. We want three consecutive boxes under our belt before we bring in the DOT witness and we can't get past box number one. You know we are already in DV and must go straight into PV. That obviously ties our hands as to what we can try, and we are running out of options. This has the potential to be a showstopper."

"Yes, Al has mentioned the issue, but I didn't understand the gravity. They are lighting that thing right now. Do we need to go inside?" he asked a little nervously.

"No, we are far enough away, but with all the fireworks we have been creating around here lately, I am pretty sure that will be coming to an end soon," I said. "I just lit this cigarette, but you can go in. It usually takes about 5 minutes for the fun to start."

"No, I'm curious. I've never seen one of these before. Man, that fire is raging," Tim said as he lit another cigarette.

"Eight-foot lengths of wood and lots of kerosene," I replied. "First events should be starting soon. Normal auto-ignitions will sound like a pop. If one explodes, you will know."

Pop, Pop, Pop, BOOM! Tim ducked, a perfectly normal reaction for the uninitiated. I took a long drag off my cigarette. Damn, I thought to myself, we might never get this thing to work.

"Holy shit, did that explode? I could of swore I heard something whiz by!" Tim exclaimed.

"Yes, sir, that was a failure, but we are far enough away." Pop, pop, BOOM! There went another.

"I've seen enough. Let's go back inside," Tim said, putting his cigarette out.

"Good idea. That's where the drawing board is anyway."

We were in a tight spot, no doubt. I was just about to schedule a teleconference with Chikaraishi to begin the difficult conversations when someone pointed out that we were using 8-foot lengths of wood for the bonfire instead of the 10-foot lengths allowed by the specification. Ten-foot lengths of wood were on a FedEx truck later that afternoon and the next day we put it to the test. And it passed. And then it passed again, and then two more times after that. The fire's increased intensity closed the thermal switch before the second chamber propellant became compromised and we squeaked by. It was right on the edge, but we had to press on and improve it later. The X-series was far superior to anything Takata was currently producing and, more importantly, it was much safer. I already had the majority of the DV results in my hands proving that. It was time to go.

We scheduled the government witness for what was probably the most stressful day of my career. Five bonfire tests for score, and if one failed, life was going to be miserable. But none did. I wore a rut in the middle of the trailer pacing back and forth, and I remember Shari Oliver, the PSDI-X engineer, refusing to look up from her desk as each excruciating PSDI-X 'pop' moved us one step closer to success. Those fifteen minutes were some of the longest of my life. With DOT under our belts and the DVs successfully behind us, we were green-lighted for the PVs.

Instead of congratulations, Douma and Paresh reprimanded me for being reckless and told us we could never use the bonfire pit again. That it was unsafe, and we would have to find an outside service for any future evaluations. Let me make something clear. We were never unsafe. Their weak minds simply didn't have the capacity to celebrate another's success. We didn't care. We had laid waste to Paresh's death match cage and were off to the races.

Our New Digs

Spring is an incredible time of year in Michigan and this one wasn't disappointing. We were out of winter, leaving the trailers, and heading confidently into the X-Series PV's. The last thing on the checklist was the presentation of the DV results in Monclova. These would be some of the first design reviews held in the new plant, which was just down the road from the old one and gorgeous. It was fitting that the X-Series should launch there. A fresh start all around.

Schumann, McCormick and KK made the trip with me. When we arrived, we went straight to the new X-Series assembly lines, still under construction. The plant was massive, close to 4000 employees, and the inflator area was a pretty good walk. I never had a problem getting my steps in while visiting Monclova. Kelli stayed with me as McCormick and Schumann dove into the equipment.

"This is exciting," KK said. "After all that work everybody put in, to see the lines actually being installed is just really cool."

"Yeah, everybody on the team needs to see this. We have to make a point of that," I said.

"Why only three lines?" she asked.

"SDI-X and SDI-X 1.7 will share a line as will SPI-X and PSPI-X. The PSDI-X has no sibling and its volumes demand a dedicated line. So yes, five inflators on three lines."

"Thanks. They look great from here, but I'm sure those two will find something if there is anything to be found," she said motioning her head at McCormick who already had grease on his shirt.

"That I am sure of KK. Fifteen minutes Dave," I yelled at him. "Make sure you bring Schumann with you. KK and I are heading up front to the conference room."

"Okay, boss. See you up there," he yelled back.

KK and I took our seats across the table from Jorge Gutierrez, the Plant Manager of Inflators that replaced Luis, who left shortly after the Monclova recovery for an exciting career opportunity. Next to him was Carlos Iruegas, Bob Phillion's Quality Manager and Jorge's right-hand man. Most people were still milling around the room with their coffees, exchanging small talk.

"Gentlemen," I said to the pair.

"Kevin, KK," Jorge nodded to us.

"We are going to share some really good news with you today," I continued. "All of the X-Series inflators passed their DVs. No gimmicks, No tricks. They are the real deal."

"Well, I'll believe that when I see it," Gutierrez said skeptically.

"Believe it, Jorge," I said, having none of that. "There is more, and Carlos, you will appreciate this. The variability that existed with the previous driver inflators is gone. Even the new passenger inflators are better despite using wafers."

Carlos smiled. He understood where I was heading, "You won't have to deal with ballistic LAT failures anymore," I said. "The culture of 'go grab another one to test' ends here."

"Now, that is some really good news, Kevin!" Carlos exclaimed.

"The spotlight will be on us, Jorge, and it will be blinding," I continued. "The X-Series inflators perform as advertised so any screw ups and operations will take it on the chin. There are 10 PVs coming at us in rapid succession, so attention to detail will be a must. This is an exciting time."

"Understood, Señor Kevin," Jorge said, as McCormick took the seat to the other side of me and Schumann went to the front of the room to start the presentations.

Did I mention spring was an incredible time of year in Michigan? It was nice to not have to look out over the frozen tundra as we touched down at DTW. I was excited to be back. The meetings had gone well, Monclova was on track, and I was told that our new building was nearing completion. The exterior and carpet installation were finished in our absence. Only office furniture was needed now, and we could finally move in. We were all so sick of the trailers and based on how we were delivering, it certainly felt like we deserved better. When I pulled into Armada the next Monday morning and saw our new building, it was clear others didn't share my sentiment. Instead of parking where I normally did, I pulled the car into one of the visitor spots in front of the main building and went right for Paresh's office.

"Wait, Kevin, Paresh is on the phone," Deana, his assistant, said. I ignored her, opened his door and closed it behind me.

"I have to go. I'll call you back later," Paresh said, hanging up the phone.

I started in on him, "Paresh, you looked me right in the eye and promised in front of Mr. Healy that you wouldn't build us a pole barn. Now I get back from Monclova and the entire building is covered with aluminum siding?!" I pointed at it like he could see it. "Please explain to me your definition of a pole barn?"

"Kevin, I don't know what you are talking about," Paresh said, squirming in his seat. "Last I checked with Peter and Jeff, they couldn't find the same façade as the main building. Apparently, it was discontinued. I knew Peter was worried about going over budget, but I never told him to use aluminum siding."

"And you never told him not to either, Paresh," I said exacerbated. "Do I need to call Mr. Healy or are you going to get this taken care of?"

"No, No, Kevin," he said, jumping out of his seat. "There is no need to call Tim!"

I could see Paresh dragging Peter into Douma's office as I left the main building for our trailers. Five minutes later the three of them were outside, traipsing around the new building in the mud, with Paresh waving his hands and yelling at Peter, whose head was down. Poor Peter. I hadn't even seen the interior yet, so his day was only going to get worse. He decided it would be a good idea to slap indoor-outdoor carpeting down and after I got a look at that, I was right back in Paresh's office for round two.

"Kevin, before you start, we are replacing the aluminum siding on the front of the building with a nice façade," he said. "Sorry for the mix-up."

"Have you seen the carpeting, Paresh?" I asked him. "The whole premise of the new building was so we could move people into more amenable workspaces. Did Peter not get the e-mail, because he glued indoor-outdoor carpeting directly to the slab? In Michigan! No padding?!" I was pissed.

Paresh just hung his head.

"Forget about the carpeting," I said. "You've already moved everything in except the office furniture. What were you thinking, Paresh?"

Later it was Al's turn to pile on. We presented him with a few modest options for new and used office furniture, which he tossed aside in favor of some old, stained furniture Takata had in storage. I was a smoker myself then, and the last time this furniture was used was when the awful habit still went on inside offices. It was disgusting and that was only half of it. The cubicle walls stretched from the floor to the ceiling and occupied 90% of the building. It was all you could see. There was no sense in even hanging pictures on the walls. Peter was, however, gracious enough to leave us a three-foot corridor around the perimeter and four intersecting aisles to move about and access the restrooms. The only thing a visitor saw as they entered our new digs was a seven-foot tall, cigarette-stained wall. How could we not take this personally? It was a dump.

We sucked it up, moved into our new pole barn, and focused on the X-Series PVs. It was time to put the ball in the back of the net, not brood. There were hiccups, tons of late nights, and a few flared tempers along the way, but with an amazing team effort, we pulled it off. The PVs themselves were uneventful, just like they were supposed to be. The same near flawless performance demonstrated in our DVs was reproduced on the Monclova production lines. Echigawa's yarn spinners could finally put their pens down. We would be releasing the PV reports ourselves, and proudly. Life was changing at Takata. It was nearing the close of 2008 and the respectable X-series inflator family was in production.

Act Two

Part B: The Takata Roller-Coaster

2009-2011

(KEVIN)

9

A Nissan Tale

MY FIRST performance appraisal at Takata was with Bill Martin just one month before I dropped the corrected Honda PSDI PV report on him and Paresh in LaGrange. Since he had no idea Tom and I were working on it, I couldn't point to that for my disappointing score. He was just a tough grader. I considered the source and shrugged it off, but there was one thing he said that stuck with me.

"You get too close to your people, Kevin. You need to work on separating your work life from your personal life."

I gave him a quizzical look and said, "Why, Bill? We spend three-quarters of our waking hours with co-workers. It puzzles me when people say that. What does 'get too close' mean to you?"

"That's two questions," he replied, "I'll tackle the second one first. You go to happy hour with your folks. You have them over for parties on the weekends. That's too close, and it can cloud your thinking when you're presented with difficult choices. That last bit is the answer to your first question."

"Well, on that we'll just have to agree to disagree, Bill. I can work on improving some of my behaviors, but I can't change who I am."

It did make some things harder, but to me there was no other way. These were my friends and it was part of what made us work. My family and I would never trade our memories with Schumann just so it wouldn't hurt if he had to be released in a downsizing, or if he were to tell me he was moving on. That was just life and why let it pass you by? I got a text from him one night after work that he needed to talk with me. Sandy and I were rooting through the refrigerator trying to figure out what to make for dinner, so we asked if he was hungry. Dave never turned down Sandy's cooking and an hour later, the three of us were standing at the kitchen island with our wine glasses full.

"Kevin and Sandy, you know I love you guys," Dave said.

"Oh boy, are you sure you don't want to eat first," I said smiling, and trying to ease his obvious discomfort. We'd been talking about what was coming next for a couple of months now.

He smiled back, "No, let's talk first."

"Douma was the final straw?" I asked him, already knowing what he was going to say.

"Yep. One lousy comp day is all I was asking for after all those weekends spent in Monclova. That may sound trivial, but it's not to me."

"Obviously. The comp time denial was just another way for Jeff and Paresh to needle us, Dave. They had me over a barrel and both knew Al wouldn't back us."

"I get that, Kevin, but you know I've been looking for an excuse and this one is as good as any. I am not happy with the person I have become at Takata," he continued. "I spend evenings and weekends with work on my mind and my Blackberry in my hand. Too much of it is negative, driven by politics, and I find myself saying and writing things that are out of character. I can't have that."

"I hear you, bud....," was as far as I got.

"There's more," he continued. "Obviously, I know about the corrected Honda PSDI PV report from 2000. Now having to watch our test and prototype departments bottlenecked with PSDI field returns because Takata failed to act when they should have...It's just not healthy for me, Kevin. I hope you understand."

"It's okay Dave," Sandy said. "You have to follow you heart."

"I'm so glad you said that, Sandy, because I have been spending more time with my entrepreneurial friends, dreaming a little more and wondering if I could start my own business. That's the direction I want to take my life even if I will miss working with Kevin tremendously."

I put my arm around his shoulder, "man, that smells good, doesn't it? Let's eat. Sandy, who's going to teach the kids piano now?"

"Hey, I am not going anywhere soon and will definitely need the spending money!" Dave exclaimed as we laughed and made our way to the table.

The conversation was a wakeup call. Until then, I thought I was doing a decent job shielding the group from the sins of the past. But KK's disgust at having to file our own version of the Nissan PSDI-5 report, accounts of PSDI field anomalies starting to trickle in, and now my good friend's imminent departure were all sober reminders of just how futile that effort was. Nevertheless, I had to keep fighting. There were no jobs to be had in Michigan. It's economy was in a tailspin and unearthing the roots that had grown deep here would wreak havoc on the family.

I couldn't dwell on it. I had to prepare the group for the onslaught their success was about to unleash. When we were in the throes of the X-Series launch, the color of your jersey was irrelevant. If you were needed on the field, you were called upon. Now with the rollout behind us, it was time return to a more traditional structure. Time to ready ourselves.

Applications would have no shortage of work. The disk inflators were a huge hit and demand for them was already outpacing capacity. Unfortunately, the same could not be said for SPI-X and PSPI-X. They had no takers beyond Honda. Takata desperately needed a full-size disk passenger inflator and that would be core engineering's first order of business. A move was also afoot in Europe from dual- to single-stage driver inflators that was about to catch fire globally, and although SDI-X was a good inflator, that kind of revolution screamed for a more advanced device.[11] Core would start with two programs — The Programmable Disk Passenger inflator (PDP) and SDI-X2.

My plan was always to have Schumann manage applications, McCormick core, Hardenburg the test and prototype labs, and KK engineering services, but my friends' departure required that to change. During the X-Series launch the team had worked closely with Cory Martin, Armada's resident quality engineer reporting to Bob Phillion, and had really grown to like him. He was pragmatic, hardworking, well-respected and most importantly, fun. He was a perfect fit for the new applications manager opening and when I approached Phillion with the proposition, he agreed. Bob knew the loss would bring him some short-term pain but wisely viewed it as a long-term investment. With his blessing, we offered Cory the position, he accepted, and we were back in business. There was one other noteworthy change to the group dynamic. Bernat had hijacked Schubert again, this time to help deal with the ballooning PSDI investigations.

Bob got pulled that way a year earlier when Teramoto was in town to run some special tests. I passed the two of them in the lab looking over some parts on a workbench. Teramoto was one of Jim Takada's original circle and Bob was assigned to take care of his every whim.

"Mr. Teramoto, how are you?" I said, shaking his hand. "It's been awhile."

"Yes, it has, Kevin. It's nice to see you again. Please excuse me, I must take this call," he said, shuffling around me.

"What the hell is this, Bob?" I asked, picking up an odd, thin, sheet metal cap that looked like it was designed to fit over the outside of a PSDI.

"Teramoto thinks that if you strap that thing on a compromised PSDI it will stop it from fragmenting. A potential field retrofit, I suppose," Bob replied halfheartedly.

"You do realize I am still holding the part in my hand," I said trying to draw a smile out of him. "This isn't going to stop shit."

"I know that, smartass," he said. "Al told me not to let Teramoto out of my sight and to make sure he got whatever he needed."

"So, I assume those PSDIs sitting there all have an extra batwing in the second chamber to make sure they rupture, and you are preparing to show him the extent of his folly," I said, smiling.

"Exactly, Kevin. Now get out of here before he gets back," he said pushing me along.

"Okay, good luck with that. I'll catch up with you later."

I knew we were going to lose Bob. The PSDI investigation was like quicksand and he had been forced to wade in. I tried multiple times to save him, but every branch I held out, Al snapped in two. Fortunately for us, Bob's protégé was a brilliant young engineer, Schuyler St. Lawrence, and he was in the wings and eager to assume the role of group guru and ballistician.

The new building had its challenges. Some we were aware of going in, others we should have anticipated. McCormick was always known to have a booming voice and our aluminum shed with its tin roof rusted had a distinct way of amplifying it. I think Jeff and Peter did this on purpose too, because it was just too devilish to be accidental. I could have put Dave anywhere in the building and he'd be right next to you, but it was poor Cory that drew the short stick. It was crucial they sit together and feel each other's pain. It was the only way we would continuously improve.

"You know why I put Big Mac in here with you, Cory?" I asked him one day.

"Yeah, I'd been meaning to thank you for that. "I'm going to need a pair of earmuffs," he said leaning back in his chair and smiling.

"Very funny," I chuckled, "but seriously, please make sure he understands what the plant struggles with. Nothing gets to Monclova anymore without lessons learned incorporated".

"Hey, trust me, coming from quality, I am 100% on board," Cory replied.

“Good. Be wary of Gutierrez too,” I said. “He’s not a doer and fixer like Luis was. He is a whiner and most of his current issues are self-inflicted. Preventable defects are trending in the wrong direction and I put that squarely on him.”

“Agree with you, Kevin,” he said. “What’s you biggest concern?”

“Welding, another reason Dave is in here with you. He’s an expert. Helium leak is right behind that. I am worried Monclova is not up for the X-Series tsunami that is coming at them.”

“How so?”

“We just added a new SDI-X customer and failed the safety factor portion of the PV due to a lousy weld,” I answered. “We easily achieve 1.7 safety factor here in Armada, and they struggle with 1.5[12]. It’s a process issue and they won’t admit it. You must be vigilant with them, Cory.”

“Understood Kevin. Will you be issuing standard earmuffs, or do I have to purchase my own? Wes is wearing the kind that American Airlines ground crews use, and he is on the other side of the building.”

Yeah, I was going to like Cory. I already loved Big Mac. The ribbing I gave him was just my way of telling him so. The two would make a great pair and Dave would be happy to help with Monclova’s weld problems. It was in his wheelhouse. I had just sent him to the plant to look into the latest SDI-X PV failure and upon his return, I stopped by the pair’s cubicle for an update.

“How did the trip go, Dave?” I asked him.

“Just like we talked about, boss. Nothing’s wrong with the design. They had an issue with weld penetration caused by a misalignment, and as usual, they cranked up the power. You know the potential consequences of that,” he answered.

“Yes, I am keenly aware. They overheat the part, basically annealing it and tanking its strength. But that’s why we hydro-burst as well. To catch that. They can’t just measure the weld nugget and call it good. If the part was annealed, it would fail burst pressure. They have to meet both. It’s not an either-or.”

“Do we look like a choir to you, boss?” Dave asked with a smile. The ribbing went both ways. “I worry they don’t strictly adhere to that protocol,” he continued.

“Yeah, me too, Dave. Gutierrez does not like being told what to do. I’ll talk to Scott and Dal about getting a weld expert permanently stationed in Mexico. One that I hope Jorge will listen to.”

On we went, but not wholly comfortable.

The PSDI-X Disconnect

Welding was just one of many issues pressing on Cory as the X-series was growing in popularity. It was a constant struggle that we managed the best we could. Monclova was never serious about becoming proficient in the technology and never hired the experts we recommended. Instead, we had to rely on a system of checks and balances to prevent escapes. Not the best solution, but if operations was comfortable with mediocrity that was their choice. I had to move on. Our first big X-Series problem had just hit and demanded my full attention.

"Kevin, you have a minute or two?" Cory asked poking his head into my cubicle with Schuyler in tow.

"Oh, this doesn't sound good," KK said, swiveling her chair around.

There was no privacy in the new building.

"It's not." Cory was serious.

"What's up, gentlemen?" I beckoned, "have a seat."

"I just got a call from one of the Nissan module engineers in Auburn Hills," Cory said. "There was a PSDI-X second chamber no-fire at 100ms in a sled test and it happened at Nissan. The test technicians confirmed the electrical signal was sent, and that the initiator is still live."

"Did you say at Nissan?" KK asked.

"Yes, at Nissan. So you can imagine the urgency," Schuyler interjected. "The video should be in your mailbox, Kevin. Can you pull it up?"

I did so and what I saw was disheartening. Recall that the PSDI-X inflator's small size and reduced part count was enabled by allowing it to expand during deployment. The video showed the inflator morphing from a hockey puck to a baseball in milliseconds, just like I'd seen in a hundred times before. But those were static videos, shot only at the inflator level. The dynamics of the sled test environment uncovered a problem we'd never seen before. The second chamber's connector that delivered its firing pulse was dislodged immediately upon initiation of the primary chamber. The electrical signal sent at 100ms to dispose of the secondary hit a dead end. I swung my chair back around to the pair.

"Well, that's not good," I said. "Are we sure the connector was seated properly before the test?"

"I think we have to assume so," Schuyler said. "I already did a frame-by-frame walk comparing this sled test video to one of our static inflator videos, and the sled test environment increases the acceleration of the inflator's base and connectors. If the connection is marginal in the static mode, the kinematics of the sled test may be pushing it over the edge."

"Well that's really not good," I said this time with the gravity it deserved.

What does this mean functionally to an airbag? Well, in a high-severity accident where both stages are fired simultaneously, nothing. But in an accident where the computer decides to delay the second stage, then the connector can pop out and not be there to deliver the signal to fire that chamber. The restraint provided by the airbag cushion becomes less than optimal, risking passenger injury, and the auto-body shop, unbeknownst to them, could be left with a potentially compromised and dangerous inflator. Neither is a desirable situation. Nor is having your customer discover the issue for you.

"The module engineers never saw this during their development?" I asked.

"I posed that same question," Cory said. "Never. They ran plenty of static module deployments with video. This is not the first Nissan sled test either. The connector doesn't always dislodge."

"But in a sled test, its acceleration is always higher. Always. They sent me a couple of other videos to look at," Schuyler pointed out.

Cory continued, "One of their engineers also mentioned that they took a closer look at a PSDI-X module they are developing for GM and found evidence of it there too. In static tests, Kevin! We're going to get buried."

"Actually, that's better news than you think Cory," I said. "At least now we have a mule. Sled tests are way too expensive and time consuming to solve a problem of this complexity. The GM module gives us a way to turn the issue on and off with much simpler and quicker static tests. Order as many of those module as they will give us, KK."

"We are going to need Sean and Deb for this one. Big Mac, too," I continued. "Grab a conference room and set something up for tomorrow. We have a way to test for a solution. I'm just not sure what it will be."

"We're going to have to move fast," Cory said. "The guys from Auburn Hills are breathing down my neck and the e-mails from Japan are off the hook."

The Chemists Save the Day

The brainstorming session the following morning took place in the main building conference room. We liked getting out of the pole barn when the weather was nice and took every opportunity to do so. Sean and Deb were already in the room when I entered, and while we were waiting for others to join I asked Sean,

"Why are there cubicles out there with nobody using them and Auburn Hills engineer's nameplates on them?"

Sean wasn't in a playful mood, "You'll have to ask Paresh. He must have reserved them for engineers who spend a lot of time here."

"Unlike us," I said, wishing I had just let it lie.

"We are doing just fine, Kevin," Deb said. "Thanks for asking. I think we are all here now."

"Thank you, Deb," I said, smiling at her for pulling me back. "I hope you've all had a chance to review Schuyler's e-mail and summary. We are in a jam. We already have builds in process to see if there is anything we can do with the booster load. Less granules and even tablets, but we don't hold out much hope for either. Based on our margin studies, it's more of a check-the-box exercise."

"I agree, Kevin," Sean said. "Knowing how the booster behaves, both of those options are directionally correct for stopping the connector from dislodging, but performance will drop off a cliff at low temperatures."

"Exactly, Sean, so what do you suggest?" I asked.

"You know we've been experimenting with a new booster material that has its own auto-ignition function," Deb said. "It's called AIB and has some interesting characteristics that may help, and the timing seems right. Sean and I have been discussing which inflator would be best to run the validation in and it sounds like you've just answered that question."

"What are the interesting characteristics?" Schuyler asked.

"Well, we are getting the same ignition with AIB tablets as we get with the current booster in granular form." That got everyone's attention.

"Yes, it surprised us too," she continued. "It seems to be the perfect balance between hot particles and pressure, and its tablet geometry may soften that initial kick you are getting from the booster's granules. Perhaps just enough for the connector to hold on."

"Cory add AIB to the test matrix," I said excitedly. "I hope you are right, Deb. I can't see this being solved any other way than pyrotechnically. We have an idea to restrain the inflator's growth mechanically, but our modeling suggests the structure will fail if we prevent the internal volume from growing as designed. You can see our options are limited."

"We'll have the AIB material in the prototype lab by the end of the day," Deb said. "Keep me posted. I'm really interested in this one."

"Thanks, you got it. Let's get to it, guys," I said wrapping things up.

If what Deb suggested was real, it would be game changing. Granules sopped up moisture like a sponge, and nobody liked working with them. They were a necessary evil when a customer needed a faster inflator to deal with a stiff crash pulse, but if AIB could provide that faster inflator without the initial surge that was dislodging the connector, Sean and Deb would be heroes. A few tests in the PSDI-X GM module and we'd know.

We quickly marched through our test matrix. Reducing the amount of booster granules stopped the connector from dislodging. So did using it in tablet form, but in both cases, occupant protection was less than ideal. It was just too slow. The mechanical restraint idea was a spectacular failure. Let's just say the computer model was right about letting the inflator's volume grow. But AIB worked like a charm, just like Deb theorized. The problem disappeared in the GM module and did not repeat in subsequent Nissan sled tests. It was a win all around and more of a life-saver than people ever realized. Its implementation would be immediate and across the board, allowing us to address the X-Series' marginal auto-ignition performance at the same time, and a lot faster than I had hoped.

Nissan Throws a Curve

With the back-to-back home runs of 13X and AIB, Sean and Deb were busy circling the bases, but we couldn't celebrate yet. AIB still needed to be validated in Nissan's PSDI-X and that was going to take another herculean lift. The changes weren't complex or numerous. There was just no time left on the clock. I pulled Dave and Cory into a conference room to discuss what was needed.

"Okay, you guys know what we are up against," I said. "Let's discuss the changes first, but before we get started, can one of you ask KK to come in? Now that I think of it, we are going to want some slides to explain this to Japan."

Cory went off and I looked at Dave. "Here's my 'must have,' Dave, and I've already discussed this with Cory. We take this opportunity to fix the shaky contact between the booster tube and the cap, and we fix it for good. All the X-Series disk inflators."

"Understood, and any cost savings we can leverage at the same time are fair game, right?" Dave asked eagerly.

"Of course. As long as we have time."

"Where are we at?" Cory asked as he and KK walked back in.

"Dave's already up to speed and moved onto cost-saving ideas," I said with a smile. "Let's start with how we fix our thermal circuit and then we'll circle back to cost savings."

The solution was straightforward, at least to us. We made the booster tube taller so there was an interference when the cap was pressed to its final height and contact was always guaranteed. Prototype parts were ordered, samples were built, and we demonstrated that it worked. We were ready to go to PV when our plan was derailed.

Nissan was too spooked by the no-fire to continue with PSDI-X, which was understandable considering how late in the game it was. They directed Takata to go back to PSDI-5, explaining they felt more comfortable with it. The irony was numbing. Their comfort with PSDI-5 was based on a lie that Takata was still perpetuating, while their discomfort with PSDI-X was based on a schedule risk we could manage. If ever there was a time for Takata to come clean, now was it! Letting Nissan go back to PSDI-5 when PSDI-X was on the one yard line was unconscionable. My hopes were quickly dashed when I received a rare call from Robert Fisher, VP of Takata North America Engineering.

"Kevin, this is Rob Fisher. Are you in a place you can talk?"

"Yes, sir," I jumped out of my seat, cell phone in hand, and darted through our cubicle maze to a conference room. "How can I help you?"

"I'm sure Al has told you by now that Nissan does not want to use PSDI-X," he began. "We explained to them that we have a solution, but they didn't want to hear it. They feel more comfortable with PSDI-5."

"Yes, he did, Rob, but..."

"Wait, let me finish Kevin," he pressed. "Nissan knows their request to go back to PSDI-5 will require us to use an assembly line that has not been validated for them, so they want a new validation on that line too."

The irony got even more stunning. After some silence I said, "Rob, we never validated Nissan's PSDI-5 on any line. It ruptured every time we tried and Bruce...."

"Please, Kevin, I don't want to hear about the past. I just want to know if there is anything you can do now to get it to pass," he replied, hating having to fly so close to the sun.

"Well, we can try 13X desiccant," I said. "It worked in the X-Series, but we miniaturized all the AI tablets at the same time, so there are no guarantees. I don't understand this at all, Rob. In the three months Nissan is willing to wait for a new PSDI-5 PV, we can have the PSDI-X with AIB ready. We already know PSDI-X meets their brutal specification and all we have to do is swap the current booster with AIB. PSDI-5 is just crazy. We have no idea if 13X will even solve the issue or not. Answer this – both inflators require a change, both changes will take the same time to validate, one is a sure thing and one is a gamble. Which would you choose?"

"Sorry, Kevin. This is coming directly from Japan," he said flatly.

"Okay, we'll get it started." I said. "But have you and Al discussed what Takata is going to do if it doesn't pass? And if it does pass, any idea how Japan is going to explain the change in desiccants to Nissan?"

"No, we haven't gotten that far, Kevin. Thanks, and keep us posted." He hung up the phone.

If Monclova had to use new assembly line to meet Nissan's increased volumes, then Nissan had every right to demand it be validated, but only at Takata would that send people into a panic. Only when passing was a lie in the first place. If 13X worked, then great. It would be one less inflator Takata was building and shipping under false pretense. If 13X didn't work, it would trigger another report from my group that Rob and Al would either have to act upon or bury.

Al didn't seem nearly as rattled as Rob. He'd been around Takata long enough to know Japan would never tell Nissan if another PSDI-5 PV failed and he'd already mastered the art of sitting on the truth. For Rob though, this was all new, and I marveled at how Al must have convinced him to make that phone call.

10

The Plant's Struggle

NO SOONER had we popped Rob's Nissan PSDI-5s into the oven than we were beset with another predicament. I thought with the PSDI-X connector issue behind us and Nissan's PV in process, we would have time to start really advancing AIB. I was sadly mistaken, and the party crasher this time: Takata's newly launched side impact inflator, SSI-20. The application was GM's Epsilon platform; a global program being managed out of Europe, and TAIC had the inflator lead. The launch was coincident with X-Series and we were responsible for the two assembly lines planned for Monclova.

The SSI-20 was Takata's first and only PSAN side impact inflator. These types of devices are used primarily in thoracic-head protection systems and can be found in the vehicle's seat or door panel. Larger sizes are sometimes located under the dash in knee bolsters and to a lesser degree in roof rails for first-strike head curtains.

Simplistically, the SSI-20 was a φ20mm X 150mm cylinder (<"1 diameter, 6" long) with an initiator and booster at one end, propellant in the middle and exhaust ports at the other end. An internal thin-walled sleeve was used to create an air gap between the body and the propellant, necessary for bonfire survivability. The industry-leading 20mm diameter was enabled by removing the filter and using a torturous path the gas traveled to trap particulates. Gas turns easily, but particles don't, and turning the flow multiple times before the gas leaves the inflator steers the particles into dead ends. This method allowed a very small inflator, but it came at the expense of super-hot exhaust gas. To make matters worse, sometimes the molten particles found their way out of the maze and into the bag. The inflator engineers were proud of their miniature side impact inflator. The Auburn Hills module engineers hated it.

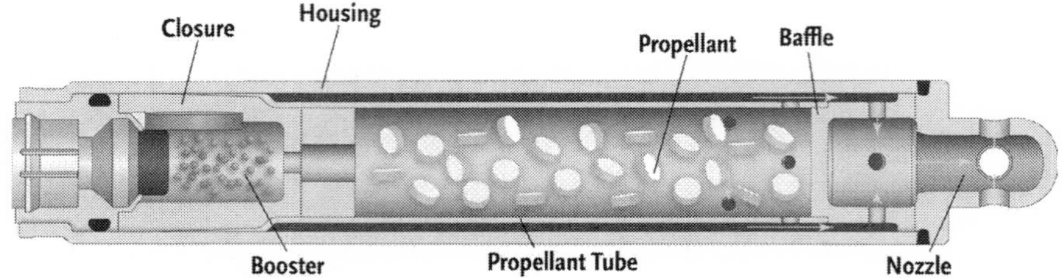

FIGURE SEVEN: CROSS-SECTION OF 'SSI-20' INFLATOR [SHOWING GAS FLOW THROUGH FILTERLESS BAFFLE DESIGN]

"So much for getting to work on AIB," Cory said plopping himself down in one of my cubicle seats.

"What do you mean, Cory?" KK asked, swiveling her chair around. "Kevin has me putting together plans to implement it everywhere!"

"Monclova just had an SSI-20 inflator rupture during a routine LAT – GM Epsilon."

I crunched a few numbers in my head and said, "Start of production was October. So worst case, we have a six-month problem. This is TAIC's baby. What do Stephen and Heiko have to say. I'm sorry, I mean Heiko. I keep forgetting Stephen has moved on to Corporate."

"Heiko says Freiberg hasn't had any issues and they've been in production a year longer than Monclova," Cory replied.

"Figures. You have Monclova pulling all their traceability records, I assume."

He nodded affirmatively.

"KK, please gather up all the DR presentations and let's meet in the conference room after lunch. We're going to need Schubert, McCormick and Hardenburg. Dave and Bob were involved in the original Armada design."

"Yes, sir," they both said taking off in different directions.

When I returned from lunch, TAIC's DR3 presentation was already projecting on the conference room screen, and KK, Schubert and Cory were sitting around the table chatting.

"Thanks, everyone. Where's Hardenburg and McCormick? Out taking swings again? Have you ever seen Hardenburg address a golf ball? We may be waiting awhile."

Cory laughed, "Here they come now."

"Good, let's get started."

"I looked over some of the presentation before you got here, Kevin," Schubert began. "Three things jumped out at me. The inflator uses an 0.060" thick propellant tablet, the thinnest and by far the weakest we make. The choke point was also relocated from the baffle to the propellant sleeve to achieve the high mass flow rate GM wanted. Lastly, it uses 13X desiccant, which surprised me."

"Yeah, I am familiar with this inflator, Bob," I responded. "It gave us fits during PV and we had a rupture after one of the USCAR environments. Cory was still working for Phillion at the time but was a huge help in the investigation. We assigned root cause to poor application of the booster cup seal which allowed the booster granules to migrate into the main propellant bed and we all know we can't let those two materials co-mingle."

"Okay, and I assume the13X was added because it was launched at the same time as the X-Series?"

"No, it had nothing to do with the X-series," I said. "Freiberg would never add an operation like that to their automated lines unless they absolutely had to. The 13X was to steady post USCAR environmental performance, which was all over the map. The moisture from that big AI tablet was really degrading the thin tablets without it."

"Thanks Kevin. One more question. What did you end up doing about the tape seal application?"

Cory answered him, "When we went to populate the fault tree branch that addressed machine issues, we found that there was none."

Bob gave Cory a confused look and said, "What do you mean 'there was none'?"

"Literally Bob, there was no machine. Operators were using their hands to remove the seal from its release liner and apply it to the booster cup. No gloves. We had to assume all the surfaces were contaminated. Also, the remains of the inflator that ruptured showed signs that the seal was missing."

"You're kidding," Schubert said. "Mario didn't have a machine built for such a critical process step? The RPN (scored risk of failure) for that operation must be through the roof."

"Monclova didn't flag it as critical in the PFMEA, Bob, and we've addressed that with them," Cory said. "But we were able to reproduce the failure in the lab. We intentionally mixed the booster and propellant inside an inflator, subjected it to shake, rattle and roll, and then deployed it at elevated temperature, and BOOM! While that activity was going on, Monclova built a machine for the process that removed any possibility of contaminants."

"Why it wasn't automated in the first place is still a wonder to me," McCormick interjected. "And the pile of crap Mario threw together in response."

"It wasn't his best effort," Cory said in agreement.

"But we thought we understood root cause," I said looking down at a picture of the ruptured LAT in my hand. "Now, I'm not so sure."

"You make decisions based on the data you have at the time, Kevin," Schubert spoke up. "You didn't have this data point then."

TAIC's SSI-20 deviated substantially from the original design. The choke point was moved to the inner propellant sleeve which created a pressure-drop across it, allowing the inflator to run at a higher internal pressure. We understood why. They had a customer application that wanted a high rate of gas flow and to do that they needed to raise the operating pressure. The inflator housing, which was designed to carry that load, could withstand 130MPa before failing. The presentation we were reviewing said the internal sleeve could take 30MPa across it. This meant the pressure inside the sleeve, where the propellant was combusted, could conceivably (minus margin) be raised to 160MPa, and the system would still stay intact. Schubert summed it up perfectly,

"That's not how I would go about raising mass flow. The approach allows for an internal pressure greater than the inflator's last line of defense, managed through a series of pressure-drops, and I don't like it."

"Bingo," I replied, "but the DR3 documentation was clean with appropriate safety factors. I checked it myself, but I must admit the data set wasn't very robust."

"Well then, let's shore it up," he said.

I looked across the table to Dave, "Big Mac, please get someone started on a heavy-wall fixture and expedite it. We'll need to measure three pressures simultaneously; inside the booster cavity and on both the inside and outside of the sleeve. We can't get those measurements on a real inflator. It's just too small."

"Got it." Then he looked at Hardenburg and laughingly said, "Hey, Bob, you do know your guys will have to clean this thing like a hundred times."

"Cory, does Phillion know?" I asked.

"Yes, he's the one who called me. He's heading down to Monclova on Monday."

"Good, so are we," I said. "I'll let Al know. Thanks, guys."

I always admired Schubert's acumen, but the way he devoured that complex problem was truly amazing. In short, changes were made to the baseline SSI-20 design to meet an extremely demanding mass flow rate, that took it from a robust inflator to what now appeared to be marginal. A deep dive in Monclova and the heavy wall fixture would tell us.

It was a pleasant March day when we touched down in Monterey. Unfortunately, American Airlines had stopped flying directly into Monclova and that forced a change to our routine. It was now a two-hour drive from the airport to the plant, northeast through the Coahuila desert and Los Zetas territory. It was the height of the Mexican drug war and there would usually be one or two military checkpoints, manned by Marines, that we would have to pass through on our way there. The stops could be unnerving at times even though we were always chauffeured by Takata drivers in company vans. As we approached the first checkpoint, we started digging for our passports.

"I hate these damn inspections," I said. "Everyone have their passports?"

"Yep. Holy shit! Are those 50 caliber machine guns on those Humvees?" Cory asked, sitting back into his seat. "I haven't seen those before. Things must be getting worse."

I squinted, "Yes, they are, and they are pointed right at us. The machine guns don't bother me as much as the ski masks. Those young soldiers are scared to death of being fingered by the cartels. There are no faces out there."

We crawled through the checkpoint without incident. It was rare that we were stopped and searched, but it was still disturbing, and we certainly weren't getting any hazard pay to compensate. As the scene disappeared in the rear window, I continued our conversation.

"There've been several gunfights in Monclova now. It's not like it used to be when we could stagger around late at night without a care. You remember when we lost the Suburban, Bob?"

"Yes, I remember," Phillion said laughing, "we found it the next morning, just 50 yards from the entrance to the last bar we were at. We didn't drive it though!"

"Good for us, Bob. We should be proud of ourselves," I said smiling. "Switching subjects. Do either of you know if GM has been clued in yet?"

"I'm not sure. We notified the GM program office in Auburn Hills," Bob said. "They are responsible for relaying the information to the customer, but your question is a good one. If we determine the problem goes beyond this one inflator lot and we don't have it all contained, then GM must be involved. The program office is contractually bound to inform them of any

LAT failure."

"Thanks, Bob, but I've lost a lot of faith in Takata lately. We'll figure out what's going on and fix it. I'm convinced of that. But if there have been escapes, I'm not so sure GM will be told anything and if there haven't been any, I'm convinced they'll be told nothing. Either way Takata will leave them in the dark."

"Don't go jumping to conclusions. We are not even at the plant yet," Bob said. "When we get there, let's split up. I'll go handle containment. If you and Cory can get started on root cause, that would be great. I'll circle back with you when I feel we have everything locked down."

"Good plan," I said as we approached the outskirts of Monclova.

When we arrived at the plant, I jumped out at the guard shack to have a quick smoke before we got started. I really wanted to kick the habit, but stress was a trigger for me and now was an impossible time. After a couple of long pulls, I made the short walk to the main entrance and into the first conference room off the main lobby where Phillion and Cory had already taken all the available power and network outlets. Smoking really was stupid. As I was unpacking my knapsack, Dal strolled into the room.

"Well, look at this sorry crew!" he exclaimed, "Phillion and Cory, I see enough of you two, but Mr. Fitzgerald, it is good to see you."

"You too, Dal," I said shaking his hand. "It's been awhile."

"Yes, it has, but I am not offended by your absence," he said with a smile. "When you're here it usually spells trouble."

"Ah, so you know about the SSI-20 LAT rupture?" I asked him.

"Yes, and I don't want to get in your way, but I do want to spend some time with you after you've poked around a bit. I have my own opinion of what may be aggravating the situation and I don't want to prejudice your thinking."

"Sounds like a plan, Dal. We are splitting up to tackle it now," I motioned to Cory and Bob, grabbing my safety glasses and heading for the floor.

There were two SSI-20 assembly lines in Monclova, both running GM product, and the LAT failure had them at a standstill. As Cory and I approached the normally bustling area, only Jorge, Mario and a few of Mario's manufacturing engineers were there, probing some of the stations for clues. Pallets of finished parts with 'hold' stickers on them were stationed at the head of each line.

"Jorge, Mario. How are you guys?" I asked, walking up.

"Señor Kevin. Señor Cory. Thanks for coming down. We can use your help," Jorge said.

"No problem," I replied. "Are the teardowns of the inflators produced just before and after the failed unit complete yet?"

"Yes, they are," Mario replied. "They're in the lab. We can talk on the way."

"Good. Did you find anything out of the ordinary in the traceability records?" Cory asked.

"No, we didn't, Cory. All the loads were to print. Nothing odd that we can find. The teardowns you can see for yourself," Mario answered as he pushed open the door to the lab.

A teardown is the practice of taking a live, fully assembled inflator and carefully disassembling it, often remotely, so that none of its internal components are disturbed. Examination of the hardware can sometimes provide valuable insight into the stability of a process at a snapshot in time. In this case, that snapshot was ten inflators on each side of the failed unit and they were neatly laid out on a table in front us. Cory and I went to opposite sides and worked our way towards the middle.

"Are you seeing the same thing I am?" Cory asked me.

"I think so."

"Mario, some of these teardowns have a bunch of broken tablets that need to be quantified. Do us a favor and have someone calculate the percentage of broken tablets for each inflator and add that to the data set."

"I noticed that too, Señor," Gutierrez said. "Is that a problem?"

"Broken tablets mean higher and faster pressures, and with everything so tightly packed in this inflator, there is no room for error." I looked at Mario and said, "Didn't you take a few of your guys over to Freiberg to review their process, their critical inspection points? I remember Dal and Scott insisting you do that before we ordered our lines." He didn't say anything, so I asked, "Do we load the propellant the same way they do? Do they vibrate as they load? Do they check the propellant height before they insert the booster cup?"

"I'm sorry, Kevin. That's too many questions. I'll have to go back to my notes and check."

"Please do, Mario." I said. "Cory, what time is it in Germany?

"Too late, Kevin. I'll set something up with Freiberg for first thing in the morning."

"You're right. Let's wrap it up for today, but we need to understand how Freiberg is performing the propellant load operation. Thanks for getting all the teardowns done, Mario. I know it was a lot of work. Please remember to check your notes and calculate the number of broken tablets for each inflator. We are damaging a significant percentage of them and that's a problem."

The next morning when we arrived at the plant, Mario had a picture of each teardown labeled with its corresponding percentage of broken tablets sitting on the conference room table for our review. Two of them had 30% of their propellant loads in pieces and that was just inexcusable!

"Holy shit," I said picking up the first of the ten pictures. "30% broken tablets! 30%!"

"No way," Phillion said reaching for the photo. Cory and I had filled him in over dinner and a few tequilas. Maybe more than a few.

"Cory, please shoot an e-mail to Armada," I said. "The heavy wall fixture should be ready soon. When it is, have them start testing with broken tablets immediately after the baselines. Begin at 30% and decrease in increments of five down to 5%. Ten each at high temperature."

"Kevin, that's 60 heavy-wall tests. Hardenburg is going to have a cow."

"Tell him we almost halved the original estimate and he should be happy about that. Get him started, bud. What time is our conference call with Freiberg?"

"Ten minutes, upstairs with Mario and his team."

"That gives us some time to talk to him about his notes before we get started. I'm heading up there."

"Kevin, I have another call I have to be on," Bob said as I walked past. "I just got a note confirming we have our arms around the suspect lot. Nothing escaped."

"That's great news, Bob. We'll fill you in."

It was a short conversation with Mario and with Freiberg. Mario couldn't find his notes and Freiberg quickly confirmed that a propellant height inspection is conducted on every unit before the booster cup is inserted, and sometimes more than once. I had to ask, at least for Mario's benefit.

"Why do you sometimes have to measure the tablet height more than once?"

"Because occasionally they don't vibrate down very nicely, and we fail the height inspection," someone on the other end answered.

"What dimension are you referencing?" Cory asked. "There is no propellant bed height called out on the drawings. I had that checked last night."

"Yes, we noticed that as well in preparing for the call, but it is in our PFMEA and control plan," Freiberg answered.

Mario had his head hung across the table. Yes, TAIC left the requirement off the drawing, but it still managed to find its way onto Freiberg's production documentation. The very documentation Scott and Dal sent Mario and his team to Germany to photocopy and bring home.

"Can you please e-mail us that dimension, so we can update our paperwork right away?" Cory asked, "and please send any information you have on your height check system."

"Yes, sure, no problem. We already told TAIC about the missing drawing dimension. So, yes, have a nice day."

I looked across the table at Mario who was still dejected and said, "Chin up bud. You have two lines that need modification. I suggest you get to it."

We were closing in on root cause, but our findings were not going to make anybody happy. Monclova hadn't checked the propellant bed height since the start of production and if cracked tablets were that primary cause, then six months of production was suspect, even if the issue had only recently flared up. That meant we'd better be damned sure about our hypothesis and for that we needed to be back in Armada with the heavy-wall fixture.

I went searching for Dal to update him on our findings and found him out by the massive plastic injection molding machines used to make module parts. He had way too much on his plate with both inflators and modules.

"Hey, I need some of your time if you can spare it," I said to him.

"Sure, let's go where it's a little quieter."

There was an exit just across the hall and we stepped outside. I said, "Dal, we are randomly cracking a significant number of tablets during the SSI-20 booster cup insertion operation. We measured as high as 30%."

"And I'm assuming that's a bad thing," he said.

"Yes, and there's more," I continued. "We had a call with Freiberg this morning and they check that propellant height 100% before inserting the booster cup."

"Let me guess, and we don't. I sent Mario and his guys to Freiberg, just so this wouldn't happen."

"I know, Dal. I don't have the data yet to be certain, but based on my experience, the cracked tablets are the culprit. They act as added booster, which this inflator does not need any more of."

"That's exactly what I wanted to talk to you about, Kevin. Why don't we take the booster and main propellant loads down to the drawing minimums, just to be on the safe side?" he asked. "Right now, we are running both at their high ends."

"That will help, but you will need to check with Steve Maurer," I answered. "It will most likely drop the inflator out of its lower acceptance limits and that will require a deviation. If Maurer is willing to run a few module tests to confirm occupant protection, I'd be willing to sign a deviation until we can get a fix in place. Listen, I need to head back to Armada to better understand the effects of these broken tablets. I'll be leaving in the morning."

"Okay, travel safe Kevin. Thanks for everything."

Before I left, I had one more mission. I wanted to test a hunch.

"Cory, have you ever heard of a snuff test?" I asked.

"No, sir. What is it?"

"It's a way of seeing if there is any effect on the main propellant from the ignition blast. I want to make sure the booster isn't smacking the crap out of those thin tablets and breaking even more of them. It could be another factor. A snuff test will show us what the tablets look like just before they start burning. Ideally, there should be no significant change," I continued. "We drill large holes in both the sleeve and housing, and everything else is normal. When the inflator is deployed, the ignition pressure will race for the vents and the combustion will never start, but the tablets, however, will have felt the full force of the booster."

"Then we disassemble it and look at the condition of the tablets. Pretty cool," Cory said.

"You got it. Here's a sketch," I said. "What do you think, an hour or two? We really need to get this done before we leave today."

Three hours later we had our answer. We found there wasn't any sign of tablets. There was propellant, but no tablets. They had been compacted into a slug now half the length of the original column that covered the sleeve's exit ports. It was completely fused in place, impossible to get out.

"I've never seen anything like this," I said. "It's a freaking slug. There is no ballistic control at all other than hoping this chaos repeats itself every time. Wow."

The snuff test results had nothing to do with Monclova, and everything to do with engineering. Now I really needed to get back to Armada and the heavy wall fixture.

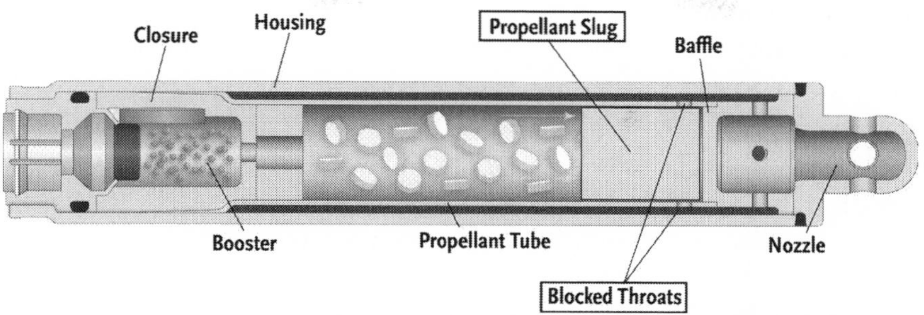

FIGURE EIGHT: CROSS-SECTION OF INFLATOR 'SSI-20' [SHOWING PROPELLANT SLUG ISSUE]

Cory's engineers already had the baseline heavy-wall tests complete when we returned to the office the following Monday and scheduled a meeting in the afternoon to begin reviewing the results.

We opened the discussion with the test fixture. I asked them if the measurements they were getting were consistent and made sense, and they were. Then we looked at the baseline results and they were clean. The team had done a great job, and I asked they thank Hardenburg for me.

But I saw what I was searching for in that first set. On the third deployment, the pressure difference across the sleeve started predictably, less than 30MPa, but then the pressure inside the sleeve suddenly rose, taking the delta over that threshold. I could picture the slug of propellant restricting flow out of the sleeve and would expect on tear-down that it had split.

"What do you say we disassemble that one?" I said. "The data suggests the sleeve should have failed. It doesn't explain an outer body rupture, but we are getting closer. TAIC's DR3 presentation missed this."

At that moment one of Hardenburg's technicians stuck his head into the conference room and asked if he could interrupt.

"We just recorded an inner sleeve pressure over 130 MPa on one of the 30% broken tablet tests."

"Nice," I said in the knowledge we were figuring it out. "Thank you and keep going."

"You're welcome, sir," the technician said. "Bob is helping us clean some the heavy-wall parts and he wanted me to pass along a message to you, but I don't think I can repeat it."

"That's a good call," I said laughing. "Tell him I said he can order another fixture or two."

130 MPa in the propellant sleeve! If it fails at that pressure, then the outer body is going right behind it. The million-dollar question now was when did Monclova start cracking those damned tablets.

We proved the catastrophic failures resulted from the design coupled with the cracking of tablets at Monclova. It took a high percentage of broken tablets and it was hard to repeat, but it was the root cause. The skeptics wanted to believe it was a flare up. They said Monclova rarely broke that many tablets and in cases where they did, the sleeve would fail first, before the outer body breached. But we showed it could happen, and furthermore, that even when built correctly, the inflator's sleeve could fail.

After Monclova made the line modifications, they X-rayed every SSI-20 LAT sample after deployment for more than a year and found many split sleeves, even in inflators that met their output specification. It was a design flaw and when TAIC and Freiberg were pressed, they confessed to similar failures in Germany.

It was easy for Takata to convince themselves that the GM rupture was only a 'flare up,' with an extremely low probability of happening again. I would be asked repeatedly, 'why only now?' and I had no better answer than the stars, moon and sun had to align. Production was released, and GM was told nothing. Senior management knew that with the line modifications and the reduced propellant loads, eventually approved by Maurer, another catastrophic rupture was unlikely. That made it easier for them to stay silent, even about the lower loads.

This was becoming all too familiar at Takata and the continued deception was taking its toll on me. Nervousness, fear, sleepless nights, and hangovers were my symptoms. Alcohol, which used to be fun and sometimes a way to release stress, was now becoming a necessary evil. A way to lighten the load of shame and guilt Takata was constantly heaping on me.

The Brazilian

There wasn't much more we could do with SSI-20 other than monitor Monclova's countermeasures. Occasionally, we would get word of a split sleeve, but since Takata had made that a de facto part of the design, nobody seemed to care anymore. We moved on to AIB, something with a point. Hopefully, this time we wouldn't be interrupted. How foolish.

"Kevin, we just had another one," Cory said.

"Please, Cory, not another rupture," I said, refusing to turn around.

"Sorry, Kevin, but I just got off the phone with our Brazil office and they had an SDI inflator come apart in a Volkswagen module LAT. It was at high temperature and the inflator was built last October in Monclova."

"Damnit! You have Monclova going through the drill?" I asked him, exacerbated.

"Yes, sir, but there is more," he continued, "TPSA (Takata Petri South America) was behind schedule and shipped the modules before the LAT was complete."

"You have got to be kidding me. Have they notified Volkswagen?"

"Yep, which Phillion says has some people pretty upset. Apparently, they didn't talk to anyone at TKH first."

"Good for them. At least we'll get everything back."

"Funny, Bob said the same thing," Cory added. "Monclova already sent me the LAT results for the suspect inflator lot. I have them here."

"Let's take a look," I motioned him to the small table in my cubicle. He spread out three Excel plots. After studying it a bit, I turned to him and said, "Oh, boy."

"Are you talking about the one riding the upper limit?" Cory asked.

"Yes. It's not that Monclova did anything wrong. It's inside the limits, but it's an outlier. It's screaming early and peaks well before the others. That's usually a good indicator of…."

"Higher than normal combustion pressure," Cory finished my sentence.

I was growing concerned. "Is the hardware on its way back?"

"Yes, and luckily, they didn't deploy all the LATs, so we will be getting some live inflators from the same lot."

"That's crucial. We will need those to figure out what the hell happened. Do we have any video or pictures yet?"

"No, not yet, but within the hour. Back to the results. If you don't think it's the hardware, then are you leaning towards a Moses Lake problem with the propellant?" Cory asked.

"Yes. Look, it's either low-density propellant or Monclova broke a bunch of tablets, and they just don't do that on SDI."

"Well, there is one more thing it could be," KK interjected. "We have a lot of different propellant tablet sizes. I know since I have to keep track of them all. Couldn't they have loaded the wrong one by mistake?"

"Yes, that's a possibility," I said. "But the SDI only uses two tablet sizes, a 5/16" diameter by 0.105" thick for Honda and a 1/4" by 0.125" thick for everybody else. They're really hard to mix up, but it needs to be on the checklist. Thanks."

"Why do we have a different Honda output?" Cory asked. "Moses Lake complains about that tablet all the time."

"As legend has it, Cory, Honda wanted a lower onset inflator and Paresh left the design to his resident engineers. They decided on a larger tablet without bothering to adjust the throat area. Moses Lake never could make it with any consistency and Paresh let it go. The inflator is a horribly inefficient, Honda-specific design."

"Now I understand," Cory said. "The e-mail with the video and pictures just came in. I'll forward it you."

"Good. Do either of you know where Phillion is?" I asked.

"He's in Greensboro," Cory answered. "I spoke to him earlier and he's heading to Monclova on Monday. The hardware from Brazil will be there early next week."

"I'll meet him there," I said, "and if I'm right, it will be a short stopover and then off to Moses Lake. I'd rather you stay back with the troops and get some work done."

"Me too!" Cory exclaimed.

The SDI was Takata's first PSAN single stage driver inflator and its eight years of virtually trouble-free production brought with it a huge fanbase. As much as we tried to steer people to the lighter and smaller SDI-X, there were always customers that wanted SDI. I liked the inflator because it used tablets and was built like a tank. Mostly because of its stout booster that held everything together. SDI didn't baseball like SDI-X. But we were about to learn that armor came with a price.

During development all inflators must demonstrate operating pressure margin, or safety factor. For most of the world, that number must be greater than 1.5. In Europe, it is 1.7. Safety factor is calculated by dividing the inflator's lowest statistical failure pressure by its maximum expected operating pressure (MEOP). MEOP is established by measuring the internal pressure of a number of high temperature deployments and calculating that population's upper statistical value. The lowest pressure at which the housing fails is calculated in the same manner, but with a data set from hydro burst tests.

What is a hydro burst test? Very simply the inflator is pumped up with water until it fails, and a transducer is used to measure that failure pressure. Why is water used? Because water is incompressible, it releases the energy in a manageable way. The same cannot be said for the compressible gas produced by an inflator.

When an SDI undergoes a hydro burst test, there are two distinct failures. The first is a tearing of the booster tube at its highest stress point, the exhaust ports. The inflator then baseballs, relatively slowly, and the cap fails with a burp leaving the insides neatly intact behind a ductile, smiley face. The pictures from Brazil that Cory just forwarded and were now up on my screen were not smiling.

"Cory, please track down McCormick, ask him to come over, and let's meet in my cube," I shouted over the wall.

A minute later Cory was standing over my shoulder, "Some picture, huh? McCormick's on his way."

"Look at that thing!" I said. "It's a baseball with a hole straight through it. Where the hell is the booster tube? The initiator holder? You can see right through it!"

Just then I heard McCormick over my other shoulder, "What the hell is that?"

"Brazil had an SDI rupture in a module LAT. That's the inflator," Cory answered.

"There's a hole straight through it! Where the hell is the booster tube?!" Dave said stunned, concern growing in his voice.

"Kevin, please open all the pictures."

"There's the booster tube," I said. "It tore at its exhaust ports, like expected, but..."

"Oh my God!" McCormick interrupted in disbelief. "The tube tore at its nozzles, but then the inflator baseballed so fast, the welds tying it to the cap and base couldn't hang on. That's two bullets. One headed into in the steering column, and the other... Kevin, I have to go."

"Go, Dave. Volkswagen knows. We'll get em back," I shouted as he turned and left. Poor guy was shaken.

I turned to Cory, "Please call Phillion and tell him we suspect a propellant problem. Ask him if one of his Moses Lake quality engineers can join us in Monclova to help with tablet density measurements. I'll call Al," I said. "At this rate, I should just have a hot line installed."

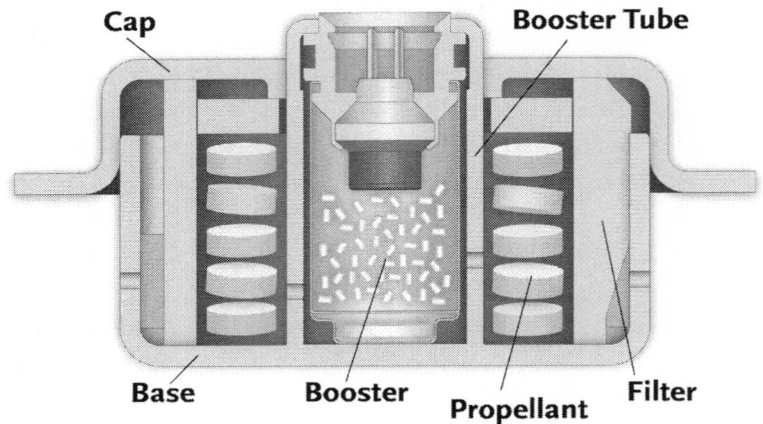

FIGURE NINE: CROSS-SECTION OF 'SDI' INFLATOR 'SDI'

We arrived in Monclova at the same time as the parts from Brazil. Carlos Iruegas' quality engineers were already pouring over traceability records in search of clues, as their counterparts in Moses Lake did the same. Gutierrez ushered us into a conference room where we quickly set up camp. On the table was a box with the ruptured Volkswagen part inside. Phillion sorted through the packing material, picked it up, and rolled it across the table towards me. I grabbed it and brought it up to my eye just in time to spy Carlos walking into the room. Already feeling foolish, I held it there and asked,

"Are they ready for us in the propellant breakdown room, Carlos?"

"Yes, Señor Kevin," he replied. "The inflators came in yesterday. Bob told us only to machine through the housing. Not to open them up. That's done, and they're waiting for us."

"Thank you, Carlos," Bob said, looking up from his laptop, his glasses at the end of his nose. "I have an e-mail here from Moses Lake that says their traceability records check out. Nothing out of the ordinary."

"Same here, Bob," Carlos said. "We haven't found anything yet."

"Well, if Moses Lake says tablet density checks out and Carlos says Monclova's traceability is clean, then you must have cracked a bunch of tablets again Jorge," I said, needling him.

"I don't think we will find that Señor Fitzgerald," he replied with his chest out.

"If not, it would mean low-density propellant," Bob said looking over his laptop again, but this time directly at his Moses Lake quality engineer.

"Let's stop speculating and go see," I said, grabbing my safety glasses.

Carlos' best quality engineer followed us. Once inside, Gutierrez motioned him to take a seat at the inspection table and handed him the first cut open inflator. The poor guy was nervous.

"Carefully separate the cap and base and pour the tablets into this vial," Jorge instructed him. "First, we want to see if there are any broken tablets and then our friend from Moses Lake will take some density measurements. OK?"

The engineer nodded. As he slowly filled the vial, it was obvious the tablets weren't broken. Jorge was grinning from ear to ear as he motioned the Moses Lake engineer to take his turn in the hot seat. He reluctantly obliged, grabbed a tablet, measured its diameter and height, weighed it, punched a few numbers into his calculator, looked up at Bob and said, "we have a problem."

"What do you mean we have a problem? How's that possible?" Bob asked, irritated. "I just finished reading an e-mail from your plant manager that said everything was fine." Bob wasn't looking for answer. He was just pissed.

"How bad is it?" I asked.

"Let me check a few more, but it's pretty bad."

I walked outside and reached for a cigarette with Bob following me.

"What the hell are you doing? You can't smoke out here."

"What is wrong with me?" I said putting the pack back in my pocket. "We need to book flights to Moses Lake right away."

"Yep. I'll call Dal and Scott and give them a rundown. After that I'll have a discussion with Thom. Neither call will be comfortable," he said.

Thom Walsh was the Moses Lake plant manager. He was always cordial and responsive, and I enjoyed his company. A good man. Bob sent him a summary report before we left Monclova and he and his team took it seriously because when we arrived, they were ready.

"Hey, Kevin and Bob. It's been awhile Kevin," Thom said.

"Yes, it has, Thom. You are normally pretty good at staying off the radar screen," I said smiling and shaking his hand.

"I suppose I have it lit up red now," he said looking at Bob.

"That's a fair assessment," I said.

"The guys will be here in a minute to go over a presentation they put together for you and Bob. We're pretty sure we know what happened."

"That helps, I said. And containment?"

"Can we table that discussion until we get through the presentation?"

"That doesn't sound good," Bob interjected as the team arrived.

It was a short investigation. They had root cause identified and countermeasures in place before we even took off from Monterey. The drive belt on the hopper that fed powder to the press was slipping, causing the press dies to be underfed. Compounding the situation, a sensor in the feed tube that should have detected the condition and halted production was incorrectly positioned. The countermeasures were a new sensor to detect further drive belt slippages and a redundant propellant feed tube sensor.

"That's great work," Bob said. "But the bad propellant lot still had to go through all our quality inspections. How did it escape?"

"All the inspections were signed off as good, Bob," Thom said, not proud. "We know we screwed up and how serious it is. Let the guys finish the presentation. The next few slides discuss the escape. They aren't going to make you any happier, but they will at least help you understand what happened and what we are doing about it."

"Go ahead," Bob said, his point made.

The next part of the presentation was hard to sit through. This was a screw-up of monumental proportions. Moses Lake's quality inspectors charged with certifying each propellant lot for density, arguably the most important of all inflator characteristics, were operating open loop. They were supposed to first weigh a tablet, measure its diameter and thickness, and then enter those values into the station's PC. If the density was good, a green accept light was displayed. If it was bad, a red reject. There was a predetermined number of tablets to verify based on the propellant lot size. The rule was that if one tablet failed, the entire lot was to be quarantined, and the quality inspector was to notify their quality engineer. Here's where the system broke down.

After interviewing several operators, it was discovered that if a sample failed but was only 'slightly out,' another sample was retrieved and tested. If a few more tested green, then the lot was accepted. When asked who gave those orders and when were they given, there were no good answers. Countermeasure proposals, ideas to make sure it would never happen again, those were plentiful. But when pressed on how Takata could guarantee this had never happened before, there was little offered. Bob and I were pissed. It was a terrible thing to realize.

"Based on the belt drive timeline, are any other customers affected? I asked. "We have to fence everything this propellant got into."

"Still checking, Kevin," Thom said.

"Okay, let's hope it's only Volkswagen. They know about the LAT failure so, I'm guessing those parts are already back at TPSA and in our control," I said, looking at Bob.

"I would expect so, Kevin," he replied, still distracted by the breakdown of such a critical process. It was unforgivable.

No One Has Any Scruples

I have a nice drive to work, I thought to myself, snaking my way around Lake Orion. It was a spectacular morning in early May, still quite brisk, and the lake was dotted with small fishing boats. Everything was in bloom, the air was fresh, I had a hot cup of coffee, good tunes on the radio and a manageable hangover. The day was off to a great start and I promised myself nothing would ruin it. I needed to attend to three things when I arrived, and McCormick was first on the list. I'd lost track of his progress on PDP and SDI-X2 and also needed his team to start a new project. As I pulled up to our pole barn, I gritted my teeth. 'Nothing was going to ruin my day.'

"Hey, Dave, do you have some time?" I asked him, weaving my way through the maze to my cubicle.

"Sure, boss. What do you have?"

"Mostly just want to catch up," I replied. "But I also want to talk about a new project for your group. Let me grab a coffee, check a few e-mails. Meet me in the conference room in fifteen. Bring your laptop."

"Can I come too?" KK asked. "I want to go over the new AIB implementation schedule with you."

"Absolutely," I said. "That was third on my list for today. We desperately need to get some cost improvement points on the board and AIB is pure gold."

"Third? What's second?" Dave asked.

"PSDI-5 with 13X. Nissan's test sequence was scheduled to finish up last week, and if I know Shari, the PV report is already finished and waiting for the last piece of data to drop. Isn't that right Shari," I yelled over the cubicles.

"Yes, Kevin, that's right. Welcome back," she said. "Is an hour okay? They're actually doing the final deployments right now."

"That's perfect Shari."

If I could clear these three items from my calendar this morning, I just might take the afternoon off and enjoy the rest of this beautiful day. I could use the break, and Al wasn't in the perpetually dark office with his nameplate on it to say 'no.' He was never in Armada. Most of our contact was via e-mail. Face to face interactions were rare, and if I absolutely had to, I could always reach him on his mobile, or what I liked to call, the 'rupture' hot line.

Dave and KK followed me into the conference room, and while Dave connected his laptop to the projector I closed the door behind us and said,

"The VW SDI inflator that ruptured at TPSA was definitely low-density propellant."

"Wow. I knew that's where the data was pointing, but I am still surprised," Dave said. "How did it make it out of Moses Lake?"

"Through their Swiss cheese quality department," I said. "If they didn't like the reading they got from one tablet, they just measured another. Unbelievable! We were able to fence this occurrence because it was tied to a press failure, but nobody could tell us it hadn't happened before. We're lucky TPSA caught it."

"I hear you. Why don't we start with PDP? That should cheer you up. The variable throat nozzles are working like a charm."

"Is that what's up on the screen now?"

"Yes, sir. You can see that by using two nozzle sizes and stainless-steel shim, we are able to keep certain nozzles closed during cold operation and open them all for hot deployments. It really clamps down our combustion pressure spread. At this low an MEOP we can take some serious metal out, and if we can convince GM's module engineers to reduce the output to three moles, like the rest of the industry is trending, the weight and size just get better."

"That's awesome, Dave," I said. "You remember Leo Knowlden told us GM is slowly moving in that direction. Their competition has already adopted the strategy. Gas is money. I can work with Auburn Hills to get GM to three moles."

"That would be great, and can you also give them a nudge on SDI-X2?" Dave asked. "They can't seem to decide on a slope or peak output, and that has us slowed at the moment. I'm using some of those people on PDP now. It's a major resource hog."

"Yes, I will, and I'm glad you mentioned our resource problem. Unfortunately, it's only going to get worse before it gets better. We can't add heads until we start showing a return on investment. That's why KK is here. We have to get AIB implementation moving. Once we start making progress on cost reductions, then we can start adding heads."

"I suppose that leads us to the new project you want me to add, but with no additional heads" Dave said with a grin.

"Yes, it does. I want to resurrect the axial ignition concept you and

Schumann were experimenting with on passenger and apply it to a side-impact inflator. That SSI-20 snuff test we ran in Monclova was an eye-opener. You can't hammer a small column of propellant like we are and expect it to behave nicely. Let's try lighting it radially, from the outside in."

"I love it!" said Dave. "What do you want to call it?"

"I gave some thought to that over the weekend. We'll advertise it as an upgrade to SSI-20 that uses the new PSAN, AIB and addresses Auburn Hills' heat and particulate concerns. Call it SL-20."

"Perfect," Dave said. "Have you talked to Heiko about it?"

"Some. He knows Auburn Hills hates SSI-20 and that there are design concerns, but to be honest, he and Christophe are consumed right now expanding Takata's GuNi portfolio. They just added a version of our SDI-X 1.7 called GDI 1.7 for Nissan/Renault and have started work on their own SSI-20 replacement called GSI. The latter will not meet USCAR requirements and that's the gap SL-20 has to fill."

"It seems such a waste," KK said. "Both groups designing a side-impact inflator."

"It is, but until there is a global organization doling out programs and resources, we have to respond to Japan and Auburn Hills," I said. "Heiko and Christophe are pursuing GuNi and I don't blame them. Look at all the difficulties we are having with PSAN. I just wish they had picked a formulation we could all use."

"Okay, you done with me?" Dave asked

"No. One more thing before we call Shari in," I said. "Do you have any idea what Paresh's R&D guys are up to? I've seen very few DRs from them lately."

"Oh, man, I'm so glad you asked. You are not going to believe this. Driver side wafers. They call them wablets. You know half-wafer, half-tablet," Dave said laughing.

I put my forehead on the table and said, "Please, no."

"Hell, yes," Dave said. "They are designing a family of disk inflators around them ranging from a small driver to a small passenger. They say it can be done with mostly the same hardware and that only the length of the cap, filter and booster tube change as the output increments. I saw the small passenger inflator in their R&D lab. It looks like Abraham Lincoln's top hat and has 50 'wablets' in it that must be stacked neatly."

"I'm sorry I asked. Please get out, and send Shari in."

Al was not paying attention to Paresh at all. This was the exact reason

Schubert and I pushed him for R&D as well. Wablets? Were they serious?

"Don't forget to talk to the GM program team in Auburn Hills," Dave said as KK tried to push him out the door. "I need to start GM's Qualified for Sourcing (QFS) for both inflators."

"I'll talk to Maurer personally, Dave. I promise."

"You're wasting your time talking to that guy. He's an idiot," Dave shot back. "All he does is complain about our inflators. Talk to Chavez."

"You know, that's been my experience with Maurer too," I said. "He's not very bright, is he? He reminds me of that cantankerous old Muppet that sits up in the balcony and is constantly complaining. What's his name?"

"Waldorf!" KK exclaimed. "Yes, he looks just like Waldorf."

"And he's crankier," Dave said. "He puts Hardenburg to shame." That had us all laughing.

"Message received, Dave, but protocol is protocol. Now would you please send Shari in."

"Your turn in the chute, Shari," Dave said on his way back to his cubicle.

A minute later she shuffled in with her laptop and said, "Dave said you're ready to talk PSDI-5 with 13X."

"That's right, Shari. Dave had nothing but good news, so please keep it coming."

"Well, I won't disappoint then," she said. "The environmental deployments completed about a half hour ago and I took a peek right before I came in. There are no ruptures. Not even close. Everything looks great. I mean better than ever. Not as tight as a PSDI-X, but pretty good."

Surprised, I asked, "Are you telling me they not only stayed intact, they passed all their performance requirements?"

"Handily," she replied. "I'll have the report ready to route for signature by the end of the day."

"Impressive. I was skeptical with those three big AI tablets. You rock, Shari," I said. "I think I will get out of here early today. Do you mind picking up with the AIB schedule tomorrow, KK? I'd like to break here and give Rob a call."

I weaved my way back to my desk. Imagine that. 13X worked. Rob was going to be thrilled. I hadn't even given the possibility serious thought but was now considering the ramifications. What would Japan tell Nissan? The PV report would list 13X desiccant, not calcium sulfate, and that would certainly catch the attention of Nissan's engineers. It would be an easy explanation. An upgrade, commonality, but oh, what a tangled web.

"Rob, it's Kevin. I have some good news for you," I said. "The Nissan PSDI-5 with 13X passed its PV. We will be routing the report for signature tomorrow and after that I will send it along to Echigawa."

"That's great news. Whew, what a relief."

"Yes, but I'm still interested in how Japan is going to explain 13X to Nissan. Our PV report will be clear."

"I don't know if they've discussed that with them, Kevin," Rob said. "All we can do is send the report over."

"I understand, Rob, but if Japan is afraid to share 13X with Nissan, it will effectively kill any chance of us adding it to products already in production. We will be sure to add it to every new design, but it should be looked at across the board."

"I understand, Kevin. Send the report over and let's see what they say. I have another call coming in.

"Okay, but we both know where this is going. Have a good afternoon," I said hanging up and swearing nothing was going to ruin my day. I packed up and headed home.

The following week I learned that Echigawa stripped 13X from our report. A few quick keystrokes and it read calcium sulfate, child's play for their accomplished report doctors. Only a small change to the bill of materials and their tracks were covered. Maybe they all took a half day off too after the simple exercise, their tangled webs doubling as hammocks.

Just after getting that news, Phillion called with an update on the SDI inflators from Brazil. They still had not shown up at TPSA and we were both anxious.

"I have some news on those Volkswagen SDI modules that seem to be MIA. Are you sitting down?" he asked.

"Ah, come on, Bob, I'm already having a shitty day," I said. "Echigawa neglected to tell Nissan that we used 13X in their latest PSDI-5 PV. You know, the only one that's ever passed."

"Well, we'll still be adding it to that inflator whether they told Nissan or not. It's what we validated," he said.

"I know, Bob, but it's just more of the same and kills any chance of across the board implementation."

"You can only affect what's in your control, Kevin. A wise man told me that once. Let's make sure we get it into everything going forward, that's the best we can do."

"What's your bad news?" I asked. "Did they lose the modules?"

"Worse. Volkswagen decided to leave them in cars. Apparently, they asked TPSA to run a couple more high-temperature tests from the same lot and when they didn't see another rupture, they approved the shipment."

"But Bob, a few extra deployments doesn't prove anything, and Takata knows that when propellant starts out at a low density it doesn't age well. This is dangerous."

"I know, Kevin. I wasn't consulted. Just informed after the fact. It sucks," he replied.

"Did it spill to anyone else or was it just Volkswagen?"

"Damnit, forgot to ask that," he replied. "I'll get back to you shortly."

The low-density propellant did spill to another customer, Honda, where it was used to make already vulnerable PSDI-5s. Unlike Volkswagen though, Honda wasn't given the chance to make the wrong decision. Echigawa made it for them.

A Large Speed Bump

Webster defines a speed bump as a low raised ridge across a roadway to limit vehicle speed. Jorge Gutierrez was the embodiment of one located every quarter mile on a Nebraska highway. He had the Monclova bus lurching from one problem to another, and my team along for the ride. He hated change, loved the status quo, and was painfully uncooperative. I didn't form this opinion hastily but do admit I have scarce patience for complainers. Why was he always complaining, anyway? The former GM, Luis, and his trusted circle had it under control. Was it because those ranks had dwindled, and he felt exposed? Regardless, his caustic personality was souring relationships at a time he needed them to be strongest.

Monclova owned all the X-Series production, including the myriad of headaches that went with first launches. Customers lined up for the new, smaller inflators and were relentless in their pursuit of cost reductions. Teamwork was central. I expected Jorge to be eager, considering Monclova's recent SSI-20 miss, but was still wary of him. We would soon see. Scott arranged a weekly teleconference between the plants and engineering to air out issues and asked if I would sit in on the inflator portion. Hoping that Jorge wouldn't devolve that exchange into a bitch session at every opportunity, I agreed.

First up on Jorge's punch list was his favorite nemesis, the SDI-X 1.7. It was a simple inflator that packed 1.7 moles of gas, looked like a top hat, and serviced a new, small-size passenger airbag market. The issue was propellant loading. Why? Because it was challenging.

"Hello, everyone, is Scott on the line?" I asked.

"No, Señor Kevin. Just us," Jorge responded cheerfully.

"I'm here," said one of Scott's lieutenants. "He asked me to sit in for him today."

"Let's get started, Jorge. What do you have for us this week?" I asked.

"We'd like to talk about the SDI-X 1.7 loading issue again," he said. "We still can't load the inflator without cracking tablets."

I turned to Cory, rolled my eyes, and put us on mute, "If he says snow cone again, I am going to lose it. How can we expect him to lead AIB implementation, if he can't even load this damn inflator?"

"Easy, Kevin. I'll do the talking if he puts on his Good Humor hat," Cory said, trying to keep the peace.

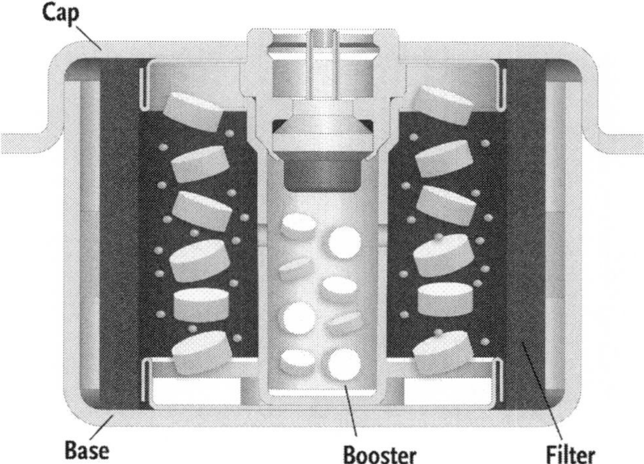

FIGURE TEN: CROSS SECTION OF INFLATOR 'SDI-X 1.7'

I used to love snow cones when I was a kid. The red, white and blue ones that melted in the paper holder faster than you could eat them. Gutierrez ruined that memory for me. The difficulty Monclova was experiencing loading X-series disk inflators was intentional. Paresh was determined to make the world's smallest inflators. He already had its most gas efficient propellant, so he challenged the space to house it. Did that make things more difficult? Yes. Could it be done? Of course. Would it take strong plant leadership? Absolutely! Was Jorge that leader? Not if embracing challenge was a job requirement. I took us off mute and said,

"Okay, Jorge. Can you share with us some of the process improvements you've been investigating to improve the situation?"

"Yes, of course," he answered. "Mario, please forward Kevin and Cory the video you showed me this morning."

"We're going to put you on mute while we look," I said. "We'll be back in a minute."

Cory and I watched the video on my laptop. Mario was still trying to load the entire 40-grams of propellant into the inflator all at once, an approach we had cautioned against previously. This time, though, he added a vibratory mechanism to help settle the tablets as they were loaded. It looked like it was slapped together in someone's garage and sounded even worse. Tablets were bouncing out of the inflator and spilling all over the weigh scale. I unmuted the phone.

"Well, Jorge, that didn't work, did it?" I asked rhetorically.

"No, Señor Kevin, and you can see we are still left with a snow cone," he said. Cory immediately muted the phone and said,

"I got this, Kevin." Taking us off mute, he continued. "Jorge did you try loading in increments or vibrating the tablet bed down under a weight like we asked. We've been able to do both successfully here."

"You don't have a 17-second Takt time in Armada," Jorge shot back.[13]

"Don't insult us, Jorge," I interrupted. "We understand the concept of line balance."

"I'm sorry, Kevin, but we are frustrated. This is impacting shipments," he said.

"All the more reason for you to figure it out, Jorge." I said with growing irritation.

Cory was done trying to restrain me. He knew I was looking for a snow cone to shove up Jorge's ass now. "Investigate the improvements we've been recommending and a tip; the next video you send over better be more than a weak attempt to embarrass us. Understood?"

"I'm not trying to embarrass you," Jorge said, getting defensive.

"Stop, Jorge. You're embarrassing yourself. Mario, do you understand?" I asked.

"Yes, Kevin. We will investigate. Cory, can you please resend the e-mail with your suggestions. We won't be ready for next week, but we'll get right on it."

"They're your shipments, Mario," I replied. "Have you talked to Dal about potentially impacting customer supply, Jorge?"

"No, I was going to bring it up here."

"I would recommend you present solutions when you deliver that message and I don't think your last attempt would have played well." I said as the line went silent. "Take another shot at it and I'll do you a favor and delete this video. Mario, I look forward to seeing your next results." After hanging up, I turned to Cory and said,

"I meant it about not trusting Jorge with AIB. There is too much at stake here. We are going to have to hold his hand every step of the way."

"I understand. We're ready to move out. The drawings are complete and trial parts on their way to Monclova. The SDI-X 1.7 is one of the first validations and we'll be sure to get the loading issue fixed at the same time."

"Good plan, Cory. Thanks," I said.

AIB wasn't a complicated integration. Really only the booster tube changed. We removed a few parts where we could, but to look at a cross section, only the tube was noticeably different. The rest of AIB's function depended on process control. We flowed tight component tolerancing to the suppliers and made sure to leave Monclova the easy part. Press the booster tube onto the initiator holder to a designed stop and weld the cap to a prescribed height. That was it. Do those two simple things and Takata would have a lower cost inflator that didn't need to be doused in holy water before every bonfire test. One dimension to hold. No finesse necessary. I sent Cory to Monclova to make sure they got it right.

"Hey, Kevin, it's Cory. Do you have a minute?"

"Hey, you're missing a beautiful day up here," I said. "How's the SDI-X 1.7 coming?"

"Good and bad," he said, not in a mood for small talk. "Would you rather start with propellant loading or AIB?"

"Deep breath, bud. Let's start with propellant loading."

"Good, that's the easier one. They upgraded the station and are now vibrating during the tablet drop and then settling the bed under a weight, all within Takt time," he answered.

"That's great news, Cory," I said. "What's the problem with AIB?"

"For some reason they are not following our recommendation to use a dead stop in the press that sets the cap height. They bought some new presses that monitor stroke and force and the machine's logic uses those parameters to set height."

"I'm confused. What could be easier than stopping the press on two precise, metal tool surfaces?" I asked. "We purposefully tightened the component tolerances to make this easy on them."

"Nothing. That's why they chose not to," Cory said frustrated. "This process is far more complicated than it needs to be and with consequences. Millimeters of over-stroke damages internal components. I just watched one trial where the final height met specification and when we took it over to the machine shop and cut it open, the booster tube and filter were smashed. The damn press over-stroked and then came back to the right dimension before the weld. The inflator would have passed all our inspections, pancaked internals and all."

"Then we'll just switch them over to the dead stop".

"That's what I said, Kevin, and their answer was that the new presses were already installed, and Jorge was dead set on using them. They even showed me a tolerance that said we are full of shit and that the smashed parts observed in the cut section were a result of the design. Jorge's position is that since the trial part met the drawing before they cut it, the problem is ours. That last part I didn't want to tell you."

"Is Phillion there?" I asked.

"No, unfortunately he's not. I tried calling but couldn't reach him," he replied. "They said he's supposed to be here week after next. He knows we have PVs to start and that they are struggling with this."

"I'll call him as well. Come on home, Cory."

"Hey one more thing. I can't go anywhere in this plant without someone chasing me down for a signature. All weld issues, so we probably need to send McCormick down again. It's disturbing the team can't stabilize such a critical process. They badly need a weld expert."

"I've been beating that drum forever, Cory. I don't think they want one. Maybe they see it as failure. I don't know. When you get back, I want to chat with you about a new piece of equipment the guys working on the recall found that measures helium concentration inside the inflator. I'd like you to think about using it to calibrate Monclova's process. Their leak station pass-fail limits are set assuming there is 100% helium inside the inflator and I'm pretty sure that's not the case."

"Agreed, Kevin. That's great. See you soon."

I hung up the phone and called Phillion, "Why is Monclova making the AIB process so difficult, Bob?" I asked. "I know you're not their process guy, but what could be easier than pressing to a dead stop? Jorge is just being stubborn."

"You are as stubborn as he is, Fitzgerald. You have to work at getting along with him," he said. "Let me see. I'm heading down there, not this week, but the week after and I'll get involved."

"Appreciate it, Bob. I don't know about you, but I'm seriously concerned about Monclova under Jorge's leadership."

"Couldn't tell," he said sarcastically.

"There is good reason for us to be uneasy. He totally botched SDI-X 1.7 and his plant is generating weld non-conformances at an alarming rate," I said.

"Have you been that direct with Dal or Scott?" he asked. "If you really feel that way, you should say something."

"I know I should, Bob, but as stupid as it sounds, I am afraid to. I know how fiercely protective Scott is of Mexican leadership and I understand why. I've seen it firsthand how they become easy prey for lazy applications engineers who never want to travel south of the border."

"It's not as stupid as it sounds Kevin. I understand. Got to run. Talk later," Bob said, hanging up.

Phillion was finally able to convince Monclova that we didn't design the SDI-X1.7 to crush all its internal parts and that maybe their process had something to do with it. He corralled Mario's engineers and together they quickly diagnosed the problem and reprogrammed the controllers. It wasn't that complicated. It just took leadership. Leadership that was absent at a time when Monclova begged for it to be at full force.

11

A Deadly Turn

IT WAS a grey September morning, just chilly enough for the heat in the car. Cold was coming. After taking care of a few things in the office, I was on my way over to Auburn Hills to market our new and improved inflators with AIB. It was always nice to get away from the steady drumbeat of issues Armada had become. The only downside was a chance encounter with my boss, or Steve Maurer. Al was always so busy with the recall that a quick pass by his office and a wave to the crowd inside would check that box. If Maurer saw me, though, he would surely corner me and remind me how crappy our inflators were. It was like he had amnesia. Every time I saw him, I would get the same lecture. I think Paresh drove him nuts, ignoring him all those years.

Anyway, if he started in, I promised myself I would just picture that old curmudgeon Waldorf sitting up in that balcony and not let it get to me. As I eased my car into a spot just off the lobby, my phone rang. It was Schubert and when I answered, I could tell he was upset.

"Kevin, I have some terrible news."

"What is it, Bob?" I was trying to remember what I could have done this time to get in trouble. Al had a gift like that.

"I just got word of the first PSDI fatality," he answered gravely.

I didn't know what to say. I feared this day would come but I wasn't prepared for it. I was removed from the investigation, immersed in the growth of X-series and constant firefighting in Monclova. Unlike Bob, I could put it out of my mind, but that didn't make the news hurt any less.

"Kevin, you there?" Bob asked.

"Yeah, I'm sorry, Bob, just taken aback," I replied. "What do you know?"

"Not much. It happened back in May in Oklahoma. They're certain it's linked to a rupture."

"And the victim?" I asked as the words hung in the air.

"A young teenage girl. She'd just graduated from high school," the pain in his voice obvious. "Also, the inflator was outside the recall population."

"Outside the recall population? We still don't have our arms around this, do we?"

"I don't know, Kevin. It could still be a manufacturing issue. We have to see the hardware, comb over the traceability records. You know the drill."

"I know the drill, Bob, but I also know my gut tells me it will come up empty. This is terrible. I have to go. I'm sorry, Bob."

Backing the car out of its spot, I pointed it in the direction of home and drove off in a daze. Work was over for me. Before today's tragic news, Takata had been notified of five prior field ruptures. The first was in 2003 in Switzerland and went unreported to NHTSA. The second was in 2004 in Alabama and Takata did not receive pictures of that incident until a year later. The next two years were quiet, but in the summer of 2007, Honda reported three more ruptures. Takata assigned those to production issues and in November 2008, Honda recalled 4000 Accords and Civics globally. That was almost a year ago now. This changed everything. This made it all too real.

'The inflator was outside the recall population.' That meant root cause was still a mystery. Yes, Bob and the team had to check all the boxes, but I was developing a sinking feeling that their singular focus on production issues was just a way to avoid the unthinkable. That PSAN was the very issue. I had to get a hold of Thom Walsh. When LaGrange was shuttered, all its documentation was shipped to Moses Lake. The corrected Honda PV report might still be there. I had to find it. I snapped out of my daze and punched Thom's number into my phone. This was the very reason Sheridan and I had the truth memorialized.

"Thom, it's Kevin. How are you?"

"Doing just fine, Kevin. If you are calling about the new tablet measurement system, its working just great..."

"No, something much more important. Do you have a minute?"

"Yes, of course. What is it, Kevin? It sounds serious."

"It is. Sadly, we just got word of the first PSDI fatality. The reason I'm calling is I think there may be more to these ruptures than just early production issues and I need your help."

"That's just awful, Kevin," Thom said pausing. "You know I wasn't around back then, but I'll help in any way I can."

"When I was in LaGrange, one of my engineers and I authored a report that I need you to find. It was filed in LaGrange's document control system and all those boxes were moved to Moses Lake. It's titled 'Revised Honda Validation Test Report' or something like that. The date on it is October 2000."

"Holy shit, Kevin. 'Revised Honda Validation Report.' I can only imagine. If it's here, we'll find it," he promised.

"Please do, Thom. It's important. Thanks, and keep me posted."

Sandy's car wasn't in the driveway when I pulled in. I wanted to talk to her, put my head on her shoulder. That would have to wait, but the stiff drink I was pouring wouldn't.

Eight years had passed since we filed that report and even though Takata's document retention policy required it still be there, I wasn't holding out much hope. I mean, why would Takata keep such an incriminating document after the great lengths they took to cover up the events it describes? Because they are idiots, that's why.

"Kevin, it's Thom. I have some good news for you," he said two days later.

"No way...shut the front door," I shouted, leaping from my chair.

"I told you if it was here, we'd find it," Thom boasted. "I hope you don't mind, but I took the liberty to peek at the Executive Summary and I must say my earlier 'Holy shit' was an understatement."

"Thank you so much, Thom. You are a life saver!" I exclaimed. "Can you still get it out tonight?"

"Yes, you will have it tomorrow."

"I mean it, Thom, you are a life saver. Talk to you later." Hanging up the phone, I swung my chair around and shouted over the wall at Schubert. Al hadn't moved him to Auburn Hills yet, but it was just a matter of time.

"Bob, you got a minute to talk in the conference room?"

"Sure," he said. "Let me grab a coffee first."

I closed the door to the room behind us, "Listen, Bob, Sheridan and I issued a pretty controversial report in LaGrange after you were reassigned. There were several ruptures in the PSDI PV that were never reported to Honda. Tom and I discovered this and published an accurate report. I presented those results to Bill Martin and Paresh, but nothing was done. Moses Lake changed their process to un-milled BHT around the same time and that seemed to fix things. Right after that they moved my group to Armada and I found another job. Last week after hearing of Ashley Parham's death, I asked Thom to find that report."

"Did he?" Bob asked seriously.

"Yes, it will be here tomorrow."

"We'll need to get a copy to Al," he said.

"Of course. That's the point. I'm also putting one in a safety deposit box and I'm not going to ask how many copies you make."

A week later, Bob and I were told we'd each be meeting separately with one of Takata's lawyers to poke at the newly unearthed landmine. The meetings would be with Ross Hamilton of the law firm Tuggle-Duggins. Their offices were in downtown Greensboro, so I thought certainly Frank's boys. Being a real southern gentleman, Ross insisted on making the trip north to see us. I called my Dad the night before. He was familiar with the history and I needed someone to talk to.

"Hey, Pop. What a mess, huh? This is all so new to me," I said. "I've never had to talk to a lawyer before. Do you think I should have my own tomorrow?"

"No, not yet Kevin," he answered. "This guy is not the law and you have nothing to hide. Just tell him the truth and you'll be fine. If they threaten you at all, then we'll talk to lawyers."

"Okay Dad. Thanks for listening. I'll let you know how it goes."

"Careful with the booze, Kevin," he said before letting me go. "It can get away from you pretty quickly, especially with the kind of stress you are always under."

"Understood, Dad. Love you." Words of wisdom from a twenty-year recovering alcoholic. He was right. I'd been hitting it harder since news of Ashley's death. As hard as I needed to. One more and I'd call it quits for the night.

The next morning, I met Ross in a conference room off the Auburn Hills Marriott lobby and he was a genuinely nice guy. Tall, well dressed, and soft spoken, I felt comfortable in his company. The conversation was easy, and after some small talk, we got around to the report. We talked for hours and I bored him with all the details, while he feverishly took notes. It was cathartic, and I thought I was helping. We broke before lunch, but before parting ways, he let me know he would be in Armada on and off over the next few months working on a special project for Frank. I reached out to shake his hand and asked.

"What's the special project?"

"Mr. Takada asked Frank to make sure his new X-series inflators are not plagued with the same problems as PSDI," Ross replied. "He wants a third party, namely me, to crawl all over the development documentation and make sure everything's legit. What's with the big grin?" he asked.

"We're an open book, Ross," I said. "Look forward to it." The smile was because I knew how much Frank's special project would get under Al and Paresh's skin.

A few weeks later Bob and I were called to meet with a second Takata lawyer, Peter Theut from Butzel-Long, and this time together. The meeting was in Takata's Auburn Hills facility and the mood was much more serious. The room was small and already cramped when we walked in. Tim Healy was sitting at the head of the table to my right. Peter Theut and his assistant, a slender, young Japanese woman, were seated directly across the table. At the other end of the room sat Al Bernat. Bob and I took our places next to each other across from Peter. The tension was palpable.

After introductions, there was an odd, almost surreal discussion about the differences between Japanese and American business cultures. To me, it was an irritating attempt to downplay the seriousness of what I was about to relate. When it was my turn, I channeled the diversion into a passionate account of Shin and Hideo's transgressions and made it clear that what they did was not acceptable in any business culture. Al and Tim squirmed. Schubert had nothing to fear and sat quietly. Theut just listened stone faced. Afterwards, Peter approached me in the hallway.

"Mr. Fitzgerald, let me shake your hand," he said with his arm outstretched. "I have a great deal of respect for what you've done. I've been at this for years and have never seen anything like this before. You should be proud of yourself."

"Thank you, Peter. That means a lot to me," I said with a smile. My faith in humanity was always easily restored.

Tim asked Bob, Al and me to follow him back to his office for a short wrap up discussion and after we were all situated Tim began the conversation.

"Let me start by saying, Al and I are thoroughly disgusted by Shin and Hideo's actions in LaGrange. That kind of behavior is unacceptable."

"Is anything going to be done about it this time, Tim?" I asked. "I reported it to Paresh and Bill Martin back in 2000."

"We are going to create a data vault, where all original test data will be preserved. Only a select few will have access, and that data can never be tampered with."

"And what happens to Shin and Hideo? How will the report impact the recall?"

"I can't answer those questions yet, Kevin," Tim said. "Peter has to submit his report to Japan first, but I promise you action will be taken."

"I sure hope so," I said as Bob and I stood to leave. Time would tell.

The Fox Gets Demoted to the Hen House

Ashley Parham was killed on May 27, 2009. Two weeks after that, in June, Honda learned of another rupture and at the end of that month expanded the November 2008 recall by 510,000 vehicles. Two months later, in September, Honda confirmed that Ashley's death was the result of an exploded airbag, notifying both NHTSA and Takata. The cumulative effect triggered the agency to open their own investigation into the scope and timeliness of Honda's two recalls. As November opened, Takata was under duress.

Paresh was under more. He was wobbling, and as we were taking bets on who would land the knockout punch, Sean Burns cold-cocked him. What? Why didn't we see that coming? He wasn't even on the scorecard. But Paresh's undoing at the hands of one of his own shouldn't have surprised us. He never let them shine. Infamously cut them off in presentations and was always grabbing the spotlight. Sean must have just reached his limit because rumor had it he gave Al and Rob an ultimatum. If Paresh didn't move on, he would. Period.

Who knows what really happened, but right after the NHTSA investigation was announced, Paresh was out. He was being moved over to a brand-new office and job in Auburn Hills. I was in my cube when I got the call from Schubert, who happened to scoop the story.

"Kevin, you are not going to believe this," he said. "Head to the conference room!" I must have been a blur navigating the maze because Schubert was rarely this excited.

"What is it?" I asked, closing the conference room door.

"Paresh is out," he said.

"Out of Takata?" I asked.

"No. When have you ever seen them do that?"

"Good point. Where is he going, then?"

"If you would just shut up for a second, I'll tell you," he laughed. "They created a new position just for him...the Director of Reoccurrence Prevention. He won't be a VP anymore. His job will be to look for gaps in our inflator and propellant processes and then work with the plants to close them. A lot of auditing, I would guess."

"And who will he have working for him?"

"Come on, Kevin. Nobody," he said. "But he will have to come through you to get anything done. When the plants revolt, which they will, Dal and Scott will send him your way. My understanding is that it is just Monclova and Moses Lake. They knew Germany would ignore him."

"Wow...so that's his window seat," was all I could say as I began to process. Paresh was out of inflator and propellant development and that was a good thing, but still, so many more questions. I collected my thoughts and said,

"Reoccurrence Prevention? Are you fucking kidding me?! That's putting the fox in charge of the hen house. We are in this mess because of him!"

"Now there's the reaction I was looking for," he said. "Yeah, it's incredible. This place never ceases to amaze me."

"Then we'll put his ass to work," I said. "Monclova has non-stop welding issues and it's about time we opened Pandora's helium concentration box. If he wants to prevent future issues, that's where he needs to focus. I can't believe I'm even saying this."

"Yeah, I know, but that's a good plan, Kevin, I would also suggest you make him write a P.O. for everything." After we both finished laughing, I asked the next logical question,

"Who is Al replacing him with? Sean?"

"No. Remember when I told you everybody over here gets a kick out of Al's organizational charts. Well, this one is no different," he answered. "He's decided to have all five of Armada's directors report directly to him. The Five Directors!"

"Let me make sure I understand you," I said. "He wants me, you, Sean, Larry, and Rich to all report directly to him, when he is never here. He has zero interest in Armada. Do you think he even knows Rich is off developing an inflator that looks like Abraham Lincoln's top hat, has over 50 wablets in it, and will never go to production?"

"A wablet? What's a wablet? Wait a minute, don't tell me. Half tablet, half wafer. Very clever," he said, yanking my chain. "Yep, The Five Directors. It does have a ring to it."

"Maybe, Five Guys. Flipping hamburgers sounds better to me. Always a pleasure to chat, Bob."

"Hang in there, Kevin. Keep fighting the good fight."

It was either laugh or cry at Takata, and Paresh's assignment to lead Reoccurrence Prevention was a perfect example why. Bob and I were laughing at the absurdity of the idea when we knew we should have been crying over its implications. Yes, Paresh was out, but by associating his name with Reoccurrence Prevention, Takata signaled they weren't serious about the important effort and stripped it of any credibility. It became a joke, his window seat, and was a telling sign of Takata's indifference.

The Oriental Project

The Oriental Project, named after Frank Roe's vacation home in NC, was one of the last things Mr. Takada would ask of Frank. Jim was battling throat cancer, but now he had more than his own mortality to think about. The death of Ashley Parham at the hands of one of his airbags had his company at risk. He asked Frank to conduct an internal audit of the X-Series development process, to make sure nothing was missed. He wanted assurance that there wasn't another PSDI looming on the horizon. Frank asked Ross and Phillion to organize the effort.

The pair would be frequent visitors to Armada over the next months, so we set them up in a conference room in the main building. KK would be doing heavy lifting from our side. She relished the thought of someone challenging her documentation and didn't mind having to schlep boxes back and forth between the buildings. That would be ending soon anyway. With Paresh gone, Sean and I agreed to end the turf wars and cohabitate again. We were scheduled to move in a few weeks, once they had all the cubicles in the main building returned to normal size.

KK and I walked over to greet Ross, who was already busy at work in to the conference room. Phillion couldn't make the trip this week.

"Ross, good to see you again," I said, shaking his hand. "Do you need a top off for that coffee?"

"No. Coffee's good and so am I. Good to see you again, Kevin," he said.

"Ross, this is Kelli. She wears many hats around here and one of them is Document Control. She will be your go-to person while you are here."

"Hi Ross, nice to meet you. They call me KK," she said. "Kevin already filled me in. Where do you want to start?"

"X-Series only, but we want to walk the entire DR process. Margin studies, FMEA's, DV and PV reports...Basically, your entire design record."

"OK, but we didn't pick up the X-series until after DR2, so I can only provide DR3 and the PVs. Everything else, you'll have to get from Sean," she said.

"I wasn't aware of that but thank you. I will add it to his list. I only had him down for the newest PSAN and AIB."

"This is pretty straightforward, Kevin," KK said. "I'll let you know if we run into a problem, but I don't anticipate any."

"Thanks, KK. You good, Ross?" I asked.

"Yes, thanks for the hospitality guys," he answered. "I'll try and make this as painless as possible."

"You both free for lunch?" I asked receiving an affirmative nod from both.

KK spent the morning filling Ross and Bob's war room with enough truthful, passing documentation to keep them busy for weeks. Having nothing to hide was making this easy for her.

Sean took a different approach to the audit and slow rolled the pair. He didn't withhold anything. He just made every request painful. Al was either directing him behind the scenes or Sean was just having a hard time shaking the secrecy Paresh ingrained in him. Either way, it was puzzling. There was no reason to stonewall. The X-series inflator DVs and PVs were near flawless, and the new propellants were fully validated as part of that process. What was the reluctance? If there were process gaps, close them. Fear of transparency just hinders progress.

Bob's tenacity eventually won out and he and Ross published a detailed report of the lessons learned. It just took them a little longer than planned. Frank invited Al down to Greensboro to review the audit findings. I got a call from Phillion the day after the meeting.

"Hey, Kevin, I thought you might be interested in how the Oriental Project meeting with Al and Frank went yesterday. Ross was there too."

"Yeah, I'd love to hear. I'm sure Al enjoyed sitting through that."

"He didn't..." Bob said.

"I was being sarcastic, Bob. Nobody likes criticism. Constructive or not."

"No, he didn't sit through it," Bob continued. "He stormed out like a child before we could finish."

"What?! How bad could it have been?" I asked, really perplexed. "I know our work was solid and Sean's propellants all passed Nissan's specification with flying colors."

"It wasn't bad at all, Kevin. We identified a few gaps to close and recommended Al institute a separate DR system for propellants, modeled after the inflator system."

"That's a great idea, Bob. And the issue?"

"I have no idea. He just packed up his laptop, left the room in a huff, and hopped the next flight back to Detroit."

"A real leader of men," I said, disgusted.

Bob echoed, "Yeah, a real leader of men."

"We'll make the propellant DR system work, Bob. It's a great idea. We'll target their third generation PSAN. Sean calls it AMP for Advanced Main Propellant."

"Thanks, Kevin. That will work. Talk to you soon."

12

They Can't Be Serious

ON DECEMBER 24, 2009, shrapnel from a PSDI inflator took its second life, an unsuspecting mother returning home from holiday shopping with her three young children. Imagine the grief. Imagine the air hanging in Takata's Tokyo headquarters and the cubicles of Chikaraishi's inflator group in Echigawa. It had to be thick with shame. Jim Takada's dream was for a world with zero fatalities from traffic accidents, not this. Honda was deeply disappointed and wanted Takata's promise that their new X-Series inflators were different, that if one of them were to rupture, for whatever reason, nobody would die. I received an e-mail from Echigawa, titled 'Fail-Safe', outlining a project to provide Honda that assurance.

A PSDI inflator is mounted in the steering wheel with its primary chamber facing the steering column and its second chamber facing the occupant. In studying field events, Takata and Honda observed that the steering column arrested most of the shrapnel from a primary chamber rupture. The real damage was done when the second chamber fragmented directly into the cabin. This led Honda to conclude, and Echigawa to agree, that if the new X-Series inflators were engineered to always rupture in their base, or into the steering column, they would 'fail-safe.' It was nonsense. I looked down at my watch and noticed I was already running late for a meeting with Cory and Dave. This just changed what we needed to discuss.

"Gentlemen," I said closing the door and taking a seat. It was just the three of us.

"Good morning, Kevin," Cory said. "What do you have?"

"Something completely different than I did ten minutes ago," I said plugging my laptop into the projector. "Take a look at this and tell me what you think." After a quick read Cory gave his summary.

"They want the X-Series inflators engineered to always fail in the base.

That way if they rupture in a vehicle, the steering column will contain all the fragments. Man, they want us to intentionally weaken a pressure vessel that carries nearly 5000 psi!"

"That's crazy," Dave interjected.

"Agreed, Dave, but Honda doesn't know any better," I said. "They think an X-Series inflator will be safer if it fails in its base. But it won't just burp into the steering column like a PSDI. It will instantly baseball and most likely break free from its fasteners and once loose, where it fails may not be so important."

"Now that would be an interesting test!" Dave said.

"Not interested and let's hope it never gets that far. Japan's idea of an engineered solution is to add a notch to the initiator holder. If there's a runaway event, then a tear starts there, moves through the weld and out into the base. I think safety factor is going to be a real problem and let's hope I'm right, because it's just a bad idea."

Cory agreed. "I'll take Chikaraishi's concept drawings and have some trial parts made. We'll run the first hydro-burst tests here. If we can't maintain safety factor, no sense in wasting Monclova's time."

"Great, thanks, Cory," I said. "Now take a look at the last part of the e-mail. They are thinking about inviting Honda Marysville up here for a vehicle level demonstration in the near future and want to use a PSDI-X. As disturbing as that reads, let's make sure we do all our evaluations with it, so we are prepared."

"Got it, boss," Dave said. "While Cory is proving the notch will never work, I'll find where the production design fails. We'll build ten inflators with smaller tablets that will force them to rupture. If we're lucky, they'll all fail in the base and we won't have to do anything."

"Okay, Dave, but be careful," I said standing to leave. "This is why Heiko and Christophe are so adamant about using GuNi propellant. It duds when it's compromised and that's the true definition of fail-safe."

I had to find Schubert. This had the potential to become a real science project and if we were going to need Al at some point to apply the brakes, Schubert would be the one to have to stand on his feet. Fortunately, Bob was in his office and as he listened to me relate our latest assignment, he reached into his desk drawer and handed over some photos. It wasn't hard to see how Honda made the leap. The one or two PSDIs that did fail in the base were largely contained by the steering column, but they were the exception. Most of the photos depicted a second chamber cap failure. In some of those instances, a large piece was detached that would have certainly resulted in blunt force trauma. In others, only a small section was peeled back, hinged at the inflator's outside edge like an open door. A perfect escape hatch for the razor-sharp spring retainer lurking behind it. Bob made a point of showing me the twisted remains of one. He wanted it to sink in and it did.

With Cory and Dave both on the job, it wasn't long before we were back in the conference room reviewing the results.

"Please tell me the data worked its magic," I implored.

"It's not a slam dunk," Cory said. "The inflators all failed in the notch, but the burst pressure variation was awful. We lose margin but unfortunately still meet Honda's safety factor. We'll never satisfy Europe's requirement and USCAR will be a struggle, so another Honda-only design."

"Listen, I don't think we need to worry about adding the notch anyway," Dave interjected. "All ten of the bombs we built without one failed in the base. The tear doesn't always start in the same place, but each time it runs to the outside diameter then around it and pops the base off like a contact lens. Here are some pictures."

"Interesting," I said, laying my own set of photos down next to his. "Compare the results to these pictures Bob shared with me of PSDI field failures. Regardless of where the PSDI fails, it still looks like a hockey puck afterwards and is still attached to the module. That PSDI-X is a baseball. It's going to jump off the steering column like a sprinter out of the blocks."

"Makes sense," Cory said. "I'm sure once Al digests these results, he will convince Honda to call off the vehicle demonstration. He knows Monclova is struggling with welding. The suggestion that we weaken the structure is bad enough. To do it near a weld is just nuts."

"I'm not so sure Al will see it that way," Dave said bluntly. "When have you ever seen him say no to Japan?"

"Come on, Dave," I jumped in. "Why would Al retreat on safety margin, if the notch doesn't add any value. Plus, your tests proved it's not even necessary. Base failures come standard."

"We'll see," he replied, digging in.

"Okay, we're wasting time," I said closing the meeting before I let Dave's honesty upset me. "Let's get it packaged up and I'll ship it off to Japan."

That evening, as drink number two softened the day's edges, my phone buzzed with an incoming e-mail from Japan. I knew I shouldn't open it, but the booze was adamant. After quickly skimming its contents, I tossed the phone aside, poured myself another stiff drink and walked outside for a cigarette, bottle in tow. Echigawa were very pleased with themselves. Their notch had worked perfectly.

"Cory, Dave, conference room, please," I shouted the next morning, bypassing the maze for a coffee. "If Schubert's here, please see if he can join us." My head was pounding. They were already in the conference room by the time I sat down and plugged in my laptop.

"Echigawa is thrilled with your hydro-burst results, Cory. Your rupture tests, Dave, not so much." I said.

"What do you mean?" Dave asked defensively.

"They liked your results, Cory, because all the failures started in the notch, and Chikaraishi's engineers, alarmingly, don't care about losing margin. They don't like yours, Dave, because the failures didn't always start in the same place."

"Are you fuc..." he started to say before I cut him off.

"Easy there, bud. That's exactly why I turned my phone off last night. Echigawa is insisting the solution be engineered and not happenstance and they're perfectly fine sacrificing safety to get it. They have to show Honda they are being responsive."

"Dave's right to be upset. Keep reading, it gets better!" Schubert said, irritated by the nonsense. "They want to go ahead with the live demonstration. Honda Marysville is prepping a vehicle to be here in two weeks."

"Yeah, I was hoping you'd see that," I said. "Al's copied on all this, but we need to get in and see him right away. You know how things work around here. If we don't move quickly, we'll be adding pointless notches to all our new inflators. Can you let him know we need to talk, Bob?"

"Sure thing."

The next day we were in Al's office walking him through the presentation we sent to Chikaraishi. My message was simple; this was bad engineering and a waste of time. Al heard me out, sat back in his chair and articulated his thoughts.

"So, the baseline PSDI-X, the one we are making today in Monclova, fails in the base by design. The tear just doesn't always start in the same place."

"That's correct, sir."

"And Japan wants to add this notch so the failure always starts in the same place and that causes us to lose safety margin. They want to do this, so they can show Honda a controlled, engineered solution. Is that correct?"

"Right again, sir, and if we run this vehicle demonstration, the PSDI-X is not going to just burp like a PSDI. It's going to instantly baseball and jump off the steering wheel."

"Okay, I understand. I'll let you know."

A couple of days later we received our marching orders. Not only was the demonstration on, the vehicle was already en route to Armada. Thankfully, it was only one test and the hardware required wasn't complex. Auburn Hills provided the module and once we had our bomb put together, we mated the two and waited for the vehicle. The test setup was far more involved than the hardware and included several camera angles and multiple safety interlocks. The inflator literally was a bomb and there could be no chance of a stray current getting to it. When we were ready, Bob phoned the Honda Marysville representative and the demonstration was scheduled for the following day.

When he arrived early the next morning, we escorted him directly to the test bay where the vehicle was waiting. He was already familiar with test hardware and purpose, so after a quick review of the setup, he gave us the go ahead to proceed. We exited the bay, the test technicians made their final connections, the siren was activated, and the countdown began. 3...2...1... fire – and there went the fucking headrest! The module came to rest on the rear window shelf and anything in its path was toast. The headrest was blasted into the back seat and the front windshield was smashed. All as we predicted, but much more unsettling in person.

Here's the instant replay. When the electrical pulse was sent to the inflator, it instantly baseballed, snapping the module's fasteners. The motor was lit and when the base opened milliseconds later, an unimaginable thrust launched the module from the steering wheel. You might as well have walked up to Nolan Ryan and ask him to bean you in the head with one of his best fastballs. At least that way, you could keep the memorabilia. The look on the Honda representative's face was priceless. He turned to Bob and said,

"This never happened. No videos. No e-mails. Nothing."

And that was it. Bob escorted him back to the lobby and he was on his way. He might have spent an hour with us.

We let Al know what happened and both felt pretty good we'd seen the last of X-Series base failures. Who knows, maybe Al was smarter than we gave him credit for. Maybe he let the demonstration go forward knowing Honda North America would see the folly firsthand and communicate it directly to Japan. I mean the guy high-tailed it out of the place without any results.

We kept our heads down and our eyes on Monclova. To us, it was a better investment of time and money to make sure we weren't building bombs there, rather than concocting a means to defuse them at some point down the road.

Cory Leaves the Group

Two years in inflator quality, followed by sixteen months of surfing tsunamis had Cory asking himself what the hell he was doing at Takata. Not a bad question, really. His kids were young, he and Melissa had not sown deep roots in Michigan, and inflators really was the underbelly of the company. He had seen enough. He had other reasons for leaving as well. We all do.

"Kevin, can we talk?" he said to me one day. I glanced over at the rupture hotline. Nothing.

"I have some difficult news to share with you," he continued. I glanced over at the hotline again. Still nothing – Cory was leaving.

"It's okay Cory. Sit down," I said trying to ease his angst. "Are you moving Melissa closer to home?"

"Yes, the job is in the Seattle area, much closer to her parents. She's thrilled. Thank you for asking, Kevin."

"I'm happy for you guys, Cory. Listen, before you go, would you do me a favor and organize everything you have on fail-safe? I worry we haven't seen the last of base failures."

"Of course, I will, Kevin. I want you to know that I really appreciate the opportunity you gave me here and if this causes any inconvenience, I'm truly sorry."

I laughed and said, "Cory, I should be apologizing to you. The constant weld issues, SSI-20 and SDI ruptures swept under the rug, Gutierrez's snow cones and pancakes, and now fail-safe inflators decapitating headrests. Nobody should have to put up with all that."

"There was never a dull moment, was there?" he said thinking back on the whirlwind.

"Come on, let's go find Paresh," I said, getting out of my seat. "I heard he's over in the main building. We can poke him on the helium concentration levels in Monclova since he's the new Director of Reoccurrence Prevention."

"People are still scratching their heads over that move," he exhaled, relieved to have the news of his departure off his chest.

We walked over to the main building together. I would miss Cory. He was a hard worker, smart, honest and his quirky sense of humor always lifted our spirits. He made Armada less insufferable and that would be a loss. As we walked through the lobby doors I saw Paresh irritating Sean about something. They were discussing Armada's next generation PSAN-propellant, AMP and the look on Sean's face said it all. Paresh needed to be escorted back to his window seat and I was only too happy to oblige.

“Excuse me, gentlemen,” I interrupted. “Paresh, I’m sorry I missed your last Reoccurrence Prevention meeting, but can you spend a few minutes with Cory and me and bring us up to speed on Monclova’s helium concentration levels? I question whether the plant is complying with USACR test standards, and making sure our inflators are properly sealed is the single, most important thing you can be working on.”

“Yes, yes, Kevin,” he replied, immediately disengaging Sean. “I have a presentation we can review right now. Phil Simons also gave me a copy of your helium leak specification. Great work. It is very clear on the proper pass-fail limits if the plant is unable to achieve 100% helium inside the inflator.”

“I’ve been trying to get that specification released for years, Paresh. Japan keeps blocking it. I could use your help with that.”

“I will try, Kevin. Let’s review the presentation. Talk to you soon, Sean.”

Paresh had nothing but bad news. The pass-fail limits set on all of Monclova’s leak check stations required a helium concentration of 100% in the inflators being inspected. An audit of the lines finally opened Pandora’s box. There were a few lines achieving 70%, but most hovered between 50% and 60%, with some even below that. The specification we were pressuring Echigawa to release would require Monclova to measure this level at the start of each shift and verify that the station’s pass-fail limits were set to correspond. The less helium detected, the tougher the requirement. If there was a mismatch, adjustments were to be made to either the equipment or the pass-fail limits before production could resume. No wonder Japan was hesitant. The requirement had the potential to grind Monclova to a standstill.

“Paresh, this is horrible. What are we doing about it? Have you shared this with Japan?” I asked.

“They are aware,” he answered. “I also talked to them about your specification.”

“And?” It was like pulling teeth.

“They asked to try it on one or two lines first before we deploy it plant-wide but want me to focus more on improving the current process. We’ve seen some lines increase concentrations quickly. Others need a lot of work.”

“That’s great, Paresh, but what happened when you tried tightening the pass-fail criteria on one or two lines?” I asked.

“It did not go well. The scrap rate immediately shot up and the trial was cancelled. Right now, I’m doing as asked and working to raise the concentrations.”

“The only way to fix this, is to implement the specification plant wide and let the scrap rates get painful. You know that, Paresh."

"Japan won't let us do that, Kevin, and you know that. I'll keep you posted on our progress. I think we can get all the lines to 75% pretty quickly."

"I hope that's not where you're setting the bar, but thanks for the update, Paresh. This one's important and we'll help any way we can."

Then I looked to Cory, "Let's go find KK and Dave and grab some lunch."

We met Dave at the local pub in Romeo. He was on his way back from meetings in Auburn Hills for the new GM K2XX platform, an important program for both GM and Takata.

"Hey, Dave," I said as he walked up to the table where Cory, KK and I were seated. "Before you tell us how your meetings went, Cory has some news for you."

"I already know about Cory's news, Kevin," he said, "You know we sit right next to each other and with how loud he is. It would be impossible not to know."

"Oh yeah, right, Dave!" Cory laughed slapping him on the back.

"Okay, then let's talk about your meeting," I asked.

"So, I ran into Fisher and Healy on the way to the conference room. This program is really important to them!" Dave started.

"Sorry for interrupting, but you're exactly right. Those two have worked tirelessly on Takata's relationship with GM and it's really starting to pay off. Keep going," I urged.

"No problem. Anyway, GM wants the full-frontal system, driver and passenger module, from one supplier. They love our PSDI-X, but hate our PSPI-X. They want a disk inflator, so it's a PSDI-X & PDP combo, or bust. I love these kinds of challenges."

"Me too," I said. "You did tell them we'd get PDP over the finish line, right?"

"Of course, boss," he replied instantly. "Oh, and Waldorf cornered me too. Asked all the same questions."

"Thanks, Dave. You suck, Cory," I said.

"I agree, Cory, you suck," KK said.

"Yeah, you suck, Cory," Dave echoed. Cory smiled at the three of us and said,

"I'll miss you guys, too."

On we went.

Enough Lying, People Are Dead

Just when I thought I'd seen it all, Takata once again did not fail to deliver. Since the notch was working so well on PSDI-X, Honda wanted to *Yokoten* the concept to their upcoming SDI-X 1.7 launch.[14] I was stunned. Did Honda North America not talk to Honda Japan? I'm glad I asked Cory to summarize the demonstration results before he left. His presentation was sitting right at my fingertips, with links to all the photos and videos. I would just send it along to Chikaraishi, apologize for the delay and that should be the end of it.

Wishful thinking. Instead of canceling the ill-advised effort, Chikaraishi demanded we make the Honda PSDI-X notch official and get started on one right away for SDI-X 1.7. I sent another e-mail asking if Honda Marysville had discussed the Armada demonstration with Honda Japan. Not to worry was the response. Takata sold both inflators to Honda with the promise that they would rupture away from the occupant and be fail-safe; science and headrests be damned. Two people were dead, yet the lies seemed effortless. I spun my chair around in exasperation,

"KK, would you please get Dave and Hardenburg and meet me in the conference room. I'm going for a smoke." Ten minutes later I was back. Cigarettes were going down as fast as the evening's first whiskey. Closing the meeting room door behind me, we got started,

"Dave, we have to find someone to replace Cory fast. Stupid is piling up all around us. Bob, I'm going to need you to pitch in where you can until then. Read this one," I said, projecting Chikaraishi's e-mail on the screen. Dave was the first to wade in.

"Setting aside the fact that base failures don't make our inflators fail-safe, we can't do what their asking. We can't make an SDI-X 1.7 always fail in the base."

"Why?" KK asked.

"Hand me that cutaway over there," Dave said almost reaching it himself. "See how the SDI-X 1.7 cap is much taller than all our other inflators and where the nozzles are located? They're right at the cap's weakest point. It always fails there first and at a pressure 20% below the base. Good luck flipping that equation."

"What if we made the cap out of a higher strength, 980-steel to force the failure to the base?" Bob asked. "They're both 780-steel now, right?"

"That's possible, but we don't want Monclova welding a 980-steel to a 780-steel, just to say we moved a failure point. Those materials don't like each other," Dave said pointedly.

"Just a suggestion, Dave," Bob retorted.

"And one I'm sure we'll be asked to investigate, Bob," I said, inserting myself. "For now, I'll just let Echigawa know the SDI-X 1.7 will require major design changes. Considering how close we are to start of production, that should shut it down, but I emphasize should."

"That and the fact that it doesn't do anything, Kevin," Bob said. "We already proved that, and don't need to be building any more bombs."

"I know, Bob. I hate building them too," I sighed. "I've asked Al to put a stop to it but I'm not holding my breath. In the meantime, double check your safety procedures, make sure we're not missing anything, and pull your folks together for a refresher. As soon as I hear back from Echigawa, we'll reconvene."

I typed up a summary of our conversation, copied Al, and shipped it off to Chikaraishi hoping I wouldn't hear anything back that evening. He wasn't going to listen to reason anyway. NHTSA had closed the investigation into Honda's handling of the recalls back in May. The worst of the storm had been weathered and nobody was going to tell Honda now that Takata's new inflators weren't fail-safe, nor could they be made so. That's why Chikaraishi's response, when it came in the next morning, was no surprise, just another disappointment.

I gathered the team in the conference room again and turning to Hardenburg said,

"Bob, would you like to be the first to tell Dave, 'I told you so?'"

"Aw, you're shitting me?" Dave said.

I smiled at him, "Nope. I called Al and told him operations won't like welding 980-steel to 780-steel, but he said to keep going as long we had safety factor. Then I reminded him of the spectacular PSDI-X headrest decapitation, and he said just keep going."

"You can't be serious," Dave said incredulously.

"Do I look like I'm having fun Dave?"

"OK...I'll get the drawings started," he said reluctantly. "A 980-cap will need a more generous internal radius to form it. It's some pretty strong stuff. We'll have to look at what that might do to the filter..."

"I trust you'll check everything, Dave," I said. "Bob, this means more bombs, so let's keep everyone on their toes. KK, once the drawing package is ready, please expedite its release and get prototype parts on order."

"But Kevin, we don't have time. The PV is supposed to start in...."

"I know, Kelli. Just expedite everything, please."

The 980-caps arrived a few weeks later and were quickly welded to 780-bases for hydro-burst testing. All the failures still occurred at the cap's nozzles. The higher-strength material just narrowed the gap between the cap and base burst pressures. We relayed that information to Echigawa and waited, never suggesting the next move in these endless snipe hunts. No encouragement was necessary. Chikaraishi took note of the converging burst pressures and now suggested we combine a 980-cap with a notched and weakened 780-base to finish the deed. This was getting ridiculous. Yes, the failure pressures had converged, but there was still a substantial difference in favor of the cap. Echigawa's new design took this into consideration, extending the notch all the way into the weld joint between the initiator holder and base. Enough was enough. Nobody did this, it was insanity. I picked up the phone and called Al.

"Al, I don't ask for you to intervene often," I started, "but you have to get in the middle of this one. It's getting dangerous. Open that last e-mail from Chikaraishi on the SDI-X 1.7 Fail-Safe. The 980-steel did not move the failure to the base and now he wants to drill a notch into a weld pool."

"Hang on one minute. Okay, I have it up. This just came in last night. There is no way you could have tested anything yet. Why don't we discuss this when you have some data?"

"Al. Listen to me," I pressed. "We cannot add a notch to the initiator holder that extends into the base weld. If I run the evaluations here in Armada and it works, it will be forced on Monclova and they will screw it up."

"Relax, Kevin. Please get the data and then we can discuss it further with Yoshimura. Is there anything else?" he asked, ending the call.

The notch being proposed by Echigawa was obscene. It was much larger and went much deeper than the one used in the PSDI-X demonstration. That one was cosmetic. This one was meant to do damage and had to be stopped. Jorge and his band of merry welders could not be allowed anywhere near this.

But nothing was ever easy. We built and tested the samples, married a 980-cap to a notched 780-base, and just as we had warned, Echigawa got exactly what they were after. All of them failed in the base and we were still holding on to safety factor – barely. The worst of all possible outcomes. The burst pressure variation quadrupled. It would never repeat in Monclova and any sane engineer would have run the other way. But Honda never saw that data. Chikaraishi had it altered to hide the variation. He erased the decline in safety factor. The driving public was not his concern. He only had Honda to please.

"Bob, you are not going to believe this," I said the second Schubert picked up his phone.

"Do you just pull a string under your chin and that comes out?" he replied with a soft chuckle.

"Very funny. You remember the SDI-X 1.7 fail-safe disaster I was telling you about? The stupid notch they want us to drill into a weld."

He paused a second, then said "Last we left it, you sent the data over to Echigawa that showed a huge increase in the burst pressure sigma and a corresponding drop in safety factor that would only get worse in Monclova."

"That's right," I said. "Well, Chikaraishi had the data altered to bring the variation and safety factor back to baseline and sent that to Honda. Now they want us to implement the change."

This time he paused longer and said, "Maybe you should have that string under your chin."

"We need to take this to Al. Is he there today?" I asked.

"Yes, let me go down to his office and we'll call you right back," he answered.

A couple of minutes later, I was back on the phone.

"Hello, Kevin," Al said. "Bob tells me that Echigawa repackaged the SDI-X 1.7 fail-safe data you sent over before sending it to Honda. Is that correct?"

"Yes, sir. Didn't take their safe-crackers very long to break into the Shin Tanaka Memorial Data Vault did it?"

"Save the commentary," he said flatly. "Do you have a presentation you can send over that we can review together?" Bob had to be cheering on the inside.

"I'm sorry, sir, not yet. I can have that tomorrow."

"Good, thank you. In the meantime, I'll contact Yoshimura. He will be in the States next week and you can walk him through it."

"That's perfect. Thank you, Al," I said. "You'll have the presentation tomorrow." I turned to fill KK in on our assignment, but she was already on her way to the conference room, laptop in tow.

Kelli had been keeping up with the effort, so after a few simple instructions, she was off and running. I'd have the presentation in a couple of hours and after some tweaks by Schubert, it would be ready for Al. The next day it was in his inbox and the day after that, I received confirmation we would be meeting with Yoshimura the following week.

That was a waste of time. It was like talking to a bobble head doll. He just kept nodding his head up and down and when I was finished, he thanked me, and I was dismissed. The next day, the pressure from Echigawa to implement picked up intensity. They must have got wind I was fighting back and then Al got an earful from me when I called him to press further,

"Did you read that last e-mail from Japan?" I asked him in an irritated voice. "Our little discussion with Yoshimura did no good at all. I am not letting go of this one, Al. We cannot let that notch get to Monclova."

"Relax, Kevin," he said, trying to calm me down. "Shige will be in town next week and I will see if I can get you an audience with him. OK?"

"Yes, sir, but until then I am standing down."

Then it dawned on me. I was being played. I was an active participant in Al's absolution ritual. As long as he arranged an information exchange with Japan, he was free of any responsibility, even if he knew it was wrong. It happened with the corrected Honda report and Takata's lawyers and it was happening right now. Son of a bitch, Al was Pontius Pilate and I was his rag.

Even if my meeting with Shige was nothing more than a sham being orchestrated by Al, I still took my job seriously, and today it was to shake Shige of the notion that base failures would make X-Series field ruptures any less dangerous.

The first slide I put up was science, a big mistake. It could not compete with Shige's brand-new iPad keyboard. I was losing him quickly and shifted to the second slide, multi-media, or what I liked to call chum. It contrasted a benign PSDI base failure against time-phased photos of a PSDI-X module with its afterburner lit and closing in on the headrest. That got his attention. He pushed his new keyboard aside and joined me at the screen and for a second I thought I had him.

I started over again, this time slower, trying my best to get inside his head. He had his chin in his hand, listening intently, every so often nodding his head up and down in acknowledgement. And when I was finished he turned to me and spoke a total of five words. The same five words I had heard so many times before,

"Honda wants. Honda must have."

Al motioned to me to gather my things and head for the exit. I thanked Shige and shook his hand. The absolution was complete. As soon as I was out of the Auburn Hills parking lot, I called Dave,

"How did it go?" he asked before I could say a word.

"How do you think it went? 'Honda wants, Honda must have.'"

"I figured as much. You want me to order those 590-steel bases we talked about?"

"Yes, right away."

"We have no experience with that material, Kevin," he cautioned me.

"I know but what choice do we have, Dave? Al won't call off the dogs. He told me to stop resisting and implement the notch and we can't let that happen. The 590-base is the only solution I'm comfortable with. It marries the strongest possible cap to the weakest possible base with no obscenity drilled into any parts. If that doesn't work, then I am prepared to fall on my sword," I said emphatically.

"Got it, boss. I'll get KK a drawing right away."

"Thanks, Dave. Make sure you order enough hardware for weld studies and DOT bonfires. We'll have to burn some fires with a lower strength material. I'll see you in a few."

Go figure. With a 980-cap and a 590-base, the failure moved to the base every time and with a solid 1.5 safety factor. I was jazzed and with only bonfire standing in the way, I let my excitement get the better of me. We only had a limited amount of hardware left and I green-lighted a small test series using a Bunsen burner to simulate the wood fire environment. That subset passed, and I told Echigawa to go ahead and tell Honda we had decided on the 980/590 combination. One full box engulfed in flame with no explosions was all that was needed now. Should have been easy, but the first box had multiple failures. We built another box full, x-raying each part this time. Maybe we had a build error. BOOM! BOOM! BOOM! What the hell was going on? Was strength of the 590-base dropping in the intense heat of the fire? I wouldn't have believed it myself until we captured it in the lab. We fitted several inflators with pressure transducers and heated the base with a Bunsen burner and after enough samples, we captured a rupture at normal operating pressure. Oh, shit!

This was not going to be an easy conversation with Echigawa. They'd already told Honda the SDI-X 1.7 would not have a notch and now the 590-base wasn't working. Chikaraishi was furious with me as I explained the situation that evening in a teleconference, even suggesting I had somehow orchestrated the whole thing to avoid any changes. It finally came to a head in Auburn Hills. I was huddled in a conference room with Al Bernat and Hideki Mizuno, discussing the results.

"I'm sorry Mizuno. I don't know what to tell you. I feel terrible about it, but we tried to find the best solution," I explained.

"We can't tell Honda we're not using the 590-base design. It's too late," he said, his voice escalating. I'd never seen a Japanese associate so angry. It was completely out of character, but Mizuno had been in the States a long time.

"We don't have DOT authorization to ship with a 590-base, Mizuno. I'm sorry," I said looking to Al for help.

After an uncomfortable pause, Mizuno started in again, his voice even louder this time, "What is it you suggest we do then!?"

"I'm not going to suggest anything, Mizuno," I said, my voice rising to his level. "But I will tell you what's going to happen. The base is reverting to 780-steel and there will be no notch in the initiator holder. I'm done with this nonsense. The fucking notch doesn't do anything anyway. If you want to lie to Honda and tell them we're using a 590-base, that's up to you. I'm not going to jail for you or Takata and this conversation is over." I picked up my papers and left.

Al never said a word.

A Problem Resolves Itself

We only half screwed Monclova. Al conceded the cosmetic PSDI-X notch, but we never made the change to the SDI-X 1.7 base material. Solid legal footing can do wonders. The inflator instead became some bastard of a 980-cap and the original 780-base. The reason? To cover another lie. The base material was indiscernible with the naked eye. It could have been 579 for all Honda knew. The 980-cap was a different story. Its bend radius made it visibly different than the 780-cap, so it had to change, or Echigawa's house of cards would fall. They remained silent on the base material, leading Honda to believe it was 590-steel and that the inflator was now fail-safe. And people were dead.

This nonsense was doing nothing to help my already fraught relationship with Jorge and Monclova. Yes, we fought off the worst of Echigawa's fail-safe lunacy, but a do-nothing, margin sucking notch for PSDI-X, and a less robust SDI-X 1.7 weld still made it to Monclova. All to fend off even more stupidity. The golden rule of manufacturing is to not mess with a stable process. This was indefensible, and Jorge had every right to be skewering me like he was.

Phillion was right. I needed to work on my relationship with Jorge and promised myself I would when I was in Monclova the next week. Kosugi, VP of Operations and another of Jim's closest allies, was conducting a global audit of Takata's inflator plants, and Scott asked me to be present for the Monclova and Moses Lake legs. The timing coincided with NHTSA's closure of the recall investigations and it seemed Jim wanted to tie a bow around the whole thing. Unfortunately, the trip was too much of a whirlwind and I never got the one-on-one time I wanted with Jorge. Next time for sure.

When I was back in the office, I asked KK when we were scheduled to be there next for reviews,

"Let me see," she said. "We have two reviews scheduled for the first week of November. A PSDI-X AIB process validation and a PDP update. So just a couple of weeks from now."

"Perfect," I said. "Dave, Shari, you and me. Oh wait, I can't be there that week. Dillon has his orientation at Wayne State. Damnit, I really wanted to spend some time with Jorge, but you guys will have to do without me."

"Oh no! I don't think we can survive," Dave boomed over his cubicle wall. Everyone was a comedian.

I really enjoyed that day at Wayne State with Sandy and Dillon. My God, where had the time gone? Dillon was only 9 when we brought him to Michigan. The orientation started off with a great student presentation followed by a campus tour. After that, we wandered off on our own, poking our heads into all the different buildings and before we knew it was lunchtime. On our way to get some grub, my phone rang. It was KK from Monclova,

"Kevin, something terrible happened last night while we were at the restaurant across the street from the hotel."

"Is everybody okay? Is anybody hurt?" I asked concerned.

"Yes, yes, it's not like that," she said.

"Well, what is, it Kelli? Talk to me," I pressed.

"Jorge and a few others came into the restaurant after we had finished eating. We were still having some drinks, so they joined us. It was obvious they had already been drinking and must have just come from a rodeo or something because they were all wearing cowboy hats and boots," she said, struggling through it.

"Sounds like a pretty normal evening in Monclova, KK. Keep going," I nudged.

"Jorge stuck his tongue down my throat," she said finally mustering the courage. "Shari too."

"You got to be kidding me Kelli! Are you okay? Is Shari alright? I'm so sorry."

"Yes, I'm OK and so is Shari. We went back to the hotel right after it happened. We are on our way to Monterey now. We'll be in the office on Monday."

"Where was Dave?"

She sighed and said, "He'd already gone to bed and that's probably a good thing. He might have killed him."

"As soon as we hang up, I'm calling Douma. Tell Shari I'm so sorry. Can you please put Dave on?"

She didn't say anything.

"Sorry boss, I should have been there," Dave took the phone.

"Don't be silly," I replied. "Were Mario and Carlos there?"

"Yes, sir, they were. The girls said everyone scattered after it happened. I'd say there are some pretty worried people right now."

"Thanks, Dave," I paused. "Gotta go. I have some phone calls to make."

So much for orientation. After two quick phone calls an investigation was opened and a week later Jorge was summarily terminated. The following week I happened to be in Auburn Hills, and since the recall investigation had slowed, Al's office was much harder to avoid, and I found myself sitting across from him.

"What do you make of the whole Gutierrez incident?" he asked me.

"It was very unfortunate for Kelli and Shari, but I am quite happy to see Jorge gone. He was a whiner and a complainer, and now we can add dirt-bag to the list. This is a real chance for Monclova to trade up."

"Well, I think you may have some responsibility here," he scowled a little at me.

"What do you mean by that?" I responded indignantly. "I was at Wayne State with my wife and son."

"You run your group too loose. Too much partying after hours. Something like this was bound to happen," he said in a nasty tone.

"Is there anything else we need to discuss, Al?" I said, standing to leave. He knew I was finished.

"No." I heard him mutter as I headed out the door.

What was he talking about? What do you say to a man who turns a blind eye to deviants like Shin and Hideo and then tells me I was responsible for Jorge shoving his tongue down KK and Shari's throats. 'Asshole' fit the bill perfectly and was the reason I was already halfway down the hall.

13

End of an Era

I SOLDIERED ON while McCormick did his best to manage both core and applications, but as the search for Cory's replacement dragged on, his programs suffered. So did his sanity, seeing he was knee deep in fail-safe with me. When we finally hired an ex-TRW inflator engineer with some gray hair, Dave had considerable ground to make up. It was GM PDP crunch time and Auburn Hills was breathing down his neck. SDI-X2's fanbase were also getting antsy and we had the first of what would be a series of global inflator strategy meetings coming up in Japan in a few weeks. Add on-boarding a new applications manager to the list and something had to give. SL-20 was put on simmer.

Christophe's anti-PSAN crusade was in part driving the new global inflator meetings. He and Heiko were duplicating nearly every X-Series inflator with the GuNi propellant Christophe had licensed from TRW, creating rancor in the organization and confusing Takata's customers. Nobody seemed in charge and the redundancies were maddening. Something had to change.

Chikaraishi coordinated the first meeting, which was held at Takata's beautiful complex on the shores of Lake Biwa in Hikone. The accommodations were impressive, resembling a small but expensive hotel with bedrooms upstairs and conference rooms, a spacious dining area, and lounge downstairs. The campus grounds were immaculate, and as McCormick and I wandered about them on our first break, we happened across a beautiful old Japanese home, transported to this special place from days gone by.

"Whoa...look at that!" Dave exclaimed. "What do you think this is?"

"There's a plaque over here," I motioned. "It's the home Jim Takada was born in. Pretty cool, huh?"

"Amazing," Dave said as he slowly turned in a circle to take it all in. There was a lot of money here. When he finally reached sensory overload, he returned the conversation to work and asked,

"Did you know Furusawa and Shin were going to be here?"

"No, not at all. Jim must have let Furusawa out of the doghouse to help with the recalls and Shin must have been hiding under a rock next to it."

"Ain't that the truth?" Dave seconded. "And who is this Claus Rudolf?"

"Ah, Claus. He is Europe's Chief Module Engineer and Heiko's boss," I answered. "I like him. He sounds reasonable and I hear he's going places."

"I think it's great Heiko has someone in his corner," Dave said. "It would be nice if Al took that kind of interest."

"Yeah, that's not going to happen. We have to fend for ourselves, Dave, just like always. Come on, we'd better get back. We're up next."

The presentation Christophe gave before the break was a retread and a perfect example of the inflator group's dysfunction. He wanted a propellant lab in Europe to develop his own GuNi and never let a microphone pass to press his case. It produced the churn he wanted, but as usual, not the decision he needed. Paresh's guys never wanted to hear it, Japan hated the confrontation, and I'd always pass, under strict orders from Al to use only propellants provided by Armada. I had to hand it to Christophe though. He knew Japan would give him that propellant lab eventually, just to shut him up and maybe that wasn't such a bad thing. Paresh's chemistry wasn't exactly racking up admirers.

The PDP inflator I was about to pitch was also emblematic of our dysfunction. When Healy and Fisher asked us to deliver for GM, time was not on our side. We had to skip the trade studies that would have considered global outputs and focused only on the GM target. That meant pressing the thickest damn PSAN tablet Moses Lake was capable of and designing a PSDI-X on steroids around it.

Ridding Takata of wafers was always a top priority of mine, so PDP was already being fast-tracked when Healy turned up the heat. But making PSAN tablets work in a passenger application was proving far more difficult than we had anticipated. Passenger inflators output roughly three times more gas than driver inflators. The bags they fill cover more area, ranging in volume from 100-120L compared to the standard 60L driver bag. To fill these larger bags safely, gas is delivered at a slower rate and for a longer period. As we were putting the final touches on the presentation for Japan, I started to get a better understanding of what PDP's limitations might be. We had the thickest tablet Moses Lake could press and we were running at the lowest operating pressure we could tolerate, and although it met GM's requirements, it was on the fast side for a passenger inflator. Tailoring it was going to be a challenge.

I ran through our presentation, providing updates on PDP, SDI-X2 and SL-20. It was impossible for anyone in the audience to resist PDP's slimmed-down look.

"Those numbers are impressive," Claus said. "We also have a huge demand in Europe for a disk passenger inflator. When will samples be available?"

"No need, no need," Shin shouted, catching everyone's attention.

"What do you mean 'no need', Shin?" I stared intently at him.

"No need for PDP. We use cylinders in Japan."

I glared at the deviant for another moment, then turned back to Claus and continued, "I'm sorry for the interruption. They are available now and we'd like to get you some right away, on the house. We need to get a read on your crash pulses and whether they limit the inflator's reach."

"Good. Let's do that and I hope it works," he said. "It would be a shame if it didn't, since it's already a go for GM."

"Yes, sir, it would," I agreed.

Claus stood to address the crowd, "This is why these meetings are so necessary. There is a chance PDP won't work for Europe or Japan. I understand what Auburn Hills asked Kevin to do, but we must be smarter about this."

"We need a global strategy, Claus," I chimed in.

"And you'll have one when we are finished," he said, sitting back down. As I gathered my things, I thought to myself that this guy might work.

"One more thing, before I let you go," he continued. "I see you are working on a side impact inflator, SL-20, and Heiko is working on the same type of inflator in GuNi called GSI. Why the redundancy?"

"I was wondering when you were going to get to that, Claus. Here's the short answer. We started SL-20 after the SSI-20 rupture in Monclova. Our investigation showed that SSI-20's axial ignition was a problem. It whacks the crap out of the tablets. SL-20 counters that with a soft, radial ignition, producing a much more consistent output than axially ignited inflators like SSI-20 and GSI. And I would add safer, based on my observations in Monclova."

"Do you agree?" Claus asked, turning his chair towards Heiko.

"I agree with Kevin's SSI-20 findings, but we are not having that problem with GSI," he responded.

Claus turned back to me and asked,

"Will you see if North America can use GSI, so we can stop at least one duplicate effort?"

"I will, Claus, but SSI-20 really turned them off and the GSI data I have seen so far, probably won't allay their concerns over USCAR compliance. They are here so we can start that conversation. If they're satisfied, I'd support the decision."

As soon as that last word rolled off my tongue, I shot a 'please don't say a word' look at Dave and he zipped it. He hated SSI-20's ignition scheme and GSI's was the same. He was thrilled with how SL-20 was performing and knew its potential. The design was groundbreaking, but it still used PSAN – the only propellant at our disposal, and one I was growing increasingly wary of. I shared my thinking with Dave later, in private. The taxi we took into Hikone for dinner that evening presented the perfect opportunity.

"I sense something different about Claus," I told him.

"Me too. What do you think it is?"

"He wants to do the right thing," I answered as we both burst out laughing.

"Seriously, though. There's a reason I coughed up SL-20 today."

"Yeah, what was up with that?" suddenly remembering he was mad at me. "You know how much I love that inflator."

"We have to start getting out of PSAN, Dave, and GSI offers us the first real opportunity," I said, the conversation turning somber. "I think we show good faith here and it will pay off later. Trust me on this one."

"I always do, boss," he said as we pulled up to the restaurant.

We were welcomed back to Armada by a bevy of PDP orders and after two months of furious module testing in Germany and Japan, we had our answer. Echigawa couldn't resist the inflator's size and weight and made it work for Nissan and Toyota but were unable to convince Honda to abandon PSPI-X cylinders. The report out from Germany was not good. They couldn't use it at all and Claus was upset. I know he gave me a pass, told me 'I did what I had to do', but his disappointment hurt. He was a committed force for change, the boss I was missing, and I didn't like disappointing.

Glühwein and Christmas Goose

All I can remember of previous global inflator meetings were the parties. Well, most of them. That was changing. Claus brought purpose. So did two fatalities. For the first-time open discussions about the future of PSAN were taking place. Heiko and Christophe's position was clear and mine had moved in their direction. Yes, Takata's PSAN when used with 13X could meet all customer specifications, but nobody could put a shelf-life on that. The only thing I knew for sure was how the inflator would fail if it did and that wasn't comforting. The group decided early on that our deliverable would be a global inflator roadmap. One that would consider each region's interests, and if it mapped an orderly exit out of PSAN, that would be fine by me. In fact, it would be a relief.

But there was one more PSAN formulation in the pipeline to complicate matters and it was a damn good one. Paresh's second-generation PSAN was nothing than the first in disguise. The X-series hung its hat solely on 13X, but Sean and Deb's new Advanced Main Propellant (AMP) was no masquerade. It was on the cusp of revolutionary. The formulation cracked the code when it came to low-cost fuels, finally making it inexpensive. But what made it special was a wax additive that formed a moisture-resistant barrier around each tablet.

I was with Sean when he performed an early demonstration for Shige in the Armada propellant lab. He placed an X-Series and an AMP tablet side by side and carefully metered a single water droplet onto each. The surface of the X-Series tablet was immediately penetrated and within minutes the tablet was crumbling. I wondered what went through Shige's mind right then, regardless of the experiment's point. The AMP tablet behaved very differently, resisting the drop for what seemed like minutes. The visual was extremely effective. AMP was the best a PSAN propellant could get but whether it would make the roadmap, remained to be seen.

There was also Paresh's old device development group's work to consider. The same group Schubert and I begged Al to hand over to us with the X-series. They were responsible for Takata's next generation of inflators, 5+ years out, and were supposed to push the envelope. But their signature accomplishment, top hats with wablets, was just pure Imagineering, fraught with manufacturing pitfalls. The X-series had finally brought Monclova relief from prettying LAT data and here was our crack development team wanting to send us right back to the stone age. I approached Al several times about changing direction, but he was disinterested. Wablets had Japan's backing.

The Lake Biwa conference was the first real attempt to confront the myriad of woes facing the inflator organization, and, after more like it followed, the beginnings of a global strategy finally emerged. Current, near term and future offerings were arranged in an easy to read menu that helped highlight Takata's portfolio gaps. The biggest of those was future offerings. Chikaraishi was insistent that the wablet-filled top hats be at the forefront of any out-year plans, and Heiko and I were dead set against that idea. When it was clear he wouldn't relent, we acquiesced but swore to each other the design would never see the light of day. It was unfair to those assigned to the development, but we had to press on. Al was not around to help.

The roadmap was further complicated by our mixture of PSAN and GuNi inflators. Takata's GuNi was old and the inflators that used it did not satisfy global requirements, earning them a 'local inflator' designation. That irked Heiko and he never failed to remind others that his local GuNi inflators always failed safe and didn't need no stinking notches. There were still decisions to make as we marched into the last of the year's meetings, this one in Aschaffenburg, Germany, and two of them were big. Would GSI or SL-20 survive the side-impact inflator cut and what to do with AMP?

Aschaffenburg is a beautiful city at any time, but around the holidays with the snow falling, the Christkindlmarkts bustling and the Glühwein flowing, it transforms into magical. What a great place to wrap up a year of hard work and take time to celebrate. McCormick made the trip with me, and the evening before the last discussions, Claus took us all to a fabulous restaurant on the outskirts of town, where he had a Christmas goose specially prepared and all the Glühwein we could ask for. It was a wonderful time. The next day I had the last presentation on the agenda and as I closed with an update on SL-20, Claus opened the floor to discussion.

"We have seen Heiko's presentation on GSI and now yours on SL-20, Kevin. They are both good," he said. Before he could continue, I interrupted.

"I must say I was surprised by Heiko's results. It looks like GSI will meet global requirements and Takata really should down select to one inflator."

That caught Claus by surprise, and even though I saw Dave's chin drop to his chest out of the corner of my other eye, I kept going, "I think we should wind SL-20 down. We have a few more things to take care of before we're at a stopping point, and after that, we'll wrap it up with a lesson-learned report."

"Thank you, Kevin," Claus said. "We are making progress."

"One word of caution," I interrupted again. "GSI meets global requirements because it uses a very small amount of our GuNi propellant. Scale that up to a driver inflator and we start running into trouble. Passenger is completely out of the question. North America and Japan can't use Takata's GuNi, so we either need a better GuNi or Sean must continue to develop AMP."

"I agree we need a better GuNi," Claus retorted. "We recently won approval of our propellant lab here in Aschaffenburg and that will be a key part of its mission. Sean should continue to work on AMP, but for now let's be happy that we have eliminated a redundancy and are on the right track. I'll let you know after the new year, when we plan to reconvene. Thank you everybody."

And with that Takata finally had its first stab at an inflator roadmap. There were still plenty of overlaps to attack, gaps to fill and efficiencies to be had, but it was on paper and that was a start. More importantly, the GSI olive branch I extended to Claus had its intended effect. I sensed change was in the air and conceding SL-20 was a small price to pay to be on the right side of it.

A Legend Passes

I was just finishing another budget meeting with Al and the Five Guys when I heard my phone ring from across the hall. Takata's fiscal year ran from April to March, so the turn of the year always meant the meanest part of winter mixed in with budgets. Just a crappy season, but thankfully we were all under one roof again and that minimized our exposure to at least one of the elements. It was a short dash to my cube.

"Hey, Kevin, it's Scott, and I have Dal here with me. Can you talk?"

"You bet I can. Just got out of another budget review with Al and I'd rather stick sharp pencils in my ears than do that." I could hear Dal laughing.

"It is that time of the year again," Scott said. "You doing alright? I've been busy with a project for Shige and we haven't talked in a while."

"Yes, I'm fine, Scott. Always a fire to fight. How can I help you?"

"The findings of Kosugi's quality audits of the Monclova and Moses Lake plants are in and we have some work to do," Dal spoke up. "We could use your help putting our plan together to address each of his concerns. Kosugi wants us in Tokyo the first week of February to present our countermeasures and that's a short fuse."

"Man, anything to get out of the snow and these budget meetings," I said. "Where do I sign up?"

"Thanks, Kevin," Scott said. "You can handle the preparation remotely with the plants, but we'd like you to come to Tokyo with us. Christophe will be there with his senior management and you know how he is. He'll have his own agenda and we'd feel more comfortable with you along."

"I'd love to. Are you doing the presenting, Dal?"

"Not me," he answered. "This time I'll be your flipping bitch."

"I remember that. Romania, right? That had to be my first month back at Takata. Wait a minute, did I just get roped into presenting?"

"Yes, you did, Kevin, and we appreciate it," Scott said laughing.

Dal jumped back in, "I'll have the guys at Monclova and Moses Lake send you where they're at. We really appreciate the help Kevin."

"No problem. Send me your itineraries and I'll see you in Tokyo," I said as we ended the call.

I could see that the plants had already done a respectable job of pulling together a presentation when the material arrived in my inbox. It just needed a little tender loving care and KK would take care of that. The day before we were scheduled to depart, Scott called,

"Kevin, I have some terrible news. Mr. Takada passed. We all knew it was coming, but it's still devastating."

"I'm sorry, Scott. I know you were close to him and Aki."[15] I didn't know what else to say.

After a short pause he continued.

"Thanks Kevin. Yes, I am close to them. He's such a loss."

"I met and spoke with him several times, Scott. He had a presence," I agreed somberly. "I'll never forget that night at Los Corrales when he reached into an ice-cold barrel of beer and handed me one. He led the company through that event with a determined will. I assume the meeting in Tokyo is cancelled?"

"No, it's still on. Jim wouldn't want it any other way," he answered. "We present the day before the funeral and will stay for the proceedings."

"That would be wonderful, Scott. Thank you," I said. "I'm sorry again and I will see you in Japan."

Of course, Shige, did not attend the meeting. Kosugi ran things and when it came time for Christophe to present, he was his usual bombastic self. He decided to ignore the audit findings, instead using the forum to promote Europe's automated assembly lines over Monclova's hand-pass, semi-automatic lines. He emphasized the quality advantages of automation and impressed how important that was when working with PSAN, where mistakes could not be tolerated. I looked over at Scott and he just gave me a perplexed shoulder shrug. This was not what the audience came to hear, and they were not pleased. At least he didn't devolve the discussion into a GuNi vs. PSAN argument, but he was dancing all around it. I thanked him for going first as he handed me the laser pointer.

My presentation was well received, and Scott and Dal were happy. It could have been a piece of shit after what Christophe just did, but I took it.

Scott treated us to a fantastic dinner that evening and even though it was a sad time, it was one of my best at Takata. I was looking forward to paying my respects to Jim.

Our schedules were clear the next day, so we decided to explore Tokyo a bit. Scott was an avid bass guitarist and took us to a bustling part of the city with narrow streets that were lined with guitar shops. We roamed those alleyways for hours until Scott finally broke down and added another bass to his collection. It was great fun, but a quick glance at our watches said it was time to get back to the hotel and rest up.

When it came time, we took a taxi to the temple and asked the driver to let us out early, so we could mingle with the crowd walking the last stretch. It was a beautiful evening and an amazing sight. The massive white, stone building rising from the city streets created a peaceful backdrop to the black-attired mourners gathering outside. As we approached the greeting area, I recognized a few familiar faces. People from all over the globe were here to pay their respects to one of Japan's most esteemed business leaders.

After a few quick handshakes and introductions, we moved inside and took our seats towards the rear of the temple. Mr. Takada's body lay at the front, adorned with white flowers that stretched the entire length of the altar. A large framed picture of a younger man hung above him and reminded everyone of the huge life he had been blessed with. I found myself caught up in the grandeur of the setting and my mind wandered.

I found myself wondering whether Jim, over his months-long decline and final succumbing to cancer, ever regretted his decision to enter the airbag market? His final days saw his company struggling with recalls and a worsening public image. There were certain massive losses on the horizon and Honda's image had been tarnished. It all must have added to his suffering.

I felt lucky to have met him and blessed to be there at his funeral. As I watched the ceremony, I thought about all the good Mr. Takada had done and all the lives he had touched. It was a sad day and I let my mind wander again. Did he die knowing the full extent of the fraud that his company had perpetrated? Did he know his minions were lying to Honda even as he took his last breath? I truly believed he didn't and forced myself to refocus on the countless lives that Takata's seatbelts, child-seats, and airbags had saved over the years.

I stood in line near the end of the ceremony, waiting to light an incense stick at the front of the temple, and marveled at the order, beauty, and magnificence. It was something to behold. The reverence and respect for this man was clear.

But what had he known? Where did the buck stop for the horrific decisions? Who made them?

I believe Jim's generals had not been willing to burden him with what had become reality. They would have done anything to help him avoid shame. They would have hidden the fake report they gave to Honda in 2000. They would never have shown him Peter Theut's report of the charade Tim and Al orchestrated to absolve themselves. That was probably shoved in a bottle, corked and tossed into the Pacific. I shook it off again. He didn't know, I told myself.

The fraudulent Honda report was written and signed by Shin Tanaka and Hideo Nakajima, and then signed above them by Shin's boss, Chikaraishi, and his boss, Furusawa, who worked for Jim directly. When Tom and I dropped the corrected report, it triggered bigger decisions. They buried it, moved my group out of LaGrange, and left me little option but to resign.

Who made that call? I thought, as I reached the front of the procession, knelt and lit my incense.

I forced myself to focus and clear my conflicted mind. Now was not the time. Now was the time to pay my final respects to a man I admired. I looked up at Jim's picture one last time and prayed for two things: that he was too strong a man to have known and remained silent and that the future of his great company had not just died with him.

With Jim's passing, leadership of Takata fell to Shige. He had been preparing for some time since assuming the Presidency in 2007, surrounding himself with many of his father's closest associates. His mother, Akiko, already an influential board member, would assume an even stronger role now, and together they would oversee the Takada legacy.

A Year to Get Ready

A year earlier, Shige had begun laying the groundwork for a massive restructuring of the company's far-flung operations. The automakers had already begun their globalization efforts and were growing frustrated by Takata's multiple, local program offices. They expected, really demanded, a similar organization. To facilitate the change, Shige hired a large corporate restructuring firm and selected Claus to play a prominent role in the transition. It was a well-guarded secret that Claus never let slip in any of our inflator meetings. He had a genuine interest in our dysfunction.

Customer Business Units (CBUs), each with their own sales, program management and applications teams, would now be Takata's forward face to the customer and these multi-disciplinary teams would report to the newly created CBU Lead. A prominent position at that, but when it assumed profit and loss from Operations, it was downright powerful. Structurally, Global VPs would sit atop the functions considered shared by the CBUs, such as Development Engineering, Quality, Operations, and Purchasing, and these VPs would each have their own teams in the Americas, Europe and Asia. Our cheese was about to be moved!

Inflators did not fit nicely into this scheme. Driver and passenger airbag modules are custom made to match automakers' tastes. They require individual teams to manage all the different configurations. But one inflator can be used across multiple airbag modules. There were many inflator configurations at Takata, but they paled in comparison to airbag part numbers. Dedicated CBU inflator teams weren't necessary and rocket scientists were too hard to come by to be farmed out anyway. Claus recognized this and convinced Shige not to divide inflators. It would become the only group where development and applications stayed with the Chief Engineer. A plum job.

I started hearing whispers that something was afoot not long after returning from Japan and Jim's funeral, but nothing immediately materialized. It was now April, budgets were in the rear-view mirror and with still no word, I settled into what I hoped would be a year of less mayhem. That didn't last long.

A few days later, we were in a meeting in the main conference room when Deanna poked her head in to let me know Claus was on the line for me. As I gathered my things to head to my cube, she told me I could take the call in Paresh's old office, or what I liked to call, Al's time share. Either way, it was a waste of space big enough for a badly needed conference room.

"Claus, good to hear from you," I said. "How have you been?"

"Very well, Kevin. Thank you for asking. I have some good news to share with you."

"That's my kind of news. What is it?"

"For the past year, I have been working on a special project for Shige. Scott Caudill has been on the same team with me. The company is going through a global restructuring. I'll share the details with you later but suffice it to say there will be one Chief Engineer responsible for inflators and propellant globally."

"Holy shit!" I said.

"Yes, holy shit. It's a big change, Kevin. The Chief Inflator Engineer will report to Takata's Chief Engineer and they have selected me for that position. I will be globally responsible for seatbelts, airbags, inflators, steering wheels, electronics, systems, configuration management and administrative. Whew, that's a mouthful."

"Holy shit, Claus!" I repeated, too floored to even extend congratulations.

"Again, with the holy shit," he laughed. "I haven't even gotten to the good news yet. I want you to be my Chief Inflator Engineer, the only Chief Engineer to hold on to both development and applications. You'll understand the significance of that as the organization becomes clearer."

"Are you serious?" I asked in disbelief.

"Yes, and it was not an easy decision. I think very highly of both you and Heiko and it was a difficult choice. But when you volunteered to stop SL-20 in favor of GSI, you were leaning forward and that meant a lot to me."

"Wow. I never thought I'd see this day," I said, still stunned. This is the structure inflators so desperately needs, regardless of who is at the top. "Thank you so much, Claus."

"So, I assume you want the position," he chuckled.

"Are you kidding me? This is my dream job!" I said, overjoyed. "I won't let you down. I promise."

"I know you won't, Kevin," he continued. "We will have a meeting with all the Chief Engineers shortly to start the process. Until the new organization is announced, you must keep this quiet. You cannot even discuss this with Al. Do you understand?"

"Yes, sir. Not a word. I look forward to hearing from you soon. Thanks again, Claus."

How the hell was I going to keep this quiet? Come on. That's just not fair. I was going to be Chief Inflator Engineer, head shit in charge, kicking back in Al's time share. I realized I'd have to stop drinking to keep a lid on this, which was probably not a bad idea considering the gravity of the undertaking.

I was instantly lit up, transformed. This was the role I'd been after. I knew where all the bodies were buried. We could make immediate and significant impacts, but as Claus explained in our first Chief Engineer meeting, the company was going to take this slowly. There would be a year of preparation before the official rollout. My assignment was to develop a new global structure, and with Claus' blessing, inform a select few to map Takata's exit out of PSAN. It was official. The more-than-a-decade-long dance was coming to an end.

A few weeks after that meeting, Shige announced the new organization, naming all the CBU Leads and Chief Engineers. It was an exciting time, but Al never said a word to me, not even a congratulation. Oh well, one more year. The important thing is that we could get started in earnest now. I picked up the phone and called Schubert, who was in Auburn Hills.

"I just saw the e-mail. Congratulations, Kevin," he sounded worn out by his circumstances. I was calling to get him out of that hell.

"Thank you, Bob. You ready to rejoin the mission? We need you back, man."

"How would I fit in?" he asked with interest.

"Heiko takes Core & Applications and you take Device Development & Propellant. I've been instructed to give Mizuno a second-tier spot, so I'm thinking initiators and micro-gas generators. Not too much damage he can do there and he's even busier than you with the recall, so I don't think he'll care. Honda has their hooks in that boy."

"That would be great, Kevin, but have you discussed this with Al? He's going to have a fit when he finds out I might not be at his beckon call."

"No – and I'm under strict orders to keep the details under wraps. You, Heiko, and I will develop the organization. I'll ask Mizuno to participate, but I don't expect him to. KK will also be tied in, to help with the workload."

"I was going to ask you that. A year of preparation must have a deliverable other than naming an organization?"

"Yes, it does," I said. "Our task is to prepare a propellant and inflator strategy that maps us out of PSAN by model year 2017. We need you, Bob."

"Thanks, Kevin. You know I'd love to, but I'm still afraid of what Al will do."

"Bob, you have been approved by Shige. So was I. Forget about what Al will do."

"You're right, what am I thinking."

"You're thinking Al is a mean-spirited, vindictive man that will exact revenge, and you're probably right, but you have been called to a higher purpose."

"OK, you don't have to lay it on so thick, Kevin, I'm in. Have you talked to Heiko yet?"

"No, he's next. I'm glad you're coming back, Bob. Talk soon."

Bob was right, naming an organization was the easy part. The strategy was hard and the question of what do with AMP still remained. Takata's next generation propellant could not be PSAN. That was clear. But AMP was already developed. It was easy to integrate into running production and far superior to its predecessors. It was the logical and safest bridge out, but Heiko was understandably hesitant, and without that decided, we couldn't move the strategy forward.

"I know you're a busy man, Claus, so we won't keep you long," I said. "I have Schubert here with me. Heiko, are you on the line?"

"He's here with me," Claus said. "Let's get started."

"Yes, sir. We understand Takata's next generation propellant won't be PSAN, but that's five years off, Claus. AMP is production ready now. It's a drop-in replacement for X-Series and we know its wax barrier will extend the inflator's service life. Why wouldn't we use it as a bridge to our next propellant? If you ask me, it's incumbent on us to improve product line robustness while we wait."

"Because it's still PSAN, Kevin," Claus said. "If you can prove that AMP won't explode when it is compromised, then maybe. But I don't want my signature on another propellant that doesn't dud like GuNi."

"Okay Claus," I said. "AMP will stay in the strategy as a bridge until we have that data. If it can't do what you ask, then we'll shut it down. Agreed?"

"Bob, Heiko?" Claus asked, and with a yes vote from each the strategy was set.

Takata would limp to its next generation propellant with its outdated GuNi and AMP. If a Takata GuNi inflator met a region's requirements, it was selected first and although most would be relegated to smaller, less stringent markets, it marked the beginning of our exit out of PSAN. AMP inflators would handle the more difficult U.S., European and Asian markets.

It was a hectic year, globetrotting to all the Chief Engineer meetings, critiquing and refining each other's strategies and, in the craziness, I lost touch with Monclova. The restructuring had handed the global inflator operations to Christophe, and when that happened, Scott and Dal became scarce. I worried about Monclova on their own. There was no bench in Mexico. When Gutierrez received his walking papers, Carlos Iruegas was inexplicably promoted to Plant Manager. It was a terrible mistake. He was part of the posse the night Jorge got himself fired and worse, he was tainted. Years of being told to ignore LAT results that were just a *skosh*[16] out would numb anybody. His selection was not the trade up I was hoping for, but as the year wound down with no major catastrophes, I worried less.

With the inflator organization and strategy set it was time for Claus to present the plan to Shige. In preparation, he asked that I come to Aschaffenburg to spend some time reviewing it with him. I sent an e-mail to Schubert with the details, asking him to come along. I was still unsure if Al knew of Bob's participation in the new organization. He never said anything to me and I never said anything to him. It was a miserable situation that Bob's travel request would bring to a head. It needed Al's approval.

The following day I was in McCormick's cube getting an update on a PDP application for Nissan, the first to near production with AMP propellant, when Deanna tracked me down and let me know Al was looking for me. Great. That didn't take long. I told her I would take it in the conference room.

"Hey, Al, Good morning," I said, trying to sound cheerful.

"Why does Bob need to go to Aschaffenburg?" he asked. So much for the niceties.

"Claus asked that I come over to help him prepare for the inflator and propellant presentation he has to give to Shige. I'd like for Bob to come along for the propellant portion. Heiko will be there for inflators."

"Sean Burns is our propellant expert. Why the hell would you need Bob?" he asked angrily. He had no idea. Apparently, the rest of Takata was as good at keeping a secret as I was.

"Al, in the new organization, Bob will oversee Device Development and Propellant and will report to me. I was told not to talk to anyone about it. Nobody ever told you?" I asked, flinching, as if I were sitting across from him. There was nothing but dead air for what seemed like an eternity.

Yelling into the phone, he said, "Bob doesn't know anything about propellant! He's unqualified."

I was shocked. I had never heard Al disparage Bob like that before and I pushed back. "On the contrary, Al. By Takata's standards, I would say he is way overqualified."

And with that, what little civility that was left between us was gone.

"Bob doesn't work for you yet and he'll be busy that week. You go and present the plan by yourself," he said coldly, hanging up the phone.

I thought it best not to press the matter. I'd suck it up and go alone, but Al had been blindsided and that worried me. His political clout was a force to be reckoned with and he was not shy about wielding it. He was important, connected to the Japanese, and now a threat. What a wonderful place, this

Takata. Deciding there was nothing I could do about it other than share my pain with Bob, I walked over to his cube and filled him in on the conversation. As I did, this terrible look of anguish beset him. I asked him what could be so bad and all he said was,

"Al will get his revenge."

"It's a little late for that, Bob. We are launching soon after I get back from this trip. All the Chief Engineers will be there and once Claus is happy he's heading to Japan to present to Shige. After that, the Chief Engineers present to the CBUs and Operations and then they flip the switch."

"I sure hope so, Kevin," he said, not comforted at all by my words.

I kept my head down and went to Germany. Claus went to Japan and Shige blessed the plan. It was time for the Chief Engineers to present to the CBUs and Operations. We were at the finish line. I decided to go over to Auburn Hills to dial into the teleconference. Claus was in the States and camped out there and I needed to discuss something with Al as well.

I swung by Al's office first. I had submitted the expense report from my Germany trip as soon as I returned, and he had not approved it yet, which was unusual. When I sent him an e-mail inquiring, he responded, 'We are reviewing it,' and copied Pat Giampaolo, Vice President of Human Resources. I told Schubert and he said,

"See, he has started."

I wanted to understand what Al's concerns were, but his office was dark, so I found a conference room, dialed into the call and waited.

When it came my turn, I laid out our strategy, not sugar coating anything. We had issues, portfolio gaps, product recalls, customer apprehension, but we had a plan to deliver a competitive, non-PSAN inflator family by 2017. I presented the roadmap that would get us there – how we would address urgent gaps like the passenger disk inflator and how we would struggle through with a combination of Takata's GuNi and AMP inflators until the new product line was ready. It wasn't a plan that pleased everyone, but it was realistic, and they agreed. I stayed and listened to all the Chief Engineer's presentations after mine. We had become good friends over the past year and knowing the time and effort they had invested, there was no way I was leaving.

Bad News

After the teleconference, I tried Al's office again, but it was still deserted. On the way, I bumped into Claus, who had been on the call but in a different room. He congratulated me and asked if I could meet him for a drink in about an hour at the bar in his hotel lobby. Good, he was pleased, I thought to myself. I told him an hour was perfect.

As I walked into the hotel lobby, I thought of that first meeting with Ross. It was this hotel where I first told Takata's lawyers about the events in LaGrange. That was 2009 and now, five years later, I was on the cusp of becoming Takata's Chief Inflator Engineer. Claus hadn't arrived yet, so I ordered a beer and waited. Ten minutes later he walked in and I knew right away something was wrong. He was upset and looked like a man with bad news.

I took a sip of my beer as he made his way to the table and thought to myself, one week before the re-organization, how bad could it be? Maybe we needed to come up with a better title for Mizuno or something like that. I wasn't too concerned. He pulled up a stool, ordered a beer and dispensed with the small talk as we waited. Once the elixir arrived, he took a long pull and got right down to business.

"You will not be the Chief Engineer," he said wiping the foam from his mouth. "That position is going to Steve Maurer. You will still be promoted to VP, but you will be his deputy. Steve is being brought in as a more senior person to be the face of Takata for the Honda recall investigation. You will concentrate on Engineering. Senior management doesn't want you distracted by the recalls."

"What are you talking about, Claus? We are one week away. You can't be serious?" I felt sick.

"Unfortunately, I am, Kevin. I'm sorry," he said, taking an even longer pull. One down. I was just getting started.

"Steve Maurer?" I asked, still stunned. "What does he know about inflator engineering?"

"That's not important, Kevin," he answered. "He is there only for the Honda investigation. You are still the engineering lead."

"This is an insult, Claus. Who is responsible?" I pressed. "When we were in Japan last you told me that Frank Roe was a very powerful man, but you wouldn't explain yourself. I just chalked it up to the beers and let it go, but what did you mean by that? Was this Frank's doing? Al's? What did you let them do?"

"I'm not saying who it was, and I tried everything in my power to stop it," Claus said defensively. "Senior management doesn't want you distracted by the recalls."

"Senior management is Al and Frank, and they're afraid I'll tell Honda the truth," I clapped back. "Takata is punishing me again for my integrity, Claus. I'll see you later."

"We have a Chief Engineer call at 2:00 am local time. Please don't miss it," he said feebly as I was walked away.

Are you fucking kidding me? Waldorf was given my job? The week before liftoff?

I went home and cried in Sandy's arms for hours. She did her best to console me and not let me drink myself into a coma, but there was no stopping the latter. I had no intention of being on that conference call.

My life changed that evening. I was never a light drinker. Make no mistake about it, I loved to have a good time. Going out with the team after work for a few beers was one of my favorite ways to blow off steam. Weekend parties with co-workers on the pontoon were regular affairs in the early days. When on business in Japan, Europe or Mexico, our evenings revolved around alcohol. Drinking was ingrained in Takata. It was fun, and the camaraderie was wonderful, but over the years, it changed. I changed. The business wore on me, the constant lies angered me, and the fatalities gnawed at me. Drinking was no longer fun. It had become a way to escape. I stopped going to happy hours years earlier, yet the frequency and strength of my hangovers only increased. That night focused the floodlights on a bottom that was a lot closer than I thought.

I skipped work the next day. It was Friday, and this one had the makings of a three-day hangover. One of the restructuring consultants gave me a call that morning to see if I was alright, but nobody from Takata. I sent Frank an e-mail asking him if this was all just a bad dream, but he never responded. Later that day came the formal announcement. After a year of preparation, a year of anticipation, there was the e-mail from Shige, and as I read it a wave of nausea passed over me. Steve Maurer was the Inflator Chief Engineer. I was promoted to Vice President and named his Deputy. I was, after all this, Waldorf's balcony buddy, Statler.

That Monday I was scheduled to be in Auburn Hills. I didn't want to go. I didn't want to see anyone. I was promoted to Vice President but embarrassed to be seen. As I made my way to the conference room, I made eye contact with no one, and when the meeting was over, I stopped by Schubert's cube and let him know what had happened with Claus. How Al had been successful in seeking his revenge, and that Frank was somehow involved. We sat there, dazed, confused and in silence until Al came up from behind, tapped me on the shoulder and asked me to stop by his office on my way out.

With everything that was swirling about, it was easy to forget the expense report that he was still sitting on. I knocked on his half-open door and he motioned me to come in and take a seat. When I was settled, he picked up his phone and called Pat Giampaolo, the VP of Human Resources and asked him to join us. I looked at him quizzically as Pat entered the room, closed the door and took the seat next to me.

"What's going on, Al?" I asked suspiciously.

"I noticed something odd on your expense report, so I had an audit done on prior submissions. What was this charge by Kelli Kirkum at 12:30 in the morning at a local bar in Sterling Heights a few weeks ago?" he probed, looking over some paperwork.

"I asked her to take the Monclova associates out for me one night while they were in town. I couldn't make it, so I gave her the company card. Is there a problem with that?"

"We think so. That and a few other charges like this baby shower gift for Shari Oliver prompted us to search your e-mails," Giampaolo interjected. "We came across one where you told Kelli you loved her. Are you having an affair with her?"

Incredible. I turned in my seat to look directly at him and said,

"No, I am not, Pat. Kelli is a dear friend of mine. Would you like to get my wife Sandy on the phone right now and ask her?" Pat wasn't sure how to respond to that. Human Resources, my ass.

I turned back to Al trying to keep my cool and continued, "If you had bothered to look further, at e-mails from me to Hardenburg or McCormick, you would have found me saying the same thing. Hell, I've even told Dal I love him. Do you think I'm sleeping with all of them too, because I think McCormick would be a challenge!"

"Easy, Kevin, we were just checking," Al said, realizing his sting had failed miserably.

Pat tried to salvage what he could of the hit job and said,

"You are a VP now Kevin, an officer of the company, and as such you need to start acting like one. No more handing out the company credit card and from now on everything must go on expense reports. Understood?"

Oh, the irony. I needed to start behaving. I just nodded and waited for Pat to leave and as soon as the door closed behind him, I looked Al straight in the eyes.

"First you strip me of the Chief Engineer position and now this bullshit?"

Without hesitation he shot back, "It was an absolute disgrace that you were even considered for that position."

That was enough abuse for a lifetime. I lifted myself out of my seat and walked out.

An absolute disgrace that I was even considered?

Was Al so guilt-ridden about not being truthful to NHTSA for all these years that he felt the need to constantly attack the man responsible for the truth existing? Or was he just so petty, that taking Bob away from him required this kind of revenge? Either way, Al Bernat was a despicable man.

My mind flashed back to Mr. Takada's funeral and I wondered what he would have thought of how truth-tellers were being treated at his company. I was convinced now that Takata had taken its last breath with him. That it was functioning solely on life support and the plug was in the hands of some bad actors. The only thing I had keeping me going, besides two kids in college and increasingly larger intakes of alcohol, was that I would no longer have to work for Al Bernat.

Act Three

Off the Rails

2011-2014

(KEVIN)

"You have enemies?
Good.
That means you stood up for something, sometime in your life."
– *Winston Churchill*

14

The Global Reorganization

BEFORE HE left the States, Claus let me know he would be back in two weeks to share the new organization with the Armada team. With no space on campus large enough to accommodate that large of a crowd, we rented a conference hall at a nearby hotel. It was awful. I had spent the better part of a year with all the other Chief Engineers preparing for this day and they were all making similar presentations around the globe. Instead, I was watching Steve Maurer at the podium addressing the U.S. inflator team as their new leader. My heart was broken.

Who was this guy? Where did he come from? All the team in Armada knew of Steve was that he was the curmudgeon from Auburn Hills who never had a good thing to say about their work. Initially he was selected to be the Ford CBU Lead, a coveted position that scared the living shit out of him. He wanted nothing to do with profit and loss, or customer satisfaction. He was underqualified, and this position would expose him. Weeks before the rollout, he was asked to attend a meeting in Europe with his CBU counterparts. His itinerary was set, but he never showed up. He disappeared for days. A CBU Lead was real work and it terrified him. He was perfect for the role of Frank and Al's lackey. He had worked on inflators briefly while at TRW a century ago and they figured I would just keep drinking and prop him up.

Unlike Al, Steve took up permanent residence in Armada. It was ideal for him. Just months earlier he had purchased a new home only a mile down the road. Hmmm? But even though Steve was in the building every day, he was remarkably nonexistent. He never left his office except to relieve himself, and the man had a bladder made of steel. Sometimes he would be spotted at a birthday celebration but never at a design review. He was terrified of becoming a CBU Lead because he couldn't hide from the responsibility. In Armada, he found the perfect hiding place. Right next to his new home.

Steve also was not a clever man. The bark that he carried from Auburn Hills was much bigger than his bite and it didn't take long for the organization to catch on. He would simply not engage and forwarded all his e-mails to me. Going into his office was excruciating and to be avoided at all costs, and if you didn't carefully plan your exit, you would find yourself paying dearly. He was not there to offer guidance or support. He was vapid and only wanted to reminisce for hours on end about the good ole days with Bruce Thames. Listen up, Steve, I had no good days with Bruce Thames. On and on he'd drone, the voice of an adult in Charlie Brown's world going in one ear and out the other.

After a few of these grueling sessions, I concocted an exit plan with Deanna. Before taking my seat across from Steve, I would drop my notepad and pen on the small table by the door. At an appropriate point in the mind-numbing conversation, I would get up to stretch and move around to the back of the chair, resting my hands on it, but not breaking his attention. After a few more minutes, I would move to the table where I'd left my pen and notepad and pretend to scribble notes. This was Deanna's cue to politely tell Steve I was urgently needed somewhere else.

Come on, Al. These were explosive devices we were dealing with and two people were already dead. This was the best you and Frank could do? Waldorf?

Schubert took Steve's promotion badly. He was deeply insulted and as a result his work ground to a halt. He went the first month without calling his propellant team together at all. I gave him space but mentioned something after the second week and was told he was getting to it. By the third week, it had made it to his list. When he finally called them together, he did a fine job, but it was clear his enthusiasm for the new organization was gone. I asked him to stay behind after his team left the conference room.

"The Steve thing is really bothering you, isn't it?"

"It's an insult, Kevin. The forward face to Honda? They will never put him up in front of Honda. Never. It was a lie when Claus told you that and it's still a lie today."

"I know how you feel, Bob," I said, trying to commiserate with the man who was always put up in front of Honda, "but we have work to do. We can still make a difference if your heart is in it."

"I'm trying, Kevin, but they're making it impossible. Just last month Al asked me to assemble a customer presentation for a pending passenger recall and it's just more of the same."

"Passenger recall?" I interrupted.

"Yes, several inflator ruptures have been reported in junkyards in Japan, where they are compelled by law to deploy them. Takata is recalling a small population from 2002 and they want me to talk to some of the impacted customers."

"Let me guess, you don't agree with the story?" I looked at him.

"Yep. Japan wants to use auto-reject and propellant left out over the weekend to limit the recall boundary. The data and records show both are demonstrably false and I told them that."

"What did Al say?"

"That they would change the presenter but not the material. Like I said, Kevin, I'm trying, but it's not easy."

"I'm sorry, Bob," I said. "I'll talk to Steve about Al."

I made an appointment with Steve to see if there was any way to improve the situation, to somehow pry Bob away from Al and the recalls, but I was met by stiff resistance. As soon as I broached the subject, Steve started leaning into Bob, complaining about how long it had taken him to pull his team together and that he needed to go. This was not Maurer talking. He would have had to leave his office to form an opinion and that hadn't happened yet. I did my best to defend Bob, citing the constant pull from the recall, but that just played right into their hands.

A week later, Bob was out. His position would not be back filled, and propellant would report directly to Steve. In one short month, Schubert was exiled back to Al and my responsibilities were marginalized even further. Takata's bad actors were still very much at work.

AMP Is Not A Dud

Even though AMP was an integral part of the inflator strategy, Claus was never comfortable with its inclusion. With two fatalities already linked to PSDI, why would Takata's new Chief Engineer rush to launch another PSAN propellant? Add to that reports of three new ruptures, two in Puerto Rico and one in Maryland with a car that had spent most of its life in Florida, and there was a lot to consider.

Claus knew that AMP, with its wax barrier, was a big improvement to the X-Series' PSAN and that we could move fast. Monclova had already finished a Nissan/Toyota PDP validation and were eyeing the GM PDP line across the aisle. But Claus shared Christophe's concern with Monclova's history of quality defects and was hesitant. What if a gross leaker escaped? What if the desiccant is left out? What if a disgruntled employee spits in one? Claus drew a line in the sand.

Any new propellant, bridge or not, had to be fail-safe if compromised. Not Echigawa's definition. AMP had to dud, just like GuNi, and if it didn't, it wasn't going to production. That simple. He would rather the time and money be spent on the next-generation propellant. Hell, if AMP was up to his challenge, it would be Takata's next generation propellant. Sean was collecting the last of that data and the tollgate review was scheduled for the next month.

This was an important one. Claus traveled to Armada for the review and Steve even mustered the courage to leave his office and attend. Three environmental chambers had been delivering a continuous assault of temperature swings and moisture for months now. The first chamber contained baseline SDI-X inflators, or Takata's second generation PSAN. The second chamber had SDI-X inflators with Takata's GuNi, and the last, SDI-X with AMP. Intentional gross leaks were included in each group by punching a hole in the inflator's seal tape. Only the baseline and AMP inflators included 13X desiccant. GuNi had to weather the storm alone. Enough samples were placed in the chambers to conduct periodic measurements as the aging progressed.

Sean started first with the properly sealed inflators. The second generation PSAN and AMP inflators were well behaved, but as time progressed, the advantage of AMP's wax barrier became evident, with its inflators staying closer to nominal performance. The GuNi inflators also performed nicely and all indications were that if properly sealed, the three propellants would continue on normally for some time. We were more interested in the gross leaking inflators, the ones with the connection to the outside world.

These results were presented in the order an event occurred. The GuNi inflators were first and, as predicted, they failed to light. They met Claus' new requirement. The baseline SDI-X inflators with 13X were next, and they all eventually ruptured. For me, this was confirmation that someday an X-series inflator would explode in the field. Every inflator has a leak rate, some worse than others, and every desiccant saturates. No scientist can argue differently. How long it might take could be debated ad infinitum, but not the result. AMP's wax barrier only prolonged the inevitable and they ruptured some time later. That was the data Claus was after. AMP could not pass the new requirement and would be wound down. The roadmap would be adjusted to show only Takata's GuNi and the X-series inflators bridging the gap to the new propellant.

With AMP off the table, Sean turned his focus to the next generation propellant and Heiko and I looked to see where we could reduce our PSAN usage. We both agreed that designing new inflators around Takata's GuNi made little sense and instead, explored our existing portfolio for a good fit. After a careful review, we only found one, that might work.

SDI-X2 was designed around PSAN's gas efficiency and was the smallest driver inflator I'd ever seen. Every bit of free space was engineered out. Squeezing Takata's less-efficient GuNi into it was going to be a challenge. On paper it seemed to fit, but the propellant-loading operation would be stressed and far beyond Gutierrez's previous complaints. I wanted to reduce our PSAN usage as much as Heiko did, but this was forcing things. Plus, our GuNi formulation would continually struggle with broad specification compliance. Why go through all the effort? Why not focus our scant resources around the new propellant, and until that's ready keep using SDI-X2, just like PSDI-X and PDP? I shared my concerns with Steve and after he finished reminiscing about Bruce, he asked me to go sort it out with Heiko.

I went back to my office and typed out a quick note to the team suggesting we consider evaluating a competitive GuNi formulation alongside our own. If we were really going to do this, squeeze ten pounds of shit into a five-pound bag, I wanted an inflator at the end that Takata could use globally and that meant a different GuNi. I outlined my arguments and asked for some quick feedback. Sean was amenable, but Heiko and Roland pushed back strongly. E-mails flew back and forth across the pond all with a common thread. A GuNi SDI-X2 inflator was on the roadmap and Renault was already promised one with Takata's GuNi. There was no time to look at other propellants. I sat back and watched it unfold before re-inserting myself into the conversation, this time not making it a suggestion. Heiko flat out refused, so I forwarded that response to Steve, asking for some help. He replied later that night, launching into an alcohol-infused rant that once deciphered meant go figure it out yourself. I think.

We were in a power vacuum. If Europe did not like the direction they were receiving from Armada, they simply ignored it. Japan didn't recognize the global organization and never would. Heiko had narrowed the SDI-X2 GuNi conversion program to a local Renault application and Steve was unwilling to intervene. AMP programs were being wound down and Sean was full steam ahead on the new propellant. I was the X-Series applications manager all over again, but this time with the added responsibility of all of

Waldorf's action items.

I made several attempts to reach out to Claus to discuss my situation, but it was difficult to get on his schedule. I finally sent him an e-mail imploring him to give me something meaningful to do, something other than being Steve's training wheels. That got his attention. He stopped by my office the next time he was in Armada and promised he would make time for me later in the day. He never did. Avoidance was going to be Claus' way of dealing with me.

I called Scott to commiserate. I hadn't spoken to him in a while and missed our chats. After a year of preparation with Heiko, Bob, and the Chief Engineers, and a long, tumultuous year with Steve, we hadn't made great progress and I was feeling deflated.

"Hey, Scott, it's Kevin."

"Kevin, my God, it's been ages," he answered. "How are you?"

"I'm struggling, Scott," I told him honestly. "I feel like I have been relegated to an engineering manager again and I'm pissed off."

"Yeah, I heard what happened up there and I don't understand it," he said. "Best advice, don't dwell on it. Reengage with Monclova, instead. It will be good for you and it will help me as well. I've been out of inflators for almost two years now with this damn restructuring and we are not hearing good things about Christophe. His boss, my good friend Hiroshi Shimizu, has moved to Monclova full time and that has me concerned!"

"That's a good idea, Scott," I said my spirits brightening a bit. "It would get me out of here as well. I may need your help with Steve though."

"Of course. Not a problem. Just let me know," he said. "Keep your head up, bud."

Putting the phone back in its cradle, I considered Scott's words carefully. He was right to be concerned. We had lost touch with Monclova. I needed to get back to making a difference, and if engineering didn't want me, Scott would certainly put me to work. I wasn't ready for my window seat yet, even if the drinks were free.

Keep Your Window Seat

Inflator assembly in Mexico consisted mainly of modular stations arranged in U-shaped cells. Components started down one end and finished inflators were packaged at the other. Each station had its own internal controls, error-proofing, and interlocks to prevent bad quality product from being advanced. All the stations operated in a cadence, with an inflator being packaged about every twenty seconds. Some of the lines had over fifteen stations, and almost every station had an operator in front of it.

These modular, hand-pass lines were significantly less expensive than 'turn-key,' or more automated, operations. They were better able to deal with the inevitable configuration changes demanded by customers. Stations could easily be wheeled in and out to make the necessary adjustments. The same could not be said for Freiberg's automated lines, designed to run one or two versions of the same basic inflator with little interruption and very few people. They were perfect for high-cost labor regions, but their sophistication made them rigid and unconducive to change. Modifying a line to add something as simple as desiccant could take six months and cost a million dollars. In Monclova, the same was accomplished with another operator and a spoon, making it easy to see how it became the 'island of misfit inflators.' The number of variants they processed dwarfed Christophe's German plants and, additionally, they were the only source of the much sought-after X-series inflators. Monclova was stressed to the breaking point.

Christophe did not like the new organizational structure. He felt strongly that inflator engineering and operations should exist under one umbrella. He had valid reasons, most of them self-serving, but Shige chose differently, and he couldn't get past it. He never fully embraced his new role as global operations leader, continuing to lobby for a single inflator organization under his leadership. Instead of giving desperately needed attention to Mexico, most of Christophe's travel was to his plant in China, which produced only a fraction of Takata's inflators, but it was close to Shige and that meant more face time. Meanwhile, his boss, Hiroshi Shimizu, was in Monclova, silently struggling.

The Monclova plant was a city. Modular lines required lots of people and there were thousands of associates in the factory. That level of human interaction put a tremendous dependence on the error-proofing and traceability-systems integral to the lines. You could never let your guard down. Christophe wanted to remove that human element and was always pushing for fully automated assembly, even in Mexico. Monclova was inching its way towards a happy medium between modularity and automation, but that evolution was only in early stages. Christophe inherited a plant and system of pyrotechnic operations he was unfamiliar with.

Scott was right. I needed to re-engage with Monclova. Prior to all the changes, communication was healthy. Not always friendly and productive, but it was healthy. That all changed when Christophe took over. There had been a precipitous drop in request for our team's support. My conversation with Scott was a wakeup call. Yes, Armada was a mess, but what immediate damage could they do now? Monclova was a different story.

It was Friday when I talked with Scott, and I had the weekend to think about it. And to have one too many. My head was pounding Monday morning as I tossed my backpack into my office and went straight for a cup of coffee. I wondered if this place would be any better without the hangovers. I had tried to lay off the booze over the weekend and give some serious thought to my situation but had had no luck with either.

Two cups of coffee later and with the cobwebs clearing, I opened my door for business. McCormick was the first to plop himself down, saying immediately,

"Phillion is about to give us a call. Something about a PDP test failure in Monclova."

"Dave, it's Monday morning and I feel like shit."

"Stop whining and put your big boy pants on," he said as the phone rang.

"Hey, Bob, good morning. Dave is here with me."

"Good morning, boys. We have a problem, so I'll get right to it. We had a PDP come apart in a GM module LAT, and to compound things, the parts have already been released to the customer."

"You've got to be kidding me, Bob..." I rubbed my eyes. "Did operations learn anything from the Brazil mess?!"

"Apparently not," he replied, sounding exhausted. "Look, I've been down here a week already and I need some help."

"A week already?" I asked confused. "Why are we only hearing about this now?"

"Ask the guys responsible for the re-organization and when you're done with that, get your ass down here and do some real work."

Dave put had his hand over his mouth trying not to laugh.

"Bob, you and I both know PDP is solid. It must be a bad weld and you don't need engineering for that," I said calmly.

"I wouldn't be calling you if I didn't need your help, Kevin."

I looked up at Dave and he nodded back. The decision to re-engage with Monclova had been made for me.

"Okay, bud, McCormick and I will be there tomorrow afternoon."

When we arrived at the plant the next day we were hustled into a war room just off the main lobby that Phillion had set up camp in. The plant would soon be swarming with GM personnel and this would serve as our safe haven. Shipping parts to your customer and informing them later that one had exploded during acceptance testing had a way of souring relations.

Bob didn't waste any time. He handed Dave what was left of the ruptured part. A few rotations in his big bear claw and he looked up and said, "the laser beam is walking off the weld-joint. Something in the fixturing or drive mechanism must be flexing."

"Thanks, MOTO," Bob said, sarcastically before continuing, "Let's go out to the Nissan/Toyota line so you can see that station run before we tear it down. The GM welder is already in pieces."

MOTO was McCormick's acronym for Master of the Obvious and he loved to use it whenever he could. So, it was sweet to see Phillion turn the tables, giving us a much-needed laugh before we grabbed our safety glasses and got down to business.

There were two identical and brand-new PDP lines in the factory. One was dedicated to GM and the other to Nissan and Toyota. PDP weld-stations were the first to transition from CO2 laser welding to fiber-optic, and that's where things went sideways.

Fiber-optic welding was the cutting-edge technology, obsoleting the CO2's pesky mirrors and beam delivery method that maintenance technicians hated. It was far more manufacturing friendly and used significantly less floor space. What I expected to see was a newer, more compact laser station, coupled to our traditional mechanisms that held and turned the parts being welded. What I found was something far different.

Dave and I peered through the weld station's window and watched it cycle several times. The PDP's two initiator holders were being welded to the inflator's base. A round dial-table with nests rotated the mating parts to two separate weld heads, each of which joined one of the initiator holders to the base. That surprised both of us and was a first for Takata.

Historically, Monclova's welders used a rigidly fixed nest that was precisely aligned and pinned to stay that way. It rotated only about its own axis. The dial table in front of us was rotating about its axis while its individual nests were rotating about their own. It reminded me of a bad solar system model from grade school. The station flexed and multiplied errors, resulting in the laser beam occasionally veering off course. How did we let this get all the way to production? There was no doubt about it now. We had let the re-organization distract us.

"Come on. There's more to see," Phillion said.

The technicians had the dial table from the GM line unbolted and turned over, exposing several gouges in its underside. The grooves appeared to be caused by an interference between the dial-table and the drive-mechanism, but we couldn't tell. What was immediately clear, however, was that precision was lost and the scope of the problem was widening. After the station on the Nissan/Toyota line was disassembled, we inspected it for the same gouges, but didn't find any. Regardless, both lines were put on hold. Dave and I suspected that the grooves on the GM table were only exacerbating an inherent beam-alignment problem existing on both lines. There was just too much moving and flexing going on for a robust weld.

We set up a teleconference with the GM, Nissan and Toyota CBU leads to inform them of our preliminary findings. The Nissan and Toyota leads insisted that since the dial-table on their line had no gouges, there was no reason to question the quality of their parts. I disagreed, letting them know we suspected the weld station design to be an issue common to both lines, and that we would revisit the matter when we had all the data. Fencing the GM inflators was our first order of business and the quality team was already busy gathering that information.

A tremendous amount of information is collected and stored in a line's electronic traceability system for every inflator produced. Weld data is one of the most critical sets ensuring product safety. At the beginning, middle and end of a day's shift, several inflators are produced specially for weld verifications. The inflators are sectioned, and every weld is polished, measured, and compared to a standard. Concurrently, several other specially prepared parts are built for hydro-burst testing, which pumps the welded inflator with water until it ruptures. That pressure is compared against a minimum and the test parts are additionally inspected to ensure none of the ruptures initiated from a weld. These were not optional requirements. Every shipment required a data package showing full compliance and that is what I was anxiously waiting to get my hands on.

Finally, some of that data from the lots nearest to the failure started to trickle in. After leafing through a couple of pages, Dave and I both looked up in disbelief. Nothing passed. The weld-nugget measurements were out, the inflator hydro-burst pressures were below minimum, and many showed pictures of tears initiating from the welds. It was a trifecta, the worst of the worst, and all the paperwork was stamped and signed-off by Monclova's quality department as 'good to go'. I lifted a picture of one of the weld seams and unloaded on Dave,

"The inflator quality team is in free fall. I can't believe this was approved to go into someone's vehicle? Look at this weld. How did it ever get through the weld monitor? It should have lit the machine up red!"

"You're right, that's not possible..." he said, taking off for the lines again, knowing as I did that the expensive, real-time monitoring equipment should have easily caught this.

Ten minutes later he sat down across from me in a huff, saying in breaths, "They bypassed them – on both lines. They said they have the data to support the decision and were under tremendous pressure to meet rate."

"Bypassed them! You..."

Dave put his paw up, "Stop, it's me you're talking to."

There was no plausible explanation for ever bypassing a weld-check monitor. The inflator welds hold the structure together and are the most critical of process steps. Period. Things were out of control.

Once Dave put his hand down and I could see him again, I said, "we're going to have to go through every piece of weld data on both lines since the start of production. Every record."

"Absolutely. Are they pulling it all?"

"Yes. Bob said he would get it for us. In the meantime, we have to figure out how to get GM back into production."

Dave already had that plan and it did not include the new weld stations. They needed major modifications and had to go back. The power source and fiber optics that generated and delivered the beam were not the issue. The culprit was how the station handled and presented the part to the beam, or the dial table, and that was going to be a big job. Our best option was swap back to the standard, single-axis method. Monclova had spare stations that could be modified, and the process was already approved by GM. Dave and the team were busy laying the groundwork to reconfigure both lines in spite of resistance from the Nissan and Toyota CBUs.

That eased GM's immediate production worries but added to their quality concerns. Why did Takata make such a drastic change to its stations' design in the first place, they asked. There was no good answer, other than we took our eye off the ball and got our clocks cleaned. Despite being furious, they worked closely with us to bring the lines back up and identify the recall population.

The data packages were coming in bigger chunks now as the quality team picked up steam and what we found was even more shocking. We identified several lots that fell short of the acceptance criteria. Think about that. Monclova inflator operations shipped multiple defective and dangerous batches, over a period of months, with acceptance data that unequivocally stated the parts should have been tossed in a dumpster. There was no reason or excuse that could be offered. Dave and I highlighted what needed to be recalled, taking our time to make sure we found every errant data point.

Most of the defective hardware could be attributed to the dial-table nest adjacent to the gouges, with inflators from it showing a characteristic weld that could only be caught with a trained eye. But not always. There were also an exorbitant number of weld adjustments being made that were unrelated to the interference problem, a clear indicator that the plant was struggling with the station's wobbling fixtures. I was sure the data from the Nissan/Toyota line would show the same and I would soon have to make a renewed case against their CBU leads. But first, it was time to go home for a breather.

Three weeks had flown by, and although exhausted, we delivered root cause and fenced the GM recall population. Flying home, I pondered on how little Christophe had participated in the discussions. He showed up after we did and stayed only for a week, leaving his boss Hiroshi to manage things.

I was talking with Scott more and more these days and he was genuinely concerned about his friend Hiroshi. He was glad we were there lending support, and Hiroshi was too. It felt good to be wanted again. Scott sent me a text as I was on my way home that simply read, 'Remarkable.' I can't tell you how incredible that felt. It had been far too long.

My return home was a much-needed break, but it wouldn't be all relaxation. Takata was summoned to two high-level meetings at GM's Technical Center in Detroit because of the debacle, and they wanted me to attend the first. It was a technical deep-dive that thankfully wasn't too painful.

The second meeting occurred a few weeks later and I was not invited, but I was filled in on what had transpired. Shige was summoned to explain how one of GM's most valued suppliers had fallen so far, so quickly, and what he was personally doing to turn things around. He got so drunk the night before that his trusted circle had to keep him a comfortable distance away from the GM folks, lest they smell the alcohol emanating from his pores. Like a lot of us at Takata, his drinking was probably not for fun anymore.

15

Oh My God!

IT WAS too short a trip home, but Monclova had the Nissan/Toyota weld data ready, I was anxious to get to it and Phillion needed my help. The reorganization left him with few soldiers to deploy, and since I had little to do in Armada, I was happy to be in the trenches with him.

I didn't bother going into the office while I was home for the long weekend. I sent only two e-mails: one to Deanna asking her to make the necessary arrangements for Dave and me to return to Monclova and the second to Claus. This one was short and delicate. I let him know I had discovered some very serious issues in Monclova that needed my immediate attention and that I would be there indefinitely. I was not asking, and he never challenged me. I would learn later from Steve that Claus found my e-mail very unprofessional. I wouldn't have sent it if the pull to go hadn't been so strong.

As I sat in the airport, I had the feeling that change was coming again. I had no idea what kind, but it wasn't the darkness I felt a year earlier when Al knocked me to the ground and kicked me as I lay there. It was an optimistic feeling that I couldn't quite put my finger on. I was no further from the bottom but felt better.

Dave jarred me back to reality, "I hate this flight. The seats are too damn small for my girth."

"Maybe no one will sit next to you," I replied, knowing full well that wasn't going to happen. These flights were always overbooked with problem-solvers heading back and forth to factories south of the border.

I wondered if Nissan and Toyota had been notified that Takata had made a critical process change to their PDP line as well when Dave retired the fiber optic weld stations. My gut told me no. That would have meant acknowledgement of an issue, something the Japanese CBUs had little stomach for. One thing I was sure of was that both Nissan and Toyota knew of GM's recall, because it was in the papers. They must have pressed Takata for certification of their product, and I'm sure they were fed the 'no gouges in your dial table' crap because only Phillion, McCormick and I were interested in the data. Japan was perfectly content leaving it in the Shin Tanaka memorial data vault.

When we arrived at the plant, we found the inspection records waiting for us. The combined Nissan and Toyota PDP volumes were much smaller than GM, so it didn't take Dave and me long to work through them. As I feared, we found inflators that failed to meet acceptance criteria for both customers: more potentially deadly product shipped and signed-off on by our quality inspectors. Phillion suggested I call Scott Caudill.

Scott asked that I invite Yoshimura to the plant to explain the situation in person. That sounded reasonable since this was going to involve another recall, so I sent a delicately worded e-mail to him explaining the situation. He had business in the U.S. the following week and replied that he would make his way to Monclova following that. So far, so good, and I hoped this time, it would be for more than another bob of the head.

Mr. Bobble Head Speaks

It was nearing the end of July when Yoshimura arrived. I was outside having a cigarette in the scorching sun when his van was waved through the guard shack. I took a few last drags before joining Phillion in a small conference room off the lobby. We had all the data separated by customer in neat folders and waited patiently for Yoshimura to get settled and join us.

Entering the room, he never took a seat. Instead, he walked to the opposite side of the room and half-sat on the windowsill. He was clearly uncomfortable and listened quietly as Bob summarized the findings of the GM investigation, explaining to him that out of due care, the same data review was performed on the Nissan/Toyota line.

"Yoshimura-san," Bob started. "We found defective product from the same weld operation on the Nissan/Toyota line. It impacts both customers, and Takata will have to issue a..."

"Stop!" Yoshimura demanded forcefully. "We will not recall any of Nissan or Toyota's product. Takata cannot stomach another recall. Furthermore, you are not to say anything about this to the President of the company."

We both sat there in stunned silence. Bob was quicker to recover, saying,

"Yoshimura, one more time so we are all clear. There are dangerous Nissan and Toyota PDP inflators in the field that Takata must recall. Kevin and his team went through all the data since the start of production and he is here to talk to you about it. The recall will not be large, but it is necessary. Do you understand what I am telling you?"

"Yes," he said flatly.

"And your instruction is that Takata do nothing? We are to move on, and to not tell Shige? Is that correct?"

Another 'yes', and the conversation was over. Yoshimura did not come to Mexico to listen. He came to deliver a message: 'Shut up and toe the line.' He refused to even look at the data. These were not inflators that would take years to age and become dangerous. A bad weld means a dangerous and potentially deadly inflator from the day it is born. Who did he think he was? He was playing God with people's lives.

I stepped out of the meeting sickened, trying to calm down. I immediately called Scott. I didn't expect him to know what to say or do, I just needed to tell him. I hung up that call and dialed Maurer. That was simply a formality and I can guarantee the sequence of events that happened next. He called Rob, who then called his boss, and the phone game continued until an international call was placed to Japan, which then abruptly ended all further discussion on the matter. The absolution ritual was in full swing, and just as Waldorf was putting the phone back on the receiver from my call, I could hear him say, "Oh shit, I'd better call Rob."

There was one other thing Yoshimura said that I kept coming back to. 'Don't tell the President of the company?' Why did he say that? Was it cultural? Did it mean that Jim went to his grave unaware of the evil being perpetrated by his closest advisors? That's how I read it. I had to believe there was a sliver of humanity somewhere in Takata.

Basta

That next morning was rough even by my standards. The stinging hangover I was trying my best to fight off kept being refueled by the thought of Yoshimura's egregious actions. I needed to get some air. Get out of this damn war room. Dal was in an upstairs conference room, so I decided to go there and commiserate with him. When I got to the top of the stairs I had to grab a hold of the handrail and pause to let a wave of nausea pass over and to catch my breath. I can't keep this up, I thought to myself. Once I had my sea legs back, I walked across the aisle and cracked the frosted glass door to Dal's room.

Good. He was by himself. I sat down across the table and said,

"Man, I feel like shit."

"Man, you look like shit," he fired back.

He wasn't being playful. He was serious.

"Boy, you need to start taking it easy. You need to start slowing down," he said to me.

I looked at him with tears welling up in my eyes. I knew he was right and said, "No, Dal, I need to quit. It is killing me."

Now the tears were streaming down my face as he said matter-of-factly, "Then you have to quit. I will help you. When we go to dinner tonight, we will have a *Topo Chico con limon* and no one will be the wiser."

And that was that. I was struck sober.

My rock bottom was not a divorce. It was not a DUI. It didn't come at the destruction of my family or friends. It wasn't a night in jail or a terrible embarrassment. It was a good friend telling me to knock it off, and my moral compass reminding me that it functioned much better when it was not submerged in alcohol.

That is not to say it was a soft landing. My drinking had gotten away from me. I was a functional alcoholic. A shell of my former self, who would pick up a pint of Jack on the way home from work, hide it in the garage, still in the brown paper bag, and polish it off over the course of the night to numb the day's pain. I would repeat the cycle every day, foolishly thinking nobody noticed. I was in decline, in a vicious circle just like the plant, and it was time the both of us snapped out of it.

Topo Chico and lemon became my drink of choice, and I never looked back. I stopped drinking on August 7, 2013, on my 51st birthday. Dave quit with me for support, and Dal, Scott and Bob were never far away. I was going to have to do this on the road, in Mexico, and without my family. There was too much to be done in Monclova, but Sandy was thrilled. Her prayers had been answered. She had stuck with me through it all and the light in my eyes was back on. I had been gone for far too long.

The first week was rough, but I managed. Thankfully, I was only in Mexico for two days of it and could spend the rest recuperating at home with Sandy. Then, it was right back down again.

There was something odd going on in Monclova that Bob and I needed to get to the bottom of. The plant was having a terrible time meeting production demands. Hiroshi was there full time, but the team was losing ground. It didn't make sense. There was plenty of capacity and the lines were running full tilt. The walls should have been bursting at the seams with inflators, but the inventory position was hand to mouth. Where were they all going?

During the PDP investigation, Bob and I sensed that we had only scratched the surface. The Monclova team was embarrassed by the damage they had done to Takata and GM's relationship. They let multiple lots of defective product slip through their hands. But why? That's Quality 101. That's not who they were. When parts don't meet critical requirements, they are scrapped.

But maybe that was the problem. Maybe they had scrapped themselves out of parts and had a VP camped out in their plant, pushing them harder each day to make deliveries. Hiroshi was not there for quality improvements. He was no Sensei. Bob and I had a sinking feeling that Christophe's indifference and a drive by Hiroshi to make shipments at any cost had combined for a perfect storm.

I was feeling better than I had in years as the driver eased the Honda Odyssey up to the Monclova guard shack. One week sober, I thought to myself. I'd been here before, and had tried different approaches, but this time I felt different. This time I had my Maker by my side and armed with His presence, I was sharper, more alert and happier than ever before. I was falling in love with my wife all over again, becoming all the things I was afraid I would lose by quitting, but never had when I was drinking. And with all of this came a strengthening clarity and sense of purpose. I was beating my demons. I was outside my vicious circle looking in now, and I was on a mission to pull Monclova along with me.

I finished my cigarette and walked into the lobby where I was met by Carlos Iruegas. I gave him a big hug and asked him to pull the team together. I had something important to share with them. I was never afraid to let people in and I was going to need their help as much as they needed mine. I grabbed a cup of coffee, took a seat, and waited for everyone to get settled. They were defeated. I could see it in their faces. As I stood to address them, a calm came over me – a certainty. I let them know that something had changed in me, that I was on a mission, and that I was not going anywhere until we had this fixed. I was alive again, filled with raw emotion, and it blazed in my eyes. If I had the ability to pull people before, it was now multiplied by my sobriety.

The Offsite Warehouse

And that's all it took to open the kimono. An hour later Phillion and I were being whisked to a warehouse by Guillermo Apud, Iruegas' Continuous Improvement Manager and a long-time friend of ours. The worn facility was just miles from the plant and located in a well-traveled part of the city. On the way there, Apud filled us in on what had been happening.

"You are going to be shocked by what you see," he said. "Over the last year things have been steadily deteriorating. We are generating enormous amounts of scrap and have no time to take the lines down to investigate why. If we did, supply would be interrupted. We've been running 24/7 just to stay afloat and piling up the scrap in this warehouse I am taking you to."

I looked over at Bob afraid to ask the question, "How many are we talking about, Apud?"

"Three hundred thousand driver inflators and all for weld inspection failures," he replied rather numbly.

Bob and I sat in stunned silence and remained that way for the rest of the ride. Apud knew to do the same.

A worn facility is being kind. The were no environmental controls. No security. The place was wide open and housed nearly 15,000 pounds of explosives. It was a disorganized, hot, filthy mess with a net value of more than $4 million dollars. I turned to Apud and said,

"Oh, my God, please get this place cleaned up. Everything needs to be organized by inflator P/N and customer right away."

Bob nodded his concurrence as he walked to the center of the warehouse and slowly turned in a circle, taking in the hundreds of thousands of suspect inflators surrounding him. He still hadn't quite come to grips with it. I walked over to where he was standing and said,

"Let's go, Bob. We've got work to do."

The drive back was even quieter. Bob was staring out his window and Apud was not offering small talk. That was best. My mind was racing anyway. The plant was running 24/7, falling further behind and about to interrupt customer supply. That meant only one thing to me. Management would be coming for those inflators. Takata was not going to stop a customer's assembly line with 300,000 finished inflators miles away from their shipping docks. They were going to move what was needed to stay off the radar screen, no matter what anyone said or did. That I was convinced of. McCormick and I would have to go through every one of those inflator lots and determine if any were safe – and before boxes started disappearing.

How the hell did Iruegas fill a warehouse full of scrap inflators without anyone noticing? Why didn't Hiroshi scream for Armada's help? I had so many questions as we pulled up to the plant lobby. Hiroshi didn't have the skill set to problem solve his way out of this. He was using his position of authority to push the people harder. To produce more to cover the scrap, but the gig was up. X-series volumes were exploding, and the lines couldn't produce enough good hardware to keep up anymore. It was all about to come to a head and none of it made any sense. We were only a phone call away.

As we walked into the plant I asked Bob, "You going to call Scott?"

"Yep. You going to get started on figuring out what the hell happened?"

"Yep," and I split off.

Why were there so many inflator lots failing weld inspection? What was going on? I found McCormick and dragged him outside to suffer through a cigarette with me in the hot sun. On the way out, I told him what we had just learned.

"The plant has outgrown its life support systems," he said.

"What do you mean?"

"What is the most important operation in inflator assembly?" he asked me rhetorically.

I played along, "welding."

"Right – and look at the plant. They keep putting line after line in and what have they done to the weld inspection area?"

"Nothing…" I trailed off, but the light was on. I understood exactly where he was going.

Weld inspections were conducted at the beginning, middle, and end of every shift to ensure the process wasn't drifting. If any one of those failed, the line was immediately stopped, and every inflator produced between the last good inspection and the failure was put on hold for disposition. The engineers would then adjust the weld station based on their interpretation of the data and a repeat weld inspection would be conducted before the line was restarted. It was a huge burden on the weld and quality engineers, even under normal circumstances.

And all these inspections took time. Inflators had to be deployed, sectioned and polished to take measurements. Hydro-burst samples had to be built and tested, and all the while production marched on. The time to wait for the data was not factored into anyone's capacity plans. Operations had to produce inflators at risk and assume the results would be acceptable. Weld sectioning, grinding, polishing and hydro-burst machines were in a constant frenetic state, struggling to minimize the financial exposure. The success of the X-series line demanded additional capacity, but the old, tired equipment was just asked to work harder. Dave surmised that both man and machine were at their limits and mistakes were being made. I believed him.

Hiroshi could no longer keep a lid on the warehouse. The threat of disrupting car maker production lines was real, the associated financial penalties staggering and the hit to Takata's reputation potentially unrecoverable. Top management descended on Monclova to assess the burgeoning crisis. Claus was one of them. He was gravely concerned about his German customers, BMW, Mercedes and VW. He had worked long and hard to develop those relationships and was in danger of disappointing. Now he needed my help.

We disclosed the contents of the off-site warehouse in a tense, high-level meeting, explaining to the disbelieving crowd that we were only in the early stages of the investigation. Then we presented the consequences. All possible scenarios to prevent a disruption could not close the gap quickly enough. It was impossible. Too many inflators that were supposed to be in vehicles were sitting in the swamp. Without those, Takata was going to disrupt production lines. The question now was whose. Sitting there listening to the back and forth my worst fears were being confirmed. They were going to wade through the swamp. They were so predictable.

After the meeting, Claus approached me and asked,

"Do you think we can avoid the embarrassment of a shutdown?"

"I don't see how, Claus. The situation is pretty dire, and we still don't understand why the scrap piled up in the first place."

"We can't let that happen," he said sadly.

"We'll do what we can, sir," I went to join McCormick.

I found him parked in the test lab observing the weld inspection process from start to finish. He was convinced it was feeding questionable data to the assembly lines, which was sending the process into a tailspin.

"Hey, Dave...," he stopped me before I could get anything else out.

"They need the swamp inflators, right?"

"They're coming for them, but let's not worry about that right now. What did you find?"

"This is messed up!" he replied, shaking his head and handing me a few plots. "Let's go up front where we can talk."

Phillion was in the war room when we got back, and I closed the door behind us. It was just the three of us.

"Hey, Bob, you got a second to listen to what Dave just observed in the test lab?" I asked. "He filled me in on the way up here and I think you'll be interested."

"Absolutely," he replied. "I could use a break from what I'm doing. Please share, Dave."

"It's not good, Bob. The hydro-burst test equipment is at the point of collapsing. Valves are leaking, pumps are smoking, and the band-aids are falling off. Bad data is going out to the lines and that's causing needless, detrimental changes to the process. Plain and simple. The problem is coming from the test lab. The rest of the plant has left it in the dust."

"What needs to be done?" Bob asked.

"Order new hydro-burst equipment immediately and while you are at it order more polishing and grinding equipment."

"I'll take care of it right away. Can we hobble along with what we have?"

I fielded this one. "We can keep going, Bob, but we must slow down. Everyone needs to be retrained. Data is being misinterpreted and people should have recognized the equipment was struggling."

"I'll take care of the training," said Dave.

Bob switched subjects. "As much as it sucks, management wants us to go through all the inflators in the swamp."

"Yeah, we knew that was coming, Bob," I said. "It's the first thing Dave asked me when I found him. Does Apud have it all organized yet?"

"He does." Bob was not happy with our assignment.

"Hey, cheer up," I urged him. "At least they haven't raided the treasure yet. Nothing ships unless Dave or I say so. They have to come through us."

"Thanks, Kevin. I'll get you guys all the help you need."

Phillion assigned us a dedicated quality team to wade through the muck. It was the same gang that assisted with the PDP issue, so everyone was familiar with the drill. We found many inflators in the warehouse that were good. After the PDP embarrassment, the quality engineers became gun shy and, afraid of losing their jobs, started sending everything there. I sorted through most of the data myself, calling Dave in when I struggled with a decision. He was busy on the floor making sure no one would ever have to go through this again. If either one of us called an inflator lot bad, we weren't challenged. It went straight into the garbage, regardless of the expense.

It took me a month to get through it all, wearing away the rubber grip of a Takata pen before finishing. In the end, there were enough good lots tied up with blatant test errors to keep customers afloat and save Takata from another embarrassment. But there were inflators with horribly bad welds that were scrapped. Scary welds, like the Nissan and Toyota PDP defects that Yoshimura callously left in the field. Takata pulled back the bad GM

PDP parts because they got caught. But what if that randomly selected LAT sample didn't rupture? Takata would have put even more potentially deadly airbag modules in the field with approved paperwork. How many times that had happened before was anybody's guess.

McCormick's assignment was to standardize every weld station fixture on the floor. Phillion had already ordered the new hydro-burst machines and inspection equipment, and the plan was to introduce everything concurrently. There were process inconsistencies between stations and improvements added to newer lines that had not been deployed backward. This was our opportunity to clean the slate, start over again and the Monclova weld engineers, free of Gutierrez's grips, were all in.

Once the new equipment was installed, the fixtures standardized and people properly trained, the frequency of adjustments being made to the machines plummeted. Takata was consistently making good inflators again and we could take a moment to catch our breath. I had a great sense of accomplishment with the progress made so far, but I was saddled with a nagging suspicion that Monclova, sidetracked by the re-organization, had let a lot of bad product escape.

It was September now and with all those sober hours in a day I started walking. A couple of miles a day quickly grew to five, and without the booze, the weight started falling off me. Associates would honk and wave at me as I marched up and down Monclova's main thoroughfare after work. My physical and emotional states were steadily improving and, for once, Takata was about to do something that wouldn't screw with that.

I was sitting in the war room by myself when the call came in from Scott. I began to bring him up to speed with the latest events when he interrupted,

"Hey, I think I have some news that you will be happy with."

"What is it?" I asked enthusiastically.

"We will be announcing an interim organization that will solidify the role you have assumed in Monclova. We want to add Inflator Process Engineering to your list of duties, giving you a foothold in both Engineering and Operations. I will be assuming responsibility for Monclova inflators and Phillion will run the day-to-day operations. You two make a great team. Christophe will retain responsibility for Takata's inflator plants in China and Germany, but I don't think that will last long. The swamp really took its toll on him. You will remain a VP and report directly to me, dotted lined to Steve. What do you think?"

"I think that sounds awesome, Scott. Thank you for your trust and support."

"Eventually, I would like for you and Phillion to move to San Antonio," he continued. "That way you would be within striking distance of the plants and you won't have to take your winter walks in the mall with all the other old people."

I laughed and said, "Now that really sounds wonderful. Thanks for everything, Scott."

"No. Thank you, Kevin."

Retirement in San Antonio. Sandy and I used to visit there when we lived in Dallas and she was pregnant with Ryan. We loved the town's history and beautiful River Walk. This could finally work. There was still a great deal to be done in Monclova that would keep Sandy and me apart, but now there was a future tied to it. A future Sandy could get excited about and one that didn't have me just watching the scenery pass below. I would be an active participant again. God, it felt good to be sober.

An X-Series Ruptures

The days were long, the weeks flew by and I was loving every minute of it. Phillion and I had a routine. Each morning a Takata driver would take us straight from the hotel to the war room, where we would catch up on e-mails and down some coffee before heading out to the lines for our daily walk. The desert was cooling off nicely now that it was fall, and as I slipped my safety glasses over my head, Bob muttered something, hit the send button on his last e-mail and said,

"Don't you think it's odd the inflator offices are up here in the front of the building and the assembly lines are all the way in the back? This building is enormous, and the inflator functions are so spread out."

"I don't know Bob, I kind of like the steps. Especially with it getting darker outside so early these days."

"I'm not concerned about your step count you idiot," he replied. "Why don't we move the team to the empty office space above the tool crib. It's right next to the manufacturing engineers and the production lines?"

"That's a great idea, Bob! Make it happen."

A month later, I was sitting in Phillion's shiny new office. He was right, this was much better. I opted out of one, instead choosing a desk in the middle of the bullpen. It was important to me that people understood I was open for business. That my side job was to further their inflator knowledge and that I expected them to have a profound understanding of what they were making. Bob and I were reviewing the team's declining scrap numbers when we were interrupted by his phone.

"It's the GM CBU Lead," Bob said, his hand covering the mouthpiece. "I'll put him on speaker."

"Good morning, Gentlemen," his voice boomed from the phone. "Sorry to say, but I have some bad news."

I put my head down and waited for it.

"We just got word that an SDI-X ruptured in a MY12 Chevy Cruze. The only other information I have is that the driver was seriously injured, losing sight in one eye."

After what felt like an eternity of silence I asked. "Did you say a MY12 Cruze? That's way too early for PSAN degradation, especially with 13X. I know I shouldn't jump to conclusions, but if it's an SDI-X built last year, I'm betting it's an assembly problem."

"Call us back when you have a serial number and some pictures," Bob said, slowing me down. "We'll start what we can here, but without that number, there's not much we can do."

I waited until I heard the line go dead before saying, "Just two months ago, Bob, we learn of the third PSDI fatality and now we gravely injure someone with an SDI-X. This has to stop."

"Yeah, I know, Kevin. I feel sick, but we have to keep moving forward. That's all we can do."

The pictures hit our inboxes a couple of hours later, but they didn't come from the CBU Lead. Schubert already had photographs of the internals and unlike most pyrotechnic failures where it is next to impossible to figure out what happened from the pieces, this one was obvious. The SDI-X and PSDI-X both used a baffle system to force the flow of gas and combustion byproducts through a torturous particulate trap. The arrangement included a knitted wire cylinder sandwiched between two stamped cups or baffles. Once assembled, an entrance was formed at the top of the inner baffle and an exit at the bottom of the outer baffle that forced the gas longitudinally through the knitted wire rather than radially, as was traditional. The result was a much more efficient filtration system. Three components and the only thing that made them unique between inflators was their height. PSDI-X's were taller, but not by much.

The outer baffle in the photos was wrinkled, bulged outward and in contact with the inflator wall, creating a 360-degree damn that shut down the gas exit path just below the nozzles. Looking over Bob's shoulder at his computer screen I said,

"Houston, we got a problem."

"What is it?" Bob asked impatiently.

"It looks like we put a PSDI-X baffle in an SDI-X. It's the taller of the two and if the station processed it, which it never should have, that's exactly what it would look like."

"I see it," Bob said shaking his head. "That wrinkle in the outer baffle is too uniform to have happened after the rupture. We made it like that, and the gas had nowhere to go."

"Yep and somebody lost an eye," I said. "We need to get down to that SDI-X line right now and see if it will process a PSDI-X baffle."

"And it's GM again," Bob winced, sounding like he had been punched in the gut. "We just put the PDP issue in our rear-view mirror."

Apud walked into the conversation halfway through but caught enough of it to know what to do next. He picked up the phone and asked one of his technicians to meet us at the SDI-X line with a few of the taller PSDI-X baffles. Before he raced out of the room ahead of us, I reminded him to have the wrong baffles marked with red indelible ink. We didn't want to be adding to the problem.

When Bob and I arrived at the station, Apud handed me the taller baffle. I had the honor. It fit nicely into the fixture bolted to the upper press ram and a vacuum instantly kicked on to hold it in place. I rested my hands on the palm buttons and once Apud nodded his approval, I pressed down firmly. Cameras verified part presence and a probe touched off on the baffle, measuring its height, but instead of sounding an alarm and locking the press out, the station drove to a prescribed height, and created a catastrophic defect. There was nothing stopping me from passing the part to the next station, where it would be one step closer to becoming a bomb. I spun around and said,

"That's root cause. Containment is going to be another story. Apud, please have this part x-rayed, sectioned and brought up to Bob's office. See you up there"

I knew the poke-yoke would fail before we got out to the station. The uniformity in the baffle's wrinkle was a dead giveaway. To me, how we had let this happen was less of a concern now than containment. The station would be fixed within the hour, but there was no telling how long its defenses had been down. Everything was suspect and if we couldn't guarantee the correct baffle was used, it all had to come back.

The failure of the station's error-proofing was only half of the breakdown. The traceability system should have also locked the wrong baffle out. When a lot was exhausted, and the line needed replenishment, the material handlers were supposed to input the part number and new lot number into the station's logic before restarting production. But that didn't happen. It had become too much of a routine and the material handler only looked at the box label for the lot number and input the part number from memory. All systems failed, leaving us with little to go on to detect a component inside a finished inflator that was only grams heavier than it was supposed to be.

We moved the discussion up to Phillion's office. Apud met us there shortly after carrying the sectioned SDI-X. It was an exact match to the Cruze photos and confirmation of what we had already surmised. He also had two of our best IT and traceability engineers with him. All the SDI-X assembly operations included a pre- and post-weight measurement and with this, we had the potential to detect an incorrect baffle. But the baffle wasn't the only part being added between measurements. There was a cushion as well, and with all the tolerances, we weren't sure we had the fidelity to differentiate. The mathematicians would have to settle that. In the meantime, we had GM to get ready for. They were on their way to Monclova again, and, of course, were not happy.

It was important to have Dave in Monclova for GM. Their engineers spoke highly of his candor, technical know-how, and integrity during the PDP investigation. They trusted him. Dave was a no-bullshit person and GM appreciated that. I was never afraid to put him front and center. The rest of Takata was, though. They weren't big on candor. I walked outside to have a cigarette and give him a call.

"Hey, bud, how have you been?"

"Not good," he answered. "I'm convinced Maurer is out to get me because of my loyalty to you. Twice now he has pulled me into his office with HR to reprimand me for my performance and twice I showed them both emails where I was begging him for something to do! And they still wrote me up!"

"I'm sorry, Dave. I was afraid this would happen. He's retaliating against you. He knows that if your family didn't need you there right now, you would be down here with us. Let's at least get you out of there for a couple of days. GM is coming in next week on the SDI-X rupture and we need you. Can you make it?"

"Yes," he answered, sounding relieved.

"Good! Get your travel arrangements together and I'll send something to Scott about Waldorf. He never mentioned anything about this nonsense to me."

"Yes, sir, and thanks, Kevin. See you next week."

I put the phone down and opened my laptop. I used e-mail very sparingly and never in anger since I stopped drinking, but this pissed me off. I typed out an e-mail to Scott. I wanted to go on record. Steve was retaliating against one of Takata's best inflator engineers just because he could. An engineer that just helped drag Takata's ass out of the swamp. I stayed professional, but I got my point across because Scott called less than an hour after I hit the send button.

"Calm down," he said. "Why do you let Steve spin you up like that?"

"He can screw with me all day long, Scott, but he needs to stop with McCormick right now. Please do something about it."

"I'll see what I can do. I can try to move him into our organization, but Heiko and Claus will put up a fight. Outside of that, I'm not sure what I can do."

"Put up a fight?" I asked incredulously. "It's Heiko and Claus who are letting him die on the vine."

"I'll see what I can do, Kevin," he repeated, clearly exasperated with me.

"Thank you, Scott. Please do. I care about Dave."

It was a Friday and I was spending another weekend in Monclova. It seemed a waste to Bob and me to spend as much time on an airplane in a week as in the plant, so we switched to two-week stints. The weekends were wearing on me and I asked Dave if he would come in on Sunday, so we could have dinner. It would be good for the both of us. He was off the booze too and looking healthier than ever.

I gave him a big hug as he walked into the hotel lobby, my arms almost able to reach around him now.

"Man, it's good to see you," I said. "You look great!"

"Thanks, you too. Let's go to Los Corrales. I'm starving!"

We had a great meal and I brought him up to speed on the investigation. The next morning, we met for breakfast and took the company van into the plant. GM would be coming in the following day.

"Let's go find Phillion," I said. He wanted to get in early this morning to review the progress made on the GM presentation over the weekend. He's probably down in the new office area, which I don't think you've seen yet. You will love it. It's right next to the production lines."

The team was in a conference room right off Bob's office, adding the last and most important slides to the presentation. The baffle weight analysis had just come back positive, indicating that the press station's weight measurements could be used to detect an incorrect assembly. That was a great relief and the mood of the participants showed it. Tomorrow, they would be able to assure GM that they understood root cause, had enacted machine fixes to prevent a reoccurrence and had an algorithm that could fence the recall based on tare weights. We wouldn't have the numbers available yet, but as far as failure investigations go, this one was a slam dunk.

The meeting went as well as could be expected. We were prepared, but that didn't stop the barrage of deserved and pointed questions that persisted throughout.

"What does your design failure mode analysis (DFMEA) say will happen if an SDI-X is assembled with a PSDI-X baffle?" the lead GM engineer asked.

"It says it will blow up, sir," Dave responded without skipping a beat.

"Then why doesn't the process failure mode analysis (PFMEA) say that? I'm looking right at it and don't see it. I agree the DFMEA says it's a potential catastrophic defect, but if that doesn't transfer to the PFMEA, why bother? How were you ever going to ensure a robust machine design?"

"We had a poke yoke in place, but it didn't work, sir," one of the manufacturing engineers spoke up. Dave and I both cringed. He was lured into the trap and the hammer was about to drop.

"That's not what I asked," he said, becoming irritated. "I asked why the potential defect was not in your PFMEA. If you had simply transferred it from the DFMEA, it would have triggered an inspection point in your control plan, which would have forced you to challenge the station daily with a known bad part. PDP was a breakdown of your quality assurance system. This is a breakdown of your quality engineering system. I want to see two documents. Your Quality Manual and the equipment specification that was used to build the machine."

Ouch! The Quality Manual was easy to produce. Takata just didn't follow it. The equipment specification didn't exist. Monclova wasn't using them. It took GM all of ten minutes to identify two critical systemic breakdowns. Engineering used the appropriate vehicle to warn of a potential catastrophic defect, but Monclova never transferred the information to their documentation. They acknowledged it, modified an existing machine to incorporate error proofing, but never documented it. There never was an equipment specification, and challenging the station never made it to the daily check-list or preventive maintenance schedule. The poke yoke literally didn't exist. A complete breakdown of Takata's quality system. Again.

GM could have been much harder on us than they were. My God, we deserved it, but they appreciated the long hours we had put in ahead of time and having Dave there helped soften the blow. That didn't make the Monclova staff feel any better. Yesterday's sense of relief was replaced with frustration and embarrassment again. They were clearly overworked and stretched to the limits. After the meeting broke up and it was just Bob and I left in the room, they vented.

"Why did you give us two parts that look exactly the same and if we mixed them up it would cause an inflator to explode? That's just an accident waiting to happen."

I let that sink in and said, "Point taken. We can both do better, and I will reinforce that with my folks, but first we must put the recall list together and not just for GM. That line also ran product for our Japanese customers and their CBUs have already been notified that they too may be facing a recall. Every inflator processed by that station must be run through the algorithm and we have to move quickly."

They were so deflated, so afraid of losing the sense of normalcy that was just returning to their lives. Weekends with the family was supposed to be a right, not a privilege.

"Come on, guys, there's no quitting now," I said. "Someone was seriously injured, and we can't forget that, but we must keep moving forward. I will help you with the FMEAs and equipment specifications. That's part of my new role and we have several assembly line acquisitions coming up that we can create a standard for. Real work, with a direct impact on our future. Let's just get through this first."

We assembled the Cruze recall list first, finding only a small population of defective parts, and after turning that over to the GM CBU Lead, we continued on with our Japanese customers. When we informed those CBUs of their recall counts, the reaction we received in return was quite unsettling.

Instead of the expected disappointment followed by acknowledgement, and a commitment to act, we got serious push-back. Demands of more proof. Smoke screens and stalling. We answered all their questions, went down every rabbit hole they could find and eventually ran out the game clock. With no pristine dial table to point to, they had to acquiesce. Their parts went through the same station as GM's.

The SDI-X issue was a disappointing setback. We couldn't afford to give up any more of the hard-fought ground we had won, but two recalls in a matter of months with a PSDI fatality sandwiched in between had us fighting a headwind. We needed to rally. We were still hand-to-mouth with deliveries but were slowly replenishing safety stocks and had a line of sight to regular work schedules. We immediately undertook an audit of all the production lines to assess our error-proofing effectiveness. We had to stop getting in our own way.

We split up into teams and set to work. Controls plans were aligned to FMEAs and every poke yoke on every line was inspected for presence and challenged for robustness. Training reemphasized the importance of startup checklists that included testing of error proofing systems. We got out of our own way but found something unsettling in the process.

Typically, as lines are added to cover increased volumes, they are purchased to the same standards as their predecessor, and usually include some modest upgrades. But each successive inflator line Takata was bringing in was different and of lesser quality. Not startlingly different but enough to notice, and if you knew what you were looking for, enough to investigate further. I found Bob crawling all over another line and motioned for him to come over and said,

"I'm uneasy with some of the things I am seeing, Bob. The quality of some of the equipment on the floor is not what I would expect."

"Yeah, I hear you," he said. "Let's keep going and compare notes afterwards, but I have a growing concern with both Carlos and Mario. Things have really deteriorated around here."

Phillion Cleans House

Carlos Iruegas was not cutting it and even though his promotion floored many of us, I could see how some thought the move made sense. Carlos was the inflator quality manager. Who better to deliver a safe, world-class product? Right? But Carlos had been operating in the grey zone for far too long. He and his 'just a *skosh* out' mentality were the wrong choice for the job and Mario Ramos, his manufacturing engineering manager, was compounding the situation.

The PDP, the off-site warehouse, and the SDI-X debacles all occurred under Carlos' and Mario's watch. They were clearly in over their heads. The same dysfunction that arrested Armada had metastasized in Monclova. Armada became useless, but Monclova became dangerous. And devious.

Mario was responsible for Monclova's assembly lines. He was the first person Bob and I sought out after we compared audit notes.

"Mario, do you have a minute?" I asked him as Bob and I approached his desk.

"Sure," he said. "What's up?"

"You know we've been auditing the lines in wake of the SDI-X incident, right?"

He nodded in affirmation.

"Well, we noticed a few stations on the most recent X-series lines that seem to be of lesser quality. There are also stations across from the line that are not fully assembled, and your team is busy finishing them up. Can you explain why this is?"

Mario was rattled. He took a deep breath and few seconds to collect his thoughts and answered,

"We have been experimenting with some local suppliers. So far, we have been satisfied with their work."

"What about the half-assembled stations?" I pressed.

"I am not sure about those," he said. "It's lunchtime now and I must leave the plant. Let me get the details and I'll send you an e-mail."

I could see the steam rising from the top of Bob's head, and knew we needed to let Mario go to lunch. I grabbed Bob's arm and said, "Okay, Mario. Thank you. We will wait to hear back from you."

Bob pulled out his cell phone as we walked away and asked Apud to meet us in his office in five minutes. He didn't call Carlos.

"Apud, what do you know about Mario's use of local suppliers for some of our simpler assembly stations?" Bob asked him as soon as the door was shut.

"Ahhhh! We hate it!" he said quickly. "The stations are being delivered with poor controls and poke yokes, and my team is having to fix them after they are installed. We are supposed to be advancing manufacturing technology, not cleaning up Mario's mess!"

"Why aren't Mario's people putting the machines right?" I asked him. "Why are your guys involved?"

"Mario's guys!" he said incredulously. "They're too busy finishing the half-assembled stations across from the SDI-X line."

"Where the hell are the half-assembled stations coming from?" Bob then asked. The conversation was so surreal.

"A local supplier that Mario is working with, but I don't know much more than that," Apud answered. "Do you want me to do some digging?"

"Yes!" We both exclaimed at the same time.

Mario thrived under the status quo. Monclova was not a world class manufacturing outfit. Not by a long shot and that was largely due to his indifference. Plant managers like Gutierrez and Iruegas created a perfect environment for him. Neither one challenged him, and he showed no incentive to improve. One thing Mario did do well though was to stay in his lane. He did just enough to get by and was not a troublemaker, at least not until the damn re-organization. He never did get back to us that afternoon and I couldn't find him anywhere in the plant before we left.

The next morning Apud brought in tacos for breakfast. I loved those days. Everyone would file in and out of Bob's office until the tacos were demolished, and this time was no different. When it was just the three of us left, Apud closed the door and said,

"I did some digging like you asked and what I found is not good."

"What is it?" Bob asked, afraid of the answer.

"We need to take a short drive to one of Mario's local equipment suppliers," he said. "I can't put it into words."

Bob just shook his head and said, "I can't make it right now, Apud. Can you take this one, Kevin?"

"Sure thing, Bob. Let's go, Apud."

I could understand why Monclova would want to source a few less-complex machines in Mexico. There was enough experience at the plant and in the surrounding community to make it a viable, cost-effective approach. It was also nice to have the vendor nearby when the equipment faltered. There were pros and cons as with any sourcing strategy, but Mario was flying solo. His efforts were not part of an overarching sourcing strategy, and it was confusing.

A good example of a less-complex assembly machine is a press station, like the one that was responsible for the GM Cruze recall. The operator places one part in a fixture secured to the press ram and another in a nest below. Both hands depress palm buttons and the pneumatic press seats the two parts. The whole thing takes only about 15 seconds, but a great deal goes on behind the scenes in that short time. Critical features are checked for presence and orientation. Stroke distance, force, and dwell time are controlled, measured and recorded; their values compared to standards as the operation progresses. Finished dimensions and characteristics are verified before the part is released to the next operation. If a monitored feature is outside of its limit at any point in the operation, the machine locks the part and prevents it from being passed to the next operation. And that's a simple machine.

As we piled into Apud's pickup I said, "I just don't get it. Why would Mario source a new equipment supplier in Mexico without asking us to come take a look first?"

"You'll see," he answered me.

Ten minutes later we turned off the main highway and down a dirt road, kicking up a huge cloud of dust. After a few hundred yards he brought the vehicle to a sudden stop.

"Here we are." He motioned for me to look.

As the dust cloud subsided I could make out a small, rectangular, cinderblock building with a door, a couple of windows and a tin roof. We were in the middle of nowhere.

"This is it?!" I said, glancing around.

"Unfortunately."

We got out of the truck and made our way over to the only entrance. It was a stout, steel door with a sliding metal plate that served as a peep-hole. Apud banged on the door a few times until the plate slid open and two eyes peered out to see who it was. I felt like I was in Oz, requesting an audience with the Wizard. The door opened slowly, and we found ourselves standing face to face with one of Mario's former employees. Being an extremely awkward situation for him, he just stepped aside. There was nothing in the cement-floored building except five assembly stations in various stages of completion pushed up against one of the walls. We walked over to them and I poked around each one, politely asking our former colleague a few questions. There was no sense causing a scene here. After a few minutes, I asked Apud to take me back to the plant. I'd seen enough.

Mario started out simple, sourcing only repeat assembly stations to local suppliers. He would let them come into the plant to look at the original equipment and documentation, and even video the operation, so they could make their own knock-offs. Shady to begin with, but things got murkier when he began sourcing stations to the supplier in the block hut who would deliver them less than fully complete. Nothing glaring, but some controls, software, palm buttons and other small items would be left off. Mario would then have his people complete the machines, program them, and tie them into the traceability system. Their gig was up. Bob acted swiftly and decisively, dismissing Carlos and Mario just days later and the sense of relief among the troops was palpable. The last of the cancer had been ripped out. The test lab was healing, the welders were improving, and the 'swamp had been drained'. Phillion was loud and proud, and the plant was on the road to full recovery.

16

One of Us Heals

BOB TURNED his attention to installing new, trustworthy plant leadership and Scott filled the interview pipeline with some of his best leaders. Within weeks the Plant Manager and Manufacturing Manager positions were filled. We briefly considered Apud and he would have made a good Plant Manager, but the organization needed a clean reboot. The lack of inflator experience heading our way was not a concern. That's what I was there for. Bob and I wanted process discipline and a fresh set of eyes.

"Nacho" Salinas, a seatbelt hotshot, was announced as the new Plant Manager and I took another of Scott's stars under my wing to run Mario's group. Nacho quickly proved to be a great leader and an even better engineer. A tooling whiz steeped in tiny, intricate buckle parts, he had me following him around like a little puppy, eager to learn new tricks. Bob and I were already playing well off of each other and Nacho made the perfect third leg.

The three Musketeers. We were going to have to stick together to pull this off. The inflator business had dug itself a deep hole. The PDP and SDI-X recalls, combined with what we tossed out of the swamp, had Monclova projecting a $25M fiscal year loss. We had to turn things around and fast. Whatever we needed, Scott provided. What a difference that made.

Nacho took up the office next to Bob's and I stayed in the bullpen with Apud's team, and we got busy. Mario's replacement was attached to my hip.

"What a fine mess you've landed yourself in!" I joked, poking my head into Nacho's office on the way in one morning. "What did you do so terribly wrong to get this assignment?"

"I haven't figured that out yet," he said. "Are you going for your morning walk?"

"Yes, you want to join me? I could use some company. Bob's not coming down until tomorrow."

"Love to!" he replied, jumping out of his seat.

Nacho was full of energy and even more full of ideas. It was comforting to see the plant in such capable hands again. I thought back fondly to 2006 and the three months Luis and I locked arms to help lift the devastated plant from the ashes. Nacho snapped me back to reality.

"See how we can change this shorting clip fixture out in less than one minute now. This changeover used to have the line down for an hour!"

He was proud of the changes that were rapidly occurring and as I watched him swap the fixture out, I knew he was the right man for the job. But would he be enough? The people of Monclova were so tired, and I knew he shared my concern.

"Scott asked me to go with him to Monterey next week for the board meeting. He's going to present our recovery plan," I said.

"That's great, Kevin," he replied, somewhat impressed.

"Yeah, he will have an audience with both Shige and Stocker and he is intent on getting us some relief. We see it as well, Nacho. They need a break."

"Thank you, we are nothing without them," he said. "Who is Stocker? I don't think I've heard that name before."

"Stephan Stocker was the President of Bosch's Japanese arm before Shige hired him about a year ago to take over as President. Shige is still the Chief Executive, but its significant in that Stocker is the first foreigner to hold that position. I was told he was brought in to increase the pace of Takata's overseas growth."

"Interesting," he said quickly filing it. "Get us some help, Kevin, and this place will soar."

The trip to Monterey with Scott was memorable. I'd always admired his swagger and self-confidence, but when I saw he was a little nervous settling into his seat next to Stocker, I knew we were in the big leagues. He was impressive though, his passion on full display as he laid out our recovery plan, and he wasted no time getting to what was ailing us.

"The inflator organization is demoralized. They have been going non-stop for months and feel as if they have nothing to show for it. Bob and Kevin have stabilized the situation and laid a foundation to build from, but the next stage of the recovery is going to require significant capital investment in terms of equipment and people. If we don't act now, we will lose the hard-fought gains that have been made."

That perked the ears of one of the board's financial analysts, who interrupted by saying, "Why can't you continue at the current staffing levels? You've avoided impacting customers to date, and we don't see any interruptions on the horizon."

Scott was prepared for that.

"Let me explain something to you about Mexico," he said. "It's God, family, and then everything else. We have flipped that upside down in Monclova and that is causing unforced errors. It has to stop. Our people are our greatest asset!"

"Yes!" I said under my breath.

That was it. Shige waved off the financial analyst and told Scott to do whatever was necessary to continue the progress. Our plan had us returning to profitability in a year and we were determined to beat that. At the end of the meeting I found Scott to shake his hand.

"Great job!" I said to him. "Thanks for standing tall."

"Thank you, Kevin. Listen, Shige has decided to divert to Monclova. He would like for you and Bob to show him around firsthand. Want to hitch a ride back on his plane with us?"

"Hell, yes!" I exclaimed.

As I gazed out at the rugged desert landscape 30,000 feet below, it was just Scott, Shige and me on board. Shige was tired and fell asleep shortly after takeoff and Scott was busy catching up on e-mails. Me, I was just enjoying the moment. Sober for a couple of months now, I felt a sudden rush of euphoria. A fleeting but wonderful moment that happens to some in the first months of sobriety, and when it does you hold onto it for dear life. It reminds you why you are not drinking anymore.

The desert below was beautiful from my window seat and I smiled. Al and Steve would be furious. This was not the seat they had assigned me. They were hoping for the one with the drink cart permanently parked in front of it.

The next couple of months were some of my best at Takata and with each passing day life and work were becoming more enjoyable. I reordered my priorities, placing God before everything else, and with that done, there was plenty of time for the rest. I bought myself a camera to go along with my passion to walk and the combination of those two things still burn brightly in me today.

At work, I immersed myself in reversing Monclova's decline and staying abreast of Armada's activities. I was full-time in Monclova, travelling home on weekends or for an occasional week-long break. I had no direct reports in Monclova. I let those all flow to Nacho. Heiko was dotted lined to me and we kept in touch, but if I needed anything from Armada, McCormick was still unhappily there.

Scott put me in a sweeper role, asking me to guide equipment strategy, mentor the plant engineers and keep tabs on inflator engineering. It was a great job and Bob and I were making a real difference. The travel and time away from family were tough, but Sandy and I had hopes to get out of the cold and head south to San Antonio soon enough.

Nacho was also settling in nicely as Plant Manager and a sense of normalcy was returning to Monclova. Bob and I trusted him implicitly, and with Scott's support, he continued to surround himself with his seatbelt friends. They were seeding deeper into the inflator organization and their culture was contagious. Our plan was taking hold. Nacho and Bob worked on getting people's lives back to normal, and I worked on the lines. We immediately developed equipment specifications, and although initially basic, they were an important first step that provided Nacho's hungry engineers with plenty to chew on.

Establishing a network of reliable and trusted equipment suppliers was next. Automation in the Monclova plant was still in its infancy. Only the stored gas inflator lines incorporated some turn-key operations. That was about to change. When you witness the CEO wave his hand and say, 'Do what you need to do,' you take advantage of it. Monclova was reeling from quality issues and automation produced fewer defects. To me, 'do what you need to do' meant more automation. I focused Monclova on vendors that had experience in both turn-key operations and lean cells and started to blend the two as made sense.

Nothing but airports and hotels. Between my home base in Michigan, the plants, and new equipment suppliers, I was constantly on the move. Thirty pounds lighter and like the Energizer Bunny, I was a force to be reckoned with. A force Steve Maurer wanted no part of when I would drop in on Armada to check in on Dave and catch up with Engineering. I still stayed clear of his office but would occasionally run into him in the hallways when his bladder forced him out of hiding.

"Kevin, you look different," he said on one occasion.

"Why thank you, Steve," I replied.

I wanted to say, "Of course, I look different. I'm one less pint of Jack a night different. Notice the fire in my eyes. It's not quenched anymore," but thought better of it. There was something more important to talk about and since there was no one nearby I pressed him.

"Steve, what is Takata doing about the defective Toyota and Nissan PDPs that still need to be recalled? I told you what Yoshimura said – that Takata can't stomach another recall. What is Takata doing about that?"

"Yes, I spoke to Rob like I told you. He said he would call Japan."

"I am your Deputy, Steve, and I am telling you those parts are dangerous and need to be recalled."

"Yes, I'll give Rob another call," he said, pushing by me.

And there it was again. Absolution at the shores of the Pacific. Steve's refusal to do anything but pass it up the chain didn't stop me from coming back to it, though. His answer to that was to stop communicating entirely. He ceased answering any of Phillion's emails as well. He turned Monclova off.

The communication breakdown bothered Bob so much that he flew to Armada to see what the problem was, but Steve wouldn't make time for him. He told him he was swamped and would try do better, but he never did. Instead, he resorted to speaking only with Scott, putting his petulance on full display. It was no bother to us. I had the respect and loyalty of his people and unfettered access to them. He only had one of those.

The Recalls Win Out

Progress in Monclova was proceeding far more quickly than anyone had anticipated. The epicenter truly was the test department, and once it was firing on all cylinders, the Mexicans were off to the races. Bob and I thought it would take a year to return to profitability, but once unshackled, the team strung together a comeback the likes of which I had never seen before. We were coming up on the end of the fiscal year, April 2014, and were almost out of the red, demolishing the recovery estimate.

But just as we were hitting our stride, the recall that was always in the back of our minds, moved front and center. There had been three years between the second PSDI fatality and the third back in September, but that lull in activity was about to end. In May 2014, Takata learned of six new field ruptures, involving both driver and passenger inflators, and after reading another depressing newspaper article, I picked up the phone and called Scott to gauge his concern.

"Scott, how are you?"

"I'm doing great!" he said. "What's on your mind?"

"I just read a really disturbing article about the recalls. Do you really think we are going to weather this storm? I am not so sure." I was serious.

He did his best to keep my spirits up, "You can't believe everything you read. That's just some web article. We'll get through this, Kevin, and you know better than anybody, it's a waste of time to worry about things you can't control."

"Yeah, I guess you're right, Scott. I'll talk to you soon."

Not the shot in the arm I was after, but what else could he really say? The bad news was mounting at an alarming rate. A month later, Honda, Mazda and Nissan expanded their recalls, adding nearly three million airbags worldwide. Separately, the same three automakers plus BMW, Chrysler and Ford announced that they would begin regional recalls in high-humidity areas, like Florida and Puerto Rico. This wasn't background noise anymore and we were being called to engage.

Bob stuck his head out of his office door and yelled,

"Hey, Fitz, Scott's on the phone and he needs to talk to us."

As soon as I closed the door behind me, Scott started. "Kevin, I was just relaying to Bob what an excellent job the team has been doing soldiering on with the recall in the background, but we can't ignore the elephant in the room any longer. The numbers just announced by Honda and Nissan are upward of three million inflators. We don't have that kind of capacity and need ideas in a hurry."

"Understood, Scott," Bob said. "We'll put a plan together. Concurrently, we'll take inventory of what stations we have in storage that can be dusted off."

"Good, thanks guys," Scott said. "Today's Wednesday, let's circle back on Friday."

The equipment Bob was considering was a bunch of old mothballed stations from PSDI lines gone by. Since the automakers had no immediate options, the recalled PSDIs were simply being replaced with new ones. That may sound crazy, but it was really the only rational plan. The oldest inflators were the most dangerous and replacing a potentially lethal PSDI, with a new one would provide the same crash protection while a permanent fix could be developed, even if that meant recalling the same cars again.

The PSDI inflator had only a few operations that required custom stations. How many of those we could find would determine the number of lines we could cobble together. We needed two above what was already on the floor.

"I'll grab Apud and a couple of his guys and start searching the warehouses," I said.

"Thanks, Kevin," he replied, sounding worn out.

"I'm sorry, Bob. I know you and Nacho just got everybody back on normal shifts," I said. "They were finally enjoying evenings and weekends with their families and we're about to blow it all up again."

"This job is always asking for too much," he said, grabbing his safety glasses. He was heading for the noisy cadence of the factory floor, a place where he could get lost for a while.

When we finished the search, we only had enough equipment for one more PSDI line. A second would require drawings and machine specifications and none of that existed. It would take a year minimum and we didn't have that kind of time. We called Scott as soon as we had the inventory.

"Doesn't look good, Scott," I said. "At best we can put one line together. We can increase its output with some redundant stations, but only slightly."

"We have to have another line," he said. "The small increase in output from the extra stations won't close the gap."

Bob spoke up. "We need Maurer to investigate adapting a different production inflator to the PSDI module. One Takata has spare capacity for."

"Bob's right," I said. "The PSDI-5 has the same basic fit. Our lines are all accounted for, but Freiberg has excess capacity. They've been migrating their dual stage inflators to single stage for some time now."

"Great idea, guys! I'll call Steve," Scott said.

"Hey, one more thing before you go, Scott," I said. "Please impress upon Steve that a replacement PSDI-5 must include 13X desiccant. If he has any questions, have him talk to Schubert."

"Understood. Does that impact anything?"

"Yes, it does," I said. "There is only one PSDI-5 configuration with 13X and it is made here in Monclova for Nissan. It was the result of the PSDI-X connector ejection issue, but I won't bore you with those details. What I will tell you is that 13X takes that inflator from exploding after environments to behaving nicely and we can't, in good conscience, put any new PSDI-5s in the field without it."

"I wasn't aware," Scott said. "Why would that be a problem for Freiberg?"

"Their lines are fully automated and don't include a desiccant install station. Watch what happens when you ask for cost and schedule to add one. I guarantee you it won't be another operator with a spoon," I said.

"Now I understand. Thanks, Kevin."

About a week later the e-mails from Japan started. "Why do replacement inflators need desiccant? We are shipping PSDIs as replacement inflators and they don't include desiccant! Germany is saying it will take six months to modify their lines and we can't tell Honda that!"

At first Maurer held the line, but having no ideology or conviction, it wasn't long before he caved to the pressure and had Heiko distribute an e-mail stating engineering's official position. The PSDI-5 replacement inflators would not require any desiccant and production in Freiberg could commence immediately. It was exactly what Japan wanted to hear.

I was having none of it. Basta. I hit the reply all button, stared at my screen and thought carefully about what I was going to say. I settled on three words.

"Please see attached."

Two reports. The Nissan PSDI-5 failure analysis and the Nissan PSDI-5 with 13X process validation. The first showed the inflator's propellant tablets turned to marshmallows by Nissan's environmental exposure. The second report showed 13X stopped it. The contrast could not have been starker.

I waited for a response. Days went by, but nothing. Scott never asked me about that e-mail. Nobody did. The discussion ended abruptly and modifications to the Freiberg's lines began almost immediately. Honda was told it would take four months and not six. Somebody listened.

With Freiberg modifying their spare PSDI-5 capacity, Monclova cobbled together their one PSDI line and started producing replacement inflators. Despite the noise, Bob and Nacho soon had the plant back in the green and Apud and I kept busy continuously improving the operation. But something wasn't right. It was the other elephant in the room.

The inflator organization had become the company's odd man out. Scott oversaw Monclova, but Christophe still had the Freiberg and China plants and Maurer was completely adrift. Bob and I knew the organization was dysfunctional and that it had to change, but to what? That question drove us crazy and then, towards the end of the summer, rumors of another inflator reorganization surfaced. Crazy rumors. Some not even worth entertaining, I thought to myself, until I walked into Bob's office as he was hanging up the phone and he looked sickened.

"What's wrong, bud?"

"That was Scott," he said. "He's coming down next week and wants to have dinner with us. He has some information on the new inflator organization."

"Okay, so why do you look like you just saw a ghost?" I asked him as he stood and closed the door.

"He said Stocker is seriously considering setting up the inflator organization as a standalone entity, just like Christophe wanted, except Shin Tanaka will be the one to run it," Bob said.

"That's impossible..." I was completely stunned.

"I can't believe it either. Shin Tanaka. After all we've given this place," he said, shaking his head.

"Let's take a deep breath," I said. "They can't put Shin in that position. Not after what I told Takata's lawyers in 2009. I'll explain that to Scott."

The following Monday the three of us met for dinner at Scott's favorite Monclova restaurant. It was a great meal with good company and after we were finished eating, Scott relayed what he knew of the pending organizational changes. It was confirmation of our worst nightmare.

I went first. Shin was my sworn enemy, not Bob's.

"No way, Scott. Shin in charge is not workable under any circumstances," I said intently. "You know I spoke with Takata's lawyers about what he and Hideo did in LaGrange back in 2000. He should be charged with a felony, not with this awesome responsibility, and I certainly cannot be asked to report to him!"

"Kevin is not the only one who feels that way, Scott," Bob interjected. "No one is threatening to quit on the spot, but if this happens, it will reverberate."

"What's going on with Takata, Scott?" I pressed further. "Just last month Al Bernat is picked to lead a newly formed Product Safety Group, Frank Roe has reportedly resurfaced and now Shin will sit atop the inflator group! Sounds to me like they're putting the old band back together."

"I don't know, Kevin," Scott said, "but that was one helluva movie."

"What about us, Scott?" Bob asked not allowing for any levity yet. "Kevin and I just pulled Monclova out of a nosedive and this is the thanks we get? Shige and Stocker raved about the place on their last visit. Why are we not being considered?"

"That's a good question, Bob," he said. "And I don't know what happened in LaGrange, Kevin, but I've heard the stories. I'm meeting with Stocker next week in Japan and will communicate your concerns directly. Look, I don't like this one bit either. I love working with you guys and don't appreciate being told to go back to my corner."

"It's bad no matter how you slice it, Scott," I said. "Once Stocker learns of Shin's past, I'm sure he will change his mind. He has to. I'll be home next week and at our new initiator plant in Germany the following week. Please keep me informed. I don't need to know who will be in charge, Scott, just that it's not Shin."

"Okay, I'll let you both know how my discussion with Stocker goes," he said paying the bill. "No sense in talking about it any further until then."

Here We Go Again

What to think? How could one come away from that dinner with anything but confusion, fear and disgust? The emotions were endless. Shin Tanaka! They couldn't be serious. Was unmasking the PSDI-5 root cause report a little bit too much truth for those near the top? Did they want me silenced? Back on the sauce? I wasn't as much of a pain in the ass floating at the bottom of a bottle. How else could it be explained? Why hadn't we heard anything from Scott about his meeting with Stocker? All these questions and more raced through my mind on the long flight to Frankfurt, Germany.

I was travelling with a colleague of mine from Armada. A fine young man whom I had hired many years earlier. We were visiting a plant that Takata had recently purchased in the town of Molan. After an uneventful flight, I wheeled my black carry-on through customs, and we took a taxi to our hotel. Arriving in the room, I unpacked my bag and sat at the end of the bed. It was a typically small German hotel room. Still nothing from, Scott, was all I could think as I changed into shorts and a t-shirt, grabbed my camera and went out for a walk around the city.

The day was slightly brisk, and I meandered around the town snapping pictures. I tried to force my mind to something other than Takata, but it was impossible. What would Sandy and I do if they resorted to the unthinkable again? Stop, I told myself and scanned the old town in search of my next shot. "Beautiful," I whispered, as I lifted the camera and just as I was about to squeeze the shutter, I felt my phone vibrate with a stream of incoming e-mails. I reached for it and scanned through them until one caught my attention, with the subject line:

"IGO Organizational Announcement"

Surprised, I opened this one immediately. IGO stood for Inflator Global Organization. They wouldn't make a formal announcement regarding that before Scott talked to us about his discussion with Stocker, would they?

As I read the e-mail, the answer was quickly a definitive yes. The new leader of the IGO would be Shinichi Tanaka, and I was expected to report to him.

I stopped in my tracks in the middle of the sidewalk, struggling to comprehend the news. My body tensed and my stomach became tight. This was the proverbial 'punch to the gut.' I stared at the e-mail, lifting one hand to my forehead and across my hair. My initial shock quickly transformed into anger and I started back for the hotel at a furious pace. This was no longer a what if. The questions that had been racing through my mind, now needed answers.

They did it to me again! I thought. I told Scott I wouldn't work for Shin!

I slammed the door open to my room, sat down on the end of the bed and banged out a text to Scott:

"This isn't going to work for me. We need to talk."

I set the phone down on the night-stand and closed the door. I was fretting and pacing the room, my mind whirling about in an agitated storm. My whole day had been turned upside down, but I was certain of one thing. I would never work for Shin Tanaka.

I checked for a text from Scott, but nothing yet, so I called Sandy. She answered and could instantly hear the edge on my voice and knew something was wrong. I said to her matter-of-factly,

"Well, it happened, baby. We're done. I'm coming home and not even going back into the office."

"Just come home, Kev." She replied instantly. She knew.

Scott called later in the day,

"I can understand your frustration and anger, but you need to calm down," he said, trying to reassure me that the move was purely organizational, and that I would still have authority to fix things.

"That's bullshit, Scott, and you know it!" I said angrily. "I told you I would quit on the spot and I wasn't kidding. What the hell did Stocker say?"

There was a long pause and then Scott answered, "He said he knew about what happened with Shin in LaGrange in 2000, and he said that people change and we need to move on."

"Are you fucking kidding me, Scott? He is a felon and Takata is asking me to work for him!" I shouted through the phone.

"I tried, Kevin. I relayed your message directly and forcefully. Stocker wasn't interested. Sleep on it and we can talk in the morning."

I was even more agitated after the call. People change! Yes, I am keenly aware of that. I changed. I stopped drinking and ordered my life. That kind of change deserves reward, not the kind where you decide to stop lying after it results in people dying. I realized in that moment what this meant and what I needed to do. Takata would never do the right thing. Never.

They either change this or I quit, I thought. I'll fight them all the way.

Could I quit? I wondered as I lay down and drifted off to sleep.

The next morning, following a sleepless night, I knew my path. My mind was set. Joining colleagues, we made our way to the new plant. Before the tour started, I sat down, opened my laptop, and typed an e-mail to Ryan Brueckner, the Vice-President of Human Resources for Takata North America, that read:

> **"Please be advised that I respectively decline the position I was assigned in the new Inflator Global Organization. I can be available the latter part of next week to discuss further and determine what alternative employment options, if any, I have left with Takata. Thank you for your time."**

After the plant tour and discussions, I checked e-mails in hopes of finding a response from HR. Crickets. But something did come in from my new boss, Shin. It was sent to me and the other managers that would report to him in the new organization, with a subject line of:

"IGO Kick off meeting announcement"

The e-mail informed the new team to make travel arrangements for meetings to kick-off the new organization and discuss strategy and responsibilities. The meeting was scheduled for October 13, less than two weeks away.

I laughed and forwarded the invite to Brueckner with a simple add:

"As information, I will not be attending this meeting."

Before the group left the plant for the hotels nearer the airport, we all stood on the steps of the entrance to say our good-byes. I remember the day being overcast and chilly. I waited until the crowd dispersed and it was only me and Heiko left. He had also seen the IGO announcement e-mail, and as I shook his hand for the last time I said,

"I'm not going to take the job in the new organization. We should say our final good-byes now. I wish you a great life, my friend. We have had some amazing times together. It's been a pleasure to work with you."

He looked at me in disbelief, smiled and thought about it for a moment, and then said lightly,

"I'll see you next time in Armada or Monclova. Have a good trip, Kevin."

Heiko thought I was just being my usual quick-to-react self. He had no idea how dead serious I was.

Choices and Consequences

It was the first week of October when I returned to Detroit to nice weather and family. I told Brueckner I could meet Thursday or Friday the following week. I wanted them to sweat a little and I had no intention of going into work – ever again – or until this was fixed. I turned off my phone for the most part, stayed at home, and tried to relax.

Sandy and I talked over what we should do and could do. I knew I had to quit. She did too. I had suffered too much for Takata and it had affected us profoundly. There were family pressures too; financial, health, and emotional struggles. Our two oldest were in college and our youngest was close behind. My oldest son was struggling with a debilitating disease that doctors couldn't figure out, taking our once-brilliant piano player, to his knees with crippling pain and stiffness, forcing him to eventually move in with us. We discussed finding a new job all together. Sandy reminded me I was a smart, high-caliber executive, and that I could find something new. It wouldn't be easy, but it could be done.

The week at home passed quickly, and on Thursday, October 9, I drove to the Auburn Hills facility to meet with Ryan. It was a nice morning with sun and rolling clouds, the leaves everywhere beginning to turn. I drove the twenty minutes patiently and pensively, rehearsing what I wanted to say. Arriving in the parking lot, I walked up to the front entry and stopped to smoke half a cigarette. Mentally preparing and getting myself slightly worked up, I finished, and opened the doors to give them hell.

Making my way through cubicles of colleagues, I thought this could be the last time here, but I didn't stop to speak with anyone. I walked straight to Ryan's office, stopping a few paces short. It was adjacent to Al's and the sight of his nameplate dredged up some painful memories for me. The campaign he waged against my promotion to Inflator Chief Engineer (and won) and his later rifling of my e-mails and expense reports to twist the knife. It was traumatic and wrong, and I swore to myself right there that Al and Takata were done getting the best of me.

What did Al achieve? The terrible leadership of Maurer and Christophe had made everything worse. Was he just happy to make me miserable?

Karma, I thought. They will all get theirs in due time. They made a mess of everything.

I pondered it all some before going into Brueckner's office. Takata's inflator group was reorganizing again and why? Politics, the same fucking politics that unwound my promotion just two years earlier. It was still poisoning the organization and issues with operations and quality were the inevitable result. And all the while the recalls mounted, sending Takata's liabilities soaring. In August the business forecasted an annual loss of $235 million, and that was now at $340 million. These were serious and difficult times. Stocker was the first non-Japanese President and COO, brought in to steady the listing company. Investors wanted more diversity, a better perspective, and picked him to provide it. Instead, after repeated warnings from Scott, he promotes a felon to take over the global inflator organization.

Stoker was supposed to fix this crap…How much are these people being paid? I thought before bringing my attention back to the meeting. I knocked on Brueckner's door.

It was a typical executive office with a table and chairs in one corner. He was sitting at the table facing me when I walked in. Seeing me, he beckoned me to take a seat at the table across from him, thanked me for coming, and spent a moment on the usual small talk.

I leaned back in the cushioned chair, feeling relaxed but anxious to see what he would say. I wasn't going to speak first.

In his mid-forties with dark black hair, Ryan was new to Takata, less than a year as the Vice-President of Human Resources, responsible for all North America. It was a big job and he seemed to enjoy it. He smiled, looked me in the eye and spoke first,

"We know you have a problem with Shin…"

"Yes. You're asking me to work for a felon." I replied quickly and with an edge.

He shifted uncomfortably in his seat and glanced away. He didn't like my choice of words or the sudden realization that this was going to be hard. I took note.

I wanted to saddle them with the knowledge of who they were

promoting, what he had done, and force them to acknowledge his obvious disqualifications. Force them to put themselves on the line by knowing, and maybe then things would change. I expected the canned corporate response but considered this my opening salvo against a company that had caused me constant stress and was now trying to take my career away.

Brueckner stared blankly at me for a moment and collected himself. He replied carefully,

"We don't know that to be true."

"He will be, you'll see."

"We know you have a problem with him..."

A problem with him?! Are you kidding me? I thought. He had to know. He talked to others before this meeting, and he should know I already voiced my absolute that I would never work for Shin Tanaka.

I replied, "How could Takata put someone in charge of inflators that was responsible for what happened back in 2000?"

I paused, watching to see if it registered, if he gave me a small tell or glanced away to think about what he was supposed to say. It registered, so I continued, raising my voice slightly,

"People have died." I waited a second and then let him have more.

"Shin committed fraud that knowingly put inflators into production vehicles that had exploded during validation testing. I wrote the factual report and made sure that everyone who signed the first fraudulent one knew what really happened. They all ignored it. I talked to lawyers representing Takata twice in 2009 and told them the entire story and who was responsible. They assured me 'things will change and those responsible would be punished.' And now I'm being asked to work for Shin?!"

I let that sink in. He didn't say anything.

"You get it, right? I'm not working for him."

I leaned back into my chair again, but this time he wasn't smiling. Visibly irritated, he shifted the discussion to the job they had in mind for me.

"We understand there may be issues between you and Shin..." He said again, "...so we want you to oversee selecting and qualifying all the inflators Takata purchases from the outside..."

I interrupted him, now unable to contain my steadily rising impatience and annoyance.

"I built these teams! I'm not just going to watch and look over someone's shoulder! My entire time at Takata has been managing departments and launching products and now you're taking that all away from me. You've assigned me to a felon. You've destroyed my career. I don't think you're prepared to seriously discuss this."

I was done with him, another spineless 'yes-man' regurgitating the company line. His job was to defend me, not the felon.

It didn't matter, Takata would reverse the decision, or I would leave. Quitting didn't sound so bad anymore after how many times they had screwed me. I had given it my all, tried to fix the issues and drive some sense into the organization, but they thwarted me at each turn. Things like this moved slowly at Takata. They were tired of my rebellion, conflicts with others, and refusal to toe the line, so they kept passing me over and worse, tormenting me.

Ryan was clearly frustrated with how the conversation was going too, and ended by saying, "I'm not explaining the new position very well. Can you come back and meet with Rob Fisher? He'll be better able to explain."

I agreed to talk to Rob, after all, this was the first salvo, but as I left I told Ryan I was seriously considering separating from the company. What I got was another canned response, telling me 'they hoped that wasn't the case' and that they could 'find a way to retain me.'

I went home and spent another week with the family. Sandy and I didn't have a lawyer yet. It was just the two of us, a little scared and worried, trying not to think too much about Takata.

The week felt like an eternity and I was anxious driving back into Auburn Hills to meet with Rob. We had a friendly relationship and I felt he appreciated what I had done for Takata. I had proven myself plenty of times and saved the company in clutch moments. The night the Monclova plant exploded, I saved countless lives by ordering an immediate plantwide evacuation while others were uncertain. The markers I laid down over the years had to count for something. They certainly did not warrant the position I found myself in.

Walking through the office for what I mused, again, might be my last, I took my time. Still, I talked to no one and was shortly at Rob's office. It was impressive. Decorations, fine-quality items, leather sofas and chairs, and a very nice table made the outer room suited for entertaining customers. There was another room behind a door and that was his office – just as nice. Ryan was waiting to escort me in.

I shook Rob's hand and we exchanged greetings. He got right to the point. The position they wanted me to take, which had some authority, was important to Takata, and they wanted me to stay. Ryan nodded quietly with his hands in his lap as Rob explained everything. He did a decent job, but it was vague, and I knew it was bullshit. I was being put to the side again.

"If this position is as important as you describe, then show me where I fit in the organizational structure? Who are my direct reports? Can I see the details, please? You must have that information, if we are to have a serious discussion. It's been a week." I replied.

I knew Rob didn't have the details. They didn't care. This was my new window seat and they hoped I'd be happy with my continued VP status and the money that came with it. What a miscalculation. I was made for the fray, the big issues, the tough problems, and I was finally sober and at full strength.

Being unable to fix any of Takata's many serious issues, it was time for me to go and find greener pastures. I had been disgraced for the last time. This was proof they would never take the recalls seriously. With the promotion of Shin, Takata would keep on marching in their errant and dangerous ways, hiding the truth where they could. No face could epitomize this reality better than his.

They're not getting off this easy, I thought, and started to lay out my case against Shin's selection, his disqualifications and transgressions, making sure I dropped the 'felon' word from time to time for good measure. Rob eventually interrupted saying he didn't want to and wasn't going to talk about the past. He didn't want to hear it. He didn't want to acknowledge it. He just looked back at me, and it was clear that he wasn't going to engage. So finally, I asked,

"You're telling me that Takata is okay with this?"

Nobody said a word. A long, dead, and awkward silence ensued. I looked at them each, waiting for a response. Ryan looked at me and then Rob. He realized Rob wasn't going to touch the question, so he replied,

"Takata made the move, so it's official. It's done."

"Okay, fine. Let me go home and talk it over with Sandy." I said after a few moments of thought.

We never discussed my final separation, so I was still a Takata employee, but I never went back into the office. For too long the wrong people had been in charge and only worse would follow now. Of that I was certain. It was clear they didn't want me involved at any level anymore. They would let me stay around, but not have an impact. Scott must have been completely forced out of the process. He would have told them I would never have agreed to this.

I took a few days before calling Brueckner to tell him I was resigning and that we needed to start the separation process. He told me he wasn't ready to talk about that and needed another week to prepare, so he scheduled me to come in on October 28. A week later, I returned to Auburn Hills. This was getting old. I told Ryan all of it again, the history with Shin, I told him he was ruining my career, taking me out of my profession…etc.,' and then he offered me three months' severance, to which I replied, "I need to speak to a lawyer," and excused myself.

As I left Ryan's office, Dal Luke and Al Bernat were standing right there, in front of Al's office.

Days earlier, the *New York Times* broke a story claiming that in 2004 Al Bernat ordered data and evidence of exploding inflators to be discarded, prompting senators to immediately begin calling for a criminal investigation. When Al looked up and saw me, he was white as a ghost. I nodded to Dal and said,

"Hey, Dal, how are you doing?"

"Fine, Kevin, just fine. Thanks for asking."

Then I walked out for good. Al had to know I wasn't coming back. I hadn't been into the office for over a month. Takata lawyers talked to me twice in 2009 about my corrected report and the faked Shin report. Al was in that second meeting and had every reason to look like a ghost.

I hadn't officially resigned, nor had they terminated me. I'd let the lawyers figure that out. As I drove home, I knew it was time for public disclosure, time to take this outside. With the current leadership, more people were going to die. I couldn't believe it – none of it. It all seemed so surreal.

As soon as I pulled into the garage, Sandy was at the door waiting, her eyes looking to me for some good news. I wrapped my arms around her and said,

"We need to stay strong, baby. It's time to go to battle."

Going public was going to be risky, fraught with possibilities of litigation and financial uncertainties, but it was thrust upon us. We had no choice. More parts needed to be removed from vehicles, and Takata was dragging their feet, obfuscating the truth with an endless goose-chase.

We were uncertain, and afraid. The decision was the easy part. The process of making it happen would be much more difficult. I needed the evidence to prove two things: Takata was guilty of fraud, and the recall needed to grow much, much larger. Just two documents would prove my case, and I had copies of both in my home safe.

My immediate task was to find a lawyer. Litigation was a sport to Takata, and they would destroy me if they could. You never need a lawyer your entire life until you do. I began to reach out to some of my friends and closer associates for help. As luck would have it, somebody recommended an employment lawyer – one of the best, I was told. I immediately shared my plight with her and after hearing the details, she referred me to another, Sue Ellen Eisenberg, a highly respected and successful civil rights and employment lawyer. I called her office and they asked me to write my story into a chronology with as many details as I could remember. I finished it the next day, and a few days later Sue Ellen and I talked for the first time.

I sat in the kitchen with my cellphone pressed to my ear, and my chronology in front of me. Sandy stood near me, watching and listening. Sue Ellen was in her office in Bloomfield Hills, Michigan, listening on speakerphone as I recounted my story. She interrupted at times, asking many pointed questions. It was more of a grilling than I expected, and it scared me. This was serious.

"Why did you go back to work for them, if you already knew they were so bad and had committed fraud? Why would you want to work for a company like that again?" she asked at one point.

I told her about Simula collapsing and leaving me without a job. I had kids and a family to support. I explained how the offer came quick and I liked the airbag business. That I scoured the internet looking for Takata recalls, found nothing, and thought they had it fixed, or, at least, contained.

She listened but pressed further, poking at aspects of my story. Why did I wait so long to resign the second time, after I knew they were dragging their feet? Why not come out sooner? She was very serious and hammered me on this point. I was on the defensive.

Then I relayed the part of my story that wasn't in the chronology, the scope of my past drinking and bouts of depression. I poured out my heart, almost weeping as I told Sue Ellen I was a recovering alcoholic who was not drinking today and praying tomorrow would be the same. I explained that with sobriety came clarity and the courage to take on the challenge, stress and uncertainty of what might lay ahead.

I believe this was the moment we connected. It was honest and real. I needed her help and she believed me. I told her about the two bombshell documents that would indict Takata and greatly expand the recall. She listened carefully as I explained what they meant and when she ended the call she promised me she would read every word of them and agreed to meet with me in person. She still wasn't on the case, but I had passed the first step.

Sue Ellen's purpose is helping people. She only works on cases she wants to and takes the counselor part of her job very seriously. She was influential in driving new federal laws on domestic spousal abuse, writing a book in the 70's on the subject, and had always fought for the big issues. Anybody who knows her knows she is full of integrity and cares for people – like a mother. She thinks strategically and her preparation is formidable.

We met in person and after less of a grilling, Sue Ellen agreed to work with me, taking up my case because she knew it was much more than just an employment matter. In her words, she needed to 'get my ass into the Feds right away.'

This was easier said than done. I would have to resign and quickly, that much was clear, but how to handle the Takata reports in my possession was still undecided. Even though the documents likely proved that a crime had been committed, they were Takata's property, and I would be forced to return them, or they would sue me – and win.

But circumstances broke our way. The New York Times article about Al Bernat was the tipping point and the criminal investigation into Takata that senators were clamoring for was officially opened. The government began subpoenaing Takata for records and e-mails.

This presented the perfect opportunity to have my documents subpoenaed. Sue Ellen convinced me that I needed to add a criminal defense lawyer to safely navigate the process and found one of the best in Michigan, Mark Kriger, to join the team.

So instead of one, I ended up with two lawyers. Their mission was to walk me out of Takata safely, with my integrity intact, and with the crucial documents necessary to support my future testimony.

At home, Sandy and I had lots to talk about, and even more to worry about. Lawyers are expensive, and two lawyers even more so. I was also concerned about any skeletons Takata might drag up. Drinking-fueled e-mail outbursts over years of fighting issues and people would all be fair game in the court of law. Nevertheless, as John Wayne once famously said, "courage is being scared to death and saddling up anyway," so we pressed forward.

Mark began calling his contacts in the Justice Department, to have my documents subpoenaed, while Sue Ellen and I wrote my resignation letter. In the middle of November, I officially resigned, sending the letter to Rob Fisher.

It read:

This letter serves as my resignation as Vice President of Inflator Engineering and Processing for Takata, effective immediately. After almost fifteen (15) years with Takata, I have been compelled to resign due to Takata's continuing fraudulent misrepresentations and its refusal to correct the defects in products that have placed Takata's customers in danger. This letter serves as a summary of the circumstances necessitating my termination.

As you are aware, I have discharged my obligation to report what I believed to be fraudulent behavior and active misconduct on the part of Takata. In 2000, I obtained a copy of the Validation Test Report that was submitted to Honda in June of that year, which was authored by Shin Tanaka and Hideo Nakajima. It was clear to me that this report contained incorrect data, as well as data that could not be verified and data that simply did not exist. In response, I worked with Tom Sheridan to conduct research and document the actual (accurate) test results. Along with Tom, I prepared a Revised Validation Test Report, which I presented in November 2000 to Bill Martin and Paresh Khandhadia. I also distributed a copy of the Revised Report to Mr. Nakajima so that all parties were aware that the original Test Report contained material misrepresentations mandating correction. Despite my notification-and preparation of an accurate Revised Test Report to submit to Honda-no corrective action was taken by Takata upper management. The P-SDI Inflator went into mass production.

After Honda issued a recall for the P-SDI Inflator in 2008, I spoke with Takata' s attorneys on two separate occasions. The first meeting was with Ross Hamilton of Tuggle Duggins. During this meeting, I notified Mr. Hamilton of the fraudulent Test Report and identified Shin Tanaka and Hideo Nakajima as its authors. The second meeting was with Peter Theut of Butzel Long. At this time, I requested that an investigation be initiated and that the company take appropriate corrective action. Despite my requests, nothing was done. And the fraudulent report remained buried from public review or company scrutiny.

The last straw, as they say, occurred last month when the Inflator Group was reorganized, and Mr. Tanaka was given responsibility for Global Inflator Engineering and Operations. The position I was offered, in the new Inflator Global Organization, required that

I directly report to Mr. Tanaka, the individual whose fraudulent behavior I had reported on several prior occasions. I immediately notified Ryan Brueckner via e-mail that I declined to accept the position I was assigned in the new Inflator Global Organization. I could no longer work within a company where fraud was permitted to percolate and survive. Of equal consequence, I certainly could not report to the individual who brought the fraudulent Test Report into existence.

Since mid-October, I have not returned to the office, as I did not want my presence at Takata to be interpreted as tacit approval of the company's fraudulent direction and gross misconduct. As should be apparent, this has had an overwhelming emotional impact on me. The stress and anxiety have been profound, and the damaging effects are uncertain at this time.

Although I have great respect for many of the individuals with whom I have worked, I believe that Takata's leadership has failed its employees, its customers, its shareholders, and the public. If a member of Takata leadership would like to speak with me in more detail about the circumstances compelling my resignation, I would welcome the opportunity, provided that remediation is the objective.

Sue Ellen requested my personnel file, which took Takata two weeks to produce. When the massive binder of documents arrived at her office, we both went through it. There were no issues with my performance, instead all my reviews were glowing. And as for that witch hunt Al and Pat concocted to try and take me down – not a word. We began to prepare for my testimony, along with Mark. A few weeks later, I had the first of many meetings with the DOJ and FBI.

I dressed business casual and drove to downtown Detroit, to Mark's office on the 17th floor of the Penobscot Building near where the meeting would be held. I stood there nervous and looked out the large windows over the city. Mark was a little late arriving and I had too much time to think about what would happen when I began telling my story.

My mind raced. The government would eventually have all of Takata's internal e-mails and some wouldn't paint me in the best light. I was fiery, proud and emotional. I cared and always said what I thought needed to be said.

The Japanese disliked confrontation, preferring things to be unsaid.

They held certain hierarchal expectations for how one should voice their opinion and when to stop and go along with the rest. I never fit in. Japanese and Southerners dominated the leadership and they had their own unique ways. I was a New Yorker, a fast-talking, brash, and passionate person with a more confrontational style. I had skeletons, as everyone does, and as I stood waiting for Mark I started wondering if I had made the right decision.

No doubt the investigators would want to poke at my character to see if I was fit to testify in a court of law. So much was uncertain. Would my decision ruin me and my family? This is the life of the whistleblower. Those who take stands for what they think is right often don't fare well– some glory if they're lucky, but mostly just toils, struggles, and uncertain futures. As I stared at the cars and people below, I hoped for the best.

Arriving in the room, Mark could see I was nervous and pacing and asked me how I was doing.

"As long as you're there with me, I know I'll be okay," I said.

Such was the trust I already had in Sue Ellen's choice of criminal lawyer, and I held fast to my mantra that I was doing the right thing.

Mark didn't look the part of the clean-cut lawyer. Dressed in a tweed jacket with a plain brown-checkered tie, he sat down for a moment. He was bald except for a rim of gray hair, and he rubbed his beard and then looked at me and said reassuringly,

"Let's go do this. You'll be fine."

With that, we left his office and walked across the street to the Federal building on a cold December day. Making our way up the elevator, we checked in with the receptionist and sat for only a moment before we were escorted back. In a tiny room sat six federal investigators from various organizations around a table, waiting for us. Their conversation stopped when we walked in, and after some quick introductions the first interview began. It was long and grueling. They took voluminous notes, constantly making me clarify statements. At one point I asked for a soda as there was nothing in the room to drink. They obliged quickly, but the questions just kept coming. They went through my documents, listened to my story, and after nearly six hours, they thanked me. I was exhausted, but by the look on their faces, I knew I had served them up a huge piece of the case they had only just opened.

Around the same time as that first meeting, I received a threatening letter from Takata lawyers, demanding I return all of their property in my possession, including any documents I might have on my personal iPad. They knew if I kept my reports, they would be explosive in the wrong hands.

Sue Ellen, in a note sent just before the holiday break, replied:

> **This correspondence is in response to your e-mail, dated December 11, 2014, regarding Takata documents and data that Mr. Fitzgerald may have in his possession. I am responding on Mr. Fitzgerald's behalf.**
>
> **Per your request, my firm will deliver electronic copies of all materials identified in your e-mail that are currently in Mr. Fitzgerald's possession to your firm's cloud storage device. You are advised that Mr. Fitzgerald has provided information to the United States Attorney's Office for the Eastern District of Michigan. This information was provided through Mr. Fitzgerald's counsel, Mark Kriger, whom he retained to represent him in any grand jury proceedings. Based on the information provided, the government has issued a grand jury subpoena for the material requested in your e-mail. Therefore, counsel for Mr. Fitzgerald has retained copies of the returned material in order to comply with the subpoena.**
>
> **Further, as you are aware, Mr. Fitzgerald has already returned to Takata, care of your office, the company lap top and cell phone he had in his possession. Mr. Fitzgerald did not "wipe" or otherwise delete any Takata documents, data, or business/proprietary information that were not already in Takata's possession.**
>
> **If you have any questions, please feel free to contact Mark Kriger or me at any time. Wishing you and your family a Merry Christmas and joyous New Year.**
>
> **Best Regards, Sue Ellen Eisenberg**

When I read it, I laughed, and my day improved. Imagine all the turmoil generated within Takata. I thought back to the day when I walked out of that miserable place for the last time. Frank Roe called me when I got home, but I let it go to voicemail. He left a message saying he had just learned about my situation and promised to find me a better position. I was surprised he was so out of the loop. It still puzzled me. Today, I'm sure, though, that I had all of Takata's attention. Their largest internal critic was now on the outside and in their face.

Conclusion

Kevin and David Return

2015 to Present

(DAVID)

17

Into the Sunset

PICTURE THE scenes as the word spread. More than just Al had reason to worry the day Kevin walked out for good. When Scott presented the facts about Shin's past to Stefan Stoker, there were just three deaths and two of them were from years earlier. As management pushed forward with Shin's promotion, as if an omen, there were two more tragic deaths. Suddenly, Takata was everywhere in the news, and awareness of the deaths and injuries grew. Then in early November 2014, the *New York Times* wrote a story critical of Al Bernat's handling of a 2004 investigation into a PSDI rupture, and cries for criminal investigations began.

In response, the U.S. Senate called hearings to convene the week before Thanksgiving, so they could press Takata with hard questions about exploding airbags. The first to testify for Senators was Hiroshi Shimizu, whom Kevin had volunteered to help in Monclova as it was overrun by poor quality, high demand, and bad management. In his best English, Hiroshi apologized for the defects and tried to assure that the troubles were resolved, and the dangerous airbags were under recall. He blamed early manufacturing errors and a steep learning curve for Takata's woes, and insisted that beyond the first few million, the rest of their PSAN inflators were safe to stay in our vehicles in perpetuity.

Hiroshi did not represent Takata well, however, in this opening salvo. He was unsteady and failed to answer many of the Senate's probing questions, struggling most with why Takata was only recalling airbags in hot and humid environments. Senators from other states with more temperate climates wanted to know why they shouldn't be concerned. Would the airbags in their regions eventually become bad? What happens if someone bought a used car from Florida or they lived half the year in the South? Hiroshi's rehearsed responses failed to erase the frowns from the stern panel on the bench above.

It seemed evident that the company was doing what it could to limit the scope of the recall. By the end of the first hearing, Florida's Senator Nelson told reporters he was frustrated, and that Takata's testimony was a "shuffle, two-step, sidestep" characterized by "pregnant pauses," implying deception. Senator Markey went so far as to say the company was "toying with the safety of the American people." Articles and broadcasts covered the poor performance and showered criticism on the flailing company, but things were just getting started.

In the first week of 2015, Kevin walked into the federal building in Detroit for his first interview with the FBI and DOJ. He had been at home with Sandy for two months anxiously waiting the final few weeks for his lawyers to hand him over. Not easy times, but he made certain to catch every minute of Hiroshi's painful and ineffectual Capitol Hill performance.

These were the real investigators crammed into a tiny federal building room to hear Kevin. He would contradict Hiroshi and Takata's testimony, and open the case in a way no other could, describing a twisted tale they could scarcely have imagined then. He was clear in his purpose and what he shared. The recall was inadequate. The fault with PSAN was systemic and here were the reports to prove it. Fixing it would devastate Takata and they would stonewall while more died. The company was fraudulent and the new boss of Global Inflators, Shin Tanaka, lied about the inflators that were killing people. It was a mess.

Within Takata the chaos was consuming, and it wasn't long before the bombshells started to fall. The first casualty was Stefan Stoker, picked to run Takata in the wake of the scandal. He was terminated on Christmas Eve of 2014, undoubtedly for his decision to push forward with Shin as the tragedy was escalating.

Shige took over unsteadily. The family and board were in turmoil. Earlier in the year, a federal grand jury had found Takata guilty of fixing seatbelt prices and fined them $70 million. Now their eighty-year reputation was being tarnished by an even bigger scandal which had already dropped their share price by half. The hard truths began to surface. By now, Shige must have learned about the hidden failures most likely kept from his father too.

Having been exposed and tied to the fraudulent behavior, Shin, Hideo, and Chikaraishi, the top of the Japanese inflator organization, were fired next. There were no window seats for these long-serving lieutenants. Hideo and Chikaraishi had worked for Takata since 1975 and 1978, respectively, starting in seatbelts long before there were ever inflators to worry about.

A ripple was becoming a tsunami. In February of 2015, Kevin met with the FBI for a second time, and then in April, he sat with NHTSA. The Feds were interested in criminally prosecuting the company and its bad actors, but the meeting with safety regulators was about expanding the recall. He explained the true scale of the PSAN problem and how many millions of inflators were really impacted. The second report he shared, the Nissan PSDI-5 root-cause investigation, showed that even with a desiccant, PSAN couldn't survive. It was clear the recall would need to expand. There were 11 million vehicles under recall when Kevin began, but that immediately tripled to 34 million, while the real number became clear – more than 70 million in the U.S. and 120 million worldwide, a full decade of Takata's inflator production. It must have been unfathomable to NHTSA.

Since the first death in 2008, Takata met each successive failure with a constantly changing story of quality defects and process issues that stunted the growth of the recall. There was a Maginot line they had to maintain to stay in business. How can a company indict nearly every product they ever produced? Certainly, an organization as devious as Takata couldn't. They were burying their heads in the sand and praying the deaths would stop. Kevin knew the tragedy would drag on under the weight of excuses, cover-ups, and politics – that's what Shin's promotion made loud and clear.

Takata's lawyers produced reams of exculpatory documents that claimed they had met automaker specifications and had done what they could as the problems unfolded. But they were on shaky ground and a deeper rot was being unearthed by Kevin. Lawyers tell the truth while omitting as many damaging facts as possible, and Takata was amassing an army of them to help them spin their case as it tightened around them. Their employees were being subpoenaed and the threat of criminal prosecution and maximum shareholder losses was real. It's always about the money.

The defense team did their best to hide the most damaging evidence, even going so far as to scatter the pages of Kevin's corrected PSDI report in random document boxes. Since the FBI was already in possession of his copy, the ruse was quickly discovered, and the government slapped a $14,000 per day fine on the non-repentant Takata. A pittance, but a clear signal to company executives that the FBI was in possession of inside-information and that the lies had better stop.

Kevin would meet with the FBI two more times in the spring of 2016 to clarify certain events and corroborate others' testimony, but for the most part, he was finished. He needed to find new work soon and return to healing. In his mind, it was time to close the door on Takata for good. For me, this wasn't possible. Others were being called to testify, and I was one of them.

The Curtain Closes

Accused of staying in the background, the criticism of Shige mounted. He had yet to address the public or even offer his condolences, instead having others speak for him as the scandal widened, the losses mounted, and his company's reputation withered. Close associates accused him of having "little sense of crisis" and pretending as if the issues were going to "blow by in due time." His mother Akiko – matriarch of the family – was often described as yelling at him, visibly frustrated with his management of the crisis. She was called *O-okusan*, or 'big wife,' and was the largest private shareholder, but her distress and shame had Shige paralyzed to make decisions. It was a family in crisis, melting down for the world to see.

Then on May 18, 2015, after hiding the problem for more than a decade, Takata finally agreed to a consent order with NHTSA, and conceded that a motor vehicle safety defect existed within their airbags. They were forced to admit the true root-cause of the tragedy, that PSAN will inevitably lose to the environments and become aggressive.[17] It wasn't a series of manufacturing errors, as they had professed, but a deeper fault in the technology that independent experts evaluating the problem were also confirming.

More Congressional hearings followed and this time Kevin Kennedy, VP of Takata North America, was picked for the grilling. When asked specifically if PSAN was safe, he answered that when "properly manufactured and designed," it could be, but casually omitted that Takata had not done so.[18] When asked how many Takata airbags would eventually become dangerous, he failed to answer.

At the summer shareholder meeting, Shige finally apologized to the victims, but still proclaimed his company's airbags to be "fundamentally safe."[19] The criminal investigation dragged on and Takata resisted. I did too, ignoring more calls from reporters or investigators.

The bad news just kept coming for Takata. In November of 2015, regulators hit them with a $70 million fine for failing to notify authorities of the defects when they first knew. Even after being caught and publicly shamed, they kept manipulating and obfuscating information they were obliged to provide. So, the government threatened to levy one more penalty of up to $130 million, the largest ever, if they didn't come clean.[20] The scandal only widened from there, and the beleaguered stock price halved once more. Takata was in a tailspin even as the worst of their wrongdoings remained hidden from public scrutiny.

In early 2016 that would all change, as the case of Mincey vs Takata got underway, and the callous actions of Takata executives began to leak. Patricia Mincey, a woman who had been injured and paralyzed in an accident involving a Takata airbag, brought a lawsuit alleging her airbag was "overly aggressive." It hadn't exploded, but she claimed her injuries were the result of defective propellant that caused the inflator pressure to soar and the airbag to crash violently into her. A number of current and former Takata employees were called to testify, and the company vigorously fought the lawsuit in a desperate attempt to limit liability to only inflator ruptures. Al and Paresh both pleaded the 5th when called upon, refusing to incriminate themselves, but Tom Sheridan and Kevin unloaded on Takata's attorneys. Later, portions of Tom's deposition appeared in the papers, exposing Takata as liars whose behavior had killed people.

The headline from the *New York Times* ran: **Takata Discarded Evidence of Airbag Ruptures as Early as 2000.**[21] Now the public could read how sixteen years earlier, Takata had altered PSDI test data to hide deadly failures from their biggest customer, Honda. Even more damaging was that executives knew their airbag inflators could explode, especially in hot and humid environments, and nonetheless continued to push their PSAN designs by falsifying reports.

The hatchets were out again. The next heads to fall were the two who kept silent, Al and Paresh, though both managed to secure lucrative severance packages on their way out. One can only imagine the information they assumed Kevin had shared with investigators and how difficult a bind they now found themselves in. Their names were in the papers, the deaths were rising, associates were pointing fingers, and they were under real risk of prosecution.

Better still, there was a strong possibility that Shige would be forced to testify in the Mincey case by the presiding federal judge. Consequently, just moments before a hearing to determine that, Takata's lawyers quickly settled with her family for an undisclosed sum. Unfortunately, Patricia had passed away from her injuries two months prior.

That summer my involvement resumed. Kevin had come to work for the company I was with, leaving Detroit for the sunny California coast. We were finally able to sit and catch up, and it was then I learned the manner of his departure from Takata and what he was grappling with still. The weight of his pain sank in and I raised the idea of a book to help, but it was quickly brushed aside. The week after our reunion, I was presented with another surprise, and of course, it was connected.

One evening I was drumming with my son before dinner, when a knock came at our door. My wife was in the shower and I wasn't expecting anyone, so I ignored it. More knocks came a bit louder and then again with even more intensity. I became a little impatient. Who was banging at my door at this hour? I went downstairs for a polite but quick dismissal.

I didn't bother to put a shirt on before I opened the door in just my shorts to find three badges staring at me and someone asking if I was David Schumann. Federal agents were standing on my porch with a subpoena to appear before the Grand Jury investigating Takata, and all I could do was smile and try to cross my arms over my bare chest. They got me.

I thought for sure they had learned everything from my former colleagues who knew more and had stayed around longer. I left in 2008 and never looked back, but here they were, clearly wanting me to talk about those days. They were gracious, and we shared a conversation about my home and Arizona, but it wasn't long before they asked if I had received any of the messages they left me. I acknowledged I had, apologized for not getting back to them, but explained there was some confusion because of the many calls from reporters I received as well.

As I was handed the subpoena, they asked if I would agree to interview right then and there at my dinner table, but I declined. With all the weight of what Kevin had shared, I felt that it was better to recall a few things first, rather than wing it there in front of my family.

A few days after they left I called to schedule my appearance. Since we had a vacation already planned for Michigan for the following month, I asked if they were interested in meeting when I was there to save them money on airfare. They seemed amenable to the idea and told me I would hear back shortly.

I called Kevin and told him I was a little concerned. I remembered how the Armada residents had forged reports with my signature, but he laughed and told me not to worry, and that they were just cleaning up loose ends. Everyone that mattered had already testified about the doctoring of reports and who was responsible. They were hunting for ringleaders, not me.

The following day, I got the confirmation call from the FBI I was waiting for and we agreed to meet during the tail-end of my vacation. It was all set.

Before going, I thought long about my five-years at Takata and searched the internet for the latest news. What Kevin had told me was reflected there but not in the detailed and more relevant ways he shared. The idea of the book kept stalking me. I called Kevin again to suggest it nonchalantly, or at least a long-form exposé, but he said he wasn't interested again and wished me luck. Before I hung up, I asked him to think about it some more.

When the day of the interview arrived, I rifled through my luggage to find my dress shoes, only to realize that in all the commotion, I forgot to pack them. So, I walked into the federal building wearing *Vibram Five-Finger* toe-shoes with jeans, I immediately apologized for my casual wear. They reassured me that this was an informal session but admonished me to answer their questions honestly or they could still force me to testify under oath at a later date.

I wanted to help and answered all their questions to the best of my ability, but they certainly had to remind me of more than I could help them with. They showed me e-mail chains of responses and replies, one by one in a chronological order, with conversations about failures from the past I had mostly forgotten. But they came back to me – instances where I had discovered fraud or expressed concern – and old conversations of Kevin and I discussing Paresh's antics. Overall it was a record showing that I had aligned with the good team. I was happy to talk and close loops where I could.

The day ended just in time for rush hour, but I had lots to digest as I drove. Before I left downtown, however, I stood in front of that grand Penobscot building and remembered back twelve years earlier when I had toured that stone marvel the day before my interview with ASL, in 2004. In ways that seemed to come full circle, I felt this purpose within grow, and just knew that we were going to write this book.

When I returned to Arizona a few days later, I texted Kevin to see if anything had changed. As if in sync with some higher purpose, he was already in and didn't need to talk, convinced that the recall was moving too slow and justice would never be served fully.

As we started our writing project, the criminal investigation into Takata was nearing its end. Their share price was at new lows, having moved a whole decimal from 3000 to 300 in just two years. Kevin Kennedy and Rob Fisher had been let go, and Shige announced he was stepping down as chief executive. Takata was in a desperate search for a lifeline from investors – a rescue deal to save their bleeding operations from the massive recall costs and inevitable bankruptcy. The details, however, would prove difficult. Nobody could answer the question of liability. How many airbags would need to be fixed? How many people were still to be killed or maimed? Investors gambled on an agreement materializing and the stock rose marginally, but any glimmer of hope was smashed as the hammer came crashing down.

In December of 2016, Takata pleaded guilty to fraud and criminal conduct, receiving a one billion dollar fine and legal remediations.[22] $25 million went to settle the criminal charge and the remainder was divided between the automakers and victims, $850 million and $125 million, respectively. A few days later, as the New Year began, federal criminal indictments from the Department of Justice were unsealed for Hideo Nakajima, Shinichi Tanaka, and Tsuneo Chikaraishi.[23] They were accused of a laundry list of wire-fraud charges for misrepresenting the inflators they sold, and for masterminding cover-ups and "the correcting" of reports. Shareholder value went to the floor as the final nail in the coffin was driven home. By summer's solstice of 2017, Takata surrendered to bankruptcy protection.

In the weeks leading up to the filing, there were four more deaths.

The airbag scandal caused the ruin of the company. The Takada family had built the second largest safety systems producer in the world, becoming one of the wealthiest dynasties in Japan. Now it would be remembered as the largest Japanese business to go bankrupt, while passing the buck for tens of millions of defective and potentially deadly products. Shige and Akiko watched solemnly as the sun set for good on their shining legacy. A new and menacing one had risen in its place. One that nobody wanted to look in the eye.

18

Hot Potato

JUST DAYS after the criminal indictments were unsealed, authorities announced another death, this one from an SDI inflator installed into a 2006 Ford Ranger. It was the second SDI to explode within months, claiming victims with a metal bullet aimed right at their heads. A new driver inflator was killing people with wounds coroners described appearing as gunshots.

Both inflators were built in Monclova, on the same day in 2005. This was a year before the devastating explosion that ripped through the plant and the year I first met Kevin. These vehicles were only ten and twelve years old and claimed two lives, right as the company was filing for protection from their overwhelming liabilities estimated at up to $50 billion.

When Kevin and I learned about the SDI deaths, we were busy on our book. The bankruptcy and guilty plea were good news, but inevitable. For us, it was always about what happened after that. By then, more than 300 Takata airbags had exploded in someone's face. Their passenger inflators were also failing regularly, resulting in growing numbers of horrific injuries that were settled quietly and going mostly unreported. It's the deaths that make the news. We had already written the chapters concerning SDI failures and cover-ups, so this somber news was confirmation that our path was true. Adding to these horrific injuries, hundreds of inflators were exploding in tests on airbags returned from people's vehicles, thankfully in the lab, but the evidence was clear. Millions were at immediate risk of a real hazard.

Our purpose is to rid the world of every last Takata airbag – to raise awareness about the current recall and to make the case for another. Over 100 million airbags are now under recall and need attention immediately. These could take another decade to find and repair. Beyond that are an additional hundred million Takata inflators with PSAN and 13X desiccant that have so far avoided recall and that is a massive problem. We have to dispel any notion that PSAN inflators can remain on our roads indefinitely. Takata is bankrupt, but their defective products live on. They will be passed down to our young or purchased on used car lots, mostly by the unwitting or those without the financial means to do otherwise. We can't let that happen.

Act 1 debuted PSAN's weakness as Paresh's new inflators were felled by Honda's relatively benign specifications. These first-generation airbags are thankfully all under recall, but the first Act only set the stage for our story, or better said, our mission. In the second Act, Paresh's inflator's are rupturing with an even greater frequency as automakers' specifications evolve and become more difficult. And then success. The X-Series and 13X desiccant quell the explosions, at least those that belong to Paresh, and tens of millions are fitted to vehicles. These inflators are not under recall and we, as experts, are adamant that they should be.

How the X-Series were manufactured is critical. We needed to spotlight the internal failures, quality defects swept under the rug, and fraudulent management that made one bad decision after another. This helps indict the remaining. We knew that without it, the fate of these hundred million would be judged on an incomplete picture, or on lab tests of the design with simulated environments. Too many are unaware of what really happened, and decisions are being influenced by only half the story. Three Japanese executives are indicted and the company is ruined, but lives still hang in the balance.

During the Senate testimony, Takata's executives said PSAN is safe if "designed and manufactured correctly." Tell us, after this read, would you say they were? There are good ones, probably most, but there are bad ones too, very bad ones that could be deadly today. These slipped through Takata's deteriorating quality systems led by a global VP that callously ignored lethal weld defects while the death count grew. This was Takata. Not everyone that filled the upper echelons, but those who steered much of her course. It certainly wasn't just three Japanese lieutenants.

If Takata ever stood a chance of taming PSAN, they needed world-class manufacturing and quality, and leaders who knew best. Instead, their performance was grossly inadequate and exhibited a disdain for basic industry protocols. Meeting shipments, saving face, and reducing costs was the priority. These are the conditions under which the hundred million were made. Remember this as we introduce the missing requirement that should be clear to most by now.

What's Missing?

It's what we couldn't see all those years, struggling in the fast-paced and competitive business of airbag engineering and manufacture. Was passing the automakers' current specification really enough? Everything was about meeting the requirements for us. Most products are the same, but energetic devices especially. But did the requirements represent real world conditions for twenty plus years? Takata bet they were conservative and that everything would be fine once their inflators were installed in cars. Turns out they weren't.

We were finally able to meet the automakers' evolving and increasingly difficult specifications with the X-Series generation, but in doing so, we missed the forest for the trees. We convinced ourselves that passing was good enough and, within limits, safe. The truth is that with PSAN, it only meant for a time – maybe – if the inflators were built correctly. As we patched up the holes with desiccant and improved processes, customers happily consumed more, but most saw firsthand the warning signs. Specification margins should have been challenged. If developed to simulate fifteen years, what happens after that?

Airbag failures happen all the time, like any other automotive component. Sometimes they don't deploy when they should. Other times they deploy when they shouldn't. We hear about these stories, but they don't make headlines. Sometimes things go awry, especially with age. We have to keep our cars maintained because we understand that negligence is dangerous. For airbags, if one simply didn't work after twenty years, we could be OK with that, but it can't explode and kill a family member. If it fails, it has to do so safely. There also should be a clear way to replace it if we decide to hold on to our pristine, twenty-year-old car.

Each PSAN inflator degrades uniquely and should be assessed individually. Some are sealed better which improves their survivability. Others, like those delivered with off-quality, low-density propellant, can go bad in as little as ten years. A number are in the tropics where heat and humidity accelerate the process. An X-Series inflator built with a leak or low-density propellant will eventually fail violently, and if it lives in Florida, Alabama, Mississippi, Louisiana or Texas, all the quicker. This is the data that Claus used to kill AMP.

There is no denying that all inflators leak, and all desiccants saturate, it's just a question of rate. There is no perfect seal, and Takata used O-rings and adhesive-backed shims with a quality department that had thrown in the towel. So long as the Earth spins around the sun and there is weather, PSAN inflators will degrade and become more aggressive. GuNi inflators will age as well, but their tendency will be to dud. If given the option, we're certain all would choose loss of function over the business-end of a Claymore mine.

If you can replace any part in an aging vehicle but the airbag that may eventually kill or maim you then something was missed. The very first inflator specifications should have included a requirement for Fail-Safe. After fifteen or twenty years, some performance drift beyond ballistic limits may be permissible, but fragments ripping through the cabin should be explicitly prohibited! This most basic of inflator requirements was missed.

Face Forward

Ten years into the recall one might expect it to be nearing conclusion, but the finish line is far from view. Some automakers have remedied less than 25% of their defective vehicles, and NHTSA has done little but verbally reprimand them. 25 million airbags still need to be replaced, and although it may seem a difficult task, it must be accelerated. Every day they become more dangerous and we inch closer to when NHTSA must add another 100 million X-Series inflators to the list.

The numbers are staggering, far too big for automakers to accept. Another hundred million is simply preposterous. We can only expect them to continue to delay the current recall and ignore the remaining X-Series inflators altogether. But no matter the cost, we must hold the institutions accountable. Anything less is passing the buck to those who did nothing wrong and have everything to lose.

In one sense, the whole affair is a raw deal for the automakers. Airbags were mandated and there was no choice but to offer them – to develop the necessary specifications and supply base. There were less than a handful of companies at the time that could make inflators, and automakers, averse to sole-sourcing, spread their orders. Takata, not averse to lying, grew at exponential rates, ensnaring nineteen automakers in its web.

But it wasn't just greed and incompetence that led to such an epic failure. PSAN's incubation period played a major role. Like a lentivirus, by the time the virulence clearly manifested, Takata's inflator's were everywhere. The question is, were the symptoms ignored?

Most damning is that some of the automakers knew about Takata's problems. They watched us fumble. We presented results of failing PSDI-5 inflators that sometimes exploded after environments to Ford as early as 2004. Those automakers who got to see real data always asked why PSAN was more aggressive after environments – a stark difference in behavior. Mostly the data would still be in specification, but sometimes one would sail out and require a deviation that they were all to ready to sign. We never had a good answer for the performance shift, other than it came with the really small package.

Signs were missed, both blatant and subtle, and we can't change that. But we can demand that NHTSA and the automakers start taking the campaign more serious. The 25 million un-desiccated PSAN inflators still left on the deck must be cleared and with the utmost urgency. Preparation for the next 100 million, the X-Series, must begin now, or we will be at this for another decade to come. Too much foot-dragging continues, and the worst offender of all is General Motors. Their stall tactics are so egregious, so profit-before-people driven, that they deserve their very own spotlight.

GM has audaciously submitted four petitions of inconsequentiality to NHTSA to avoid repairing nearly seven million of Takata's un-desiccated passenger inflators found in their most popular pickups and trucks.[24] This makes them the only automaker to resist the deadly recall. Takata has deemed these inflators defective, yet GM continues to inundate the government with nonsensical reports, generated by so-called 'experts' they hire to say the opposite. The superfluous data and flawed arguments they advance are nothing but a poorly veiled attempt to overwhelm and confuse NHTSA, which lacks the technical competency to sort through the obfuscation. We know GM's inflators well and they are no different than any other Takata PSAN inflator under recall. Claims that they have a 'special' design that is kept safe from disaster by unique features found in their pickups and SUVs, are simply put, complete bullshit.

The only way to rationalize GM's behavior is to see it as immoral. It seems they have coldly calculated that settling with those who will be killed or maimed by their airbags is more cost effective than paying the $1.2 billion to bring them back. They are determined to wait us out, hoping we will give up the fight as they submit petition after petition. And where is NHTSA? Missing in action, devoid of an executive or a backbone since the day Trump took office. People will die if GM is not forced to remedy these vehicles. PSAN is a cancer. It has a latency period and the sooner it is cut out, the better. GM and NHTSA refuse to pick up the scalpel. We must demand they do.

There are also tens of millions of Takata's SSI-20 side-impact inflators on our roads that are not under recall. Most have no desiccant and those that do have a different catastrophic design flaw that erases any advantage. SSI-20 inflators are hidden in our seats beside our torso and some have ruptured even before making it out of the manufacturing plant. Why are they not being recalled, let alone discussed? Because you can't just tear open a seat, install a new airbag and then stitch the whole thing back together again. Replacing them will come at an astronomical cost and unless we demand otherwise, they will stay in our vehicles.

It's all too big - the X-Series, SSI-20, and GM's immune pickups and SUVs. Lumped together, automaker's liabilities will exceed $50 billion, and we are certain that will have them deflecting responsibility, not embracing it. Like Takata, they are cowering in the face of such losses and will do little to expand the recall unless forced to. Our governments must act. In a real sense, they share in the responsibility. They mandated the technology, then walked away from regulating it, and now that it has reared an ugly head, they must wrestle with the consequences. We cannot let NHTSA and car companies ignore the next 100 million.

Prognosis

In the middle of our book efforts I stalled and burned out. Writing is hard. I worked part-time in the industry throughout, and even after Kevin quit his job to focus on the book, we struggled and missed every deadline. At one point I was defeated, feeling the draft insurmountable. I was unhappy with it and everything I penned seemed terrible. Life was competing and stressful, and I quit writing for a few months to put things back together while Kevin soldiered on. He coached me and told me to have faith, while waiting patiently for me to return. Eventually I pulled up my chair again, but only for brief bouts on the glossary and to read the latest news. Then two things happened – I started reading what Kevin had been writing, and did what good engineers do first.

Opening the draft again, I was quickly disheartened because I found that Kevin had dumped more than a hundred pages right in the middle of it, in no sensible order. My heart sank at the prospect of all the hours needed to organize his ramblings, but somehow I found the courage to keep going. Then about twenty pages in, something switched in his writing. A step change – these weren't notes anymore, but writings, and they were good. Suddenly, after months of plying the trade, he had found his voice, and I discovered he was the better writer. It lifted me and brought me back. I was down but he was up.

Still, I couldn't write, and our summit seemed far away. I switched over to compiling some of the charts and recall chronology that we intended to include in the book's appendices. As I sifted through my research and read the stories I had written in earlier drafts of the victim's tragic plights, their names were seared into my mind. And then it dawned on me. I never plotted any of the data I had so painstakingly assembled. So, I did. The quick calculation in my head until then had been one to two deaths per year, on average, but I should have plotted things sooner. Here was the kick in the pants I needed.

Seeing the collection of deaths and injuries over the decade, I had mixed feelings of enthusiasm and shame – a revitalized passion to fulfill our mission and help end the tragedy, but also, a stark reminder of how time was our enemy and that the manuscript still needed more.

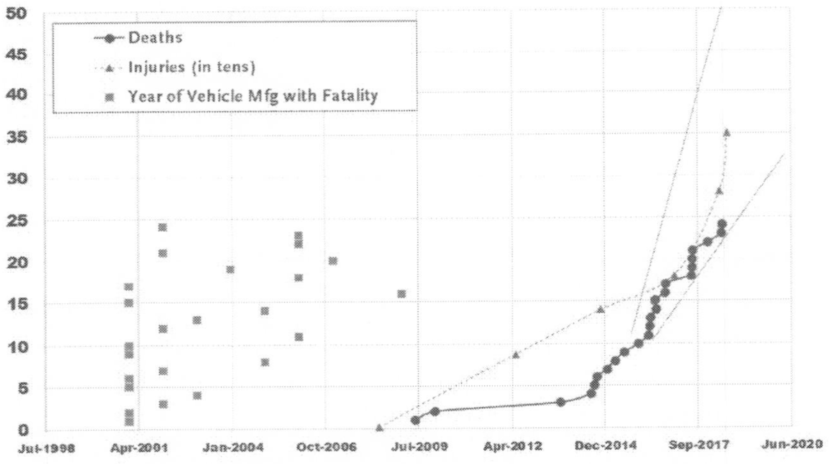

FIGURE ELEVEN: DEATHS AND INJURIES RESULTING FROM TAKATA PSAN INFLATORS

Instantly, I saw what should have been clear: the real increase in deaths and injuries didn't start until 2014, when Kevin was leaving. PSAN needed time to degrade. And when I extrapolated the data out to 2023, it suggested the death toll could reach as high as fifty souls, even one hundred, and that realization changed everything.

The square data points represent the year of manufacture of vehicles involving a fatality, beginning with the fraudulent PSDIs from 2000-2002, and expanding through succeeding generations up until 2009. For specifications that were touted to simulate fifteen years, the reality of the data is striking – 250 injuries and more than twenty deaths in that many years. Most have taken between 10 and 14 years. The later generations, with all their band-aids, may take longer, but the ultimate trajectory doesn't change. There are still tens of thousands of PSDIs with greater than 50% chance of exploding, installed into Hondas and on our roads, now twenty years old.

It's taking too long to replace what has already been recalled. Jason Levine, executive director of the Center for Auto Safety, said it best at the close of 2018.[25]

> **"The numbers speak for themselves: In a matter of weeks there will be over 25 million unrepaired, recalled Takata airbag inflators remaining on our roads, 10 years after the process started and three years after NHTSA was put in charge of the recall."**

There have been nearly twenty-five deaths and five hundred injuries to date, and with the fifteen-year shadow covering more of the un-desiccated inflators each day, we can expect at least that many injuries in the next five years. But these tragedies can be prevented, and anything less is inexcusable, unconscionable and intolerable. More inflators need to be remedied faster. Engage NHTSA! Engage!

Legacy

And then there is the X-series promising to cast its shadow over the next decade. They won't fail at the same rate as those without desiccant, but when a tenth of a billion inflators are moving in the wrong direction, this will lead undoubtedly to heartache and pain.

As we were putting the final touches on our book, another recall for 1.2 million PSDI-5D inflators was announced by Honda, for model years 2009 through 2016.[26] The PSDI-5D was the inflator Takata delivered to Nissan with Zeolite desiccant when a new validation was demanded and Takata was caught in their lie. It is the same inflator Kevin insisted Takata use early in the recall when they ran out of capacity for like-for-like PSDI replacements. Zeolite desiccant was the best armor Takata had, the same desiccant used in the X-Series inflators, but in less than five years, one has already exploded and added another name to the growing list of injured and maimed. The explanation was that Monclova introduced excessive moisture during assembly. But that is exactly our point - even desiccated PSAN inflators built poorly will become dangerous quickly. Beyond that, they will never last the test of time. All inflators leak, and all desiccants saturate. Period. This damning disclosure was our proverbial nail in the coffin as we bound the first copies of Kevin's story. How could NHTSA leave any PSAN in the field now?

The fate of the remaining is scheduled to be decided at the end of 2019 when outside experts wrap up their evaluation programs and deliver NHTSA a verdict. One of the jury members is the same hired hand GM used to stall the current recall. Their knowledge of PSAN inflators is non-existent, and their experiments in support of GM's petitions, amateurish. They should be ashamed that their deeply flawed data is being used to leave Takata's ticking time-bombs in our vehicles. How can we believe this same company will decide any differently on the desiccated X-Series? We can't. The writing is on the wall and it's blood red. Unless we demand expert and independent oversight of this looming and critical decision, it will come and go with little commotion and no further recalls. You will not know if your vehicle has a Takata PSAN inflator that could kill you one day, and there is no way to have it repaired when word eventually leaks, causing your car to become worthless.

A life is unmeasurable in money, and until we make that clear to the powers that be, it will remain an abstract calculation. Our efforts are dedicated to the victims and their families. I pray that we can help others avoid the deep suffering they have endured for the mistakes of a few, and that the senselessness of their loss is lessened by our efforts.

Our aim and purpose is clear. Help us raise awareness and end the Takata legacy in a way that heals. Every life matters is the truth that sets us free, the truth that will solve this crisis no matter how daunting a complete do-over seems. Choices matter. They flow into all facets of our lives, influencing events and tipping consequences in ways that often return hard lessons when misaligned. Tell the truth. Honesty wins. Failure is natural.

Believe in the hero that fights for causes and ideals. They may rise and fall with a will that is stubbornly their own and errant at times, but their courage and tenacity spring from a deep desire to serve others and lead the way in hard times. They are part of life's safety system. Humankind can only be bold with leaders who risk everything for truth.

Gratitude

Kevin Fitzgerald

I am thankful for my Maker who whispered "Have Faith" in my ear as he took the bottle out of my hand and replaced it with a pen. I live in the present, comforted by the knowledge that the One who controls my life is totally trustworthy.

I am thankful for my dear wife Sandy and my children, Ryan, Dillon and Kris, who stuck with me as I wrestled with and finally conquered my demons. I am forever grateful for their patience, forgiveness and love.

I am thankful for my parents Joseph and Patricia Fitzgerald for instilling in me their unbreakable faith and marking a bright line between right and wrong. And I'm thankful for my siblings John and Maureen who carry that torch with me today.

I am thankful for my co-author and brother, David Schumann, who was so dogged in his determination to see this project through. He and his dear wife Courtney have sacrificed everything because they so deeply believe in the mission. They are heroes.

I am thankful for my Takata brothers and sisters, my teammates, who helped save countless lives despite the constant headwinds of dishonesty. And I am sorry to the 99% who came to work every day to make a difference and were tarnished by the actions of a few.

I am thankful for Sue Ellen Eisenberg and Mark Krieger who so skillfully extracted me from a terrifying and threatening Takata with my integrity intact and my head held high. They were so much more than my lawyers. They were and are my dear friends.

I'm thankful to Heidi and Dennis Pack whose hospitality, graciousness and humanity couldn't have come at a more needed time. Their little bungalow in the hills of San Juan Bautista became my sanctuary while I hunkered down for a year and waited for my family to join me in California.

I'm thankful for the town of San Juan Bautista, CA, its beautiful people, and the Mission at its center. Those hollowed grounds were my place of solace, inspiration, and strength during difficult times. The energy that flows from its core is boundless.

I'm thankful to the gang at Vertigo coffee shop where I could be spotted every day for over a year, my soul pouring out onto paper. They never stopped rooting for me as I feverishly banged away at my keyboard, transported to another world by the music blaring from my earbuds . And Jess, thank you for telling me to stand up and write when you saw I was suffering. It made all the difference.

I am thankful to Damon Vander Lind and the HVSD team at Kitty Hawk for giving an ex-VP who just wanted to be an engineer again a much needed break. You helped me gain my confidence and swagger back and for that I owe you a debt of gratitude.

Finally, I'm thankful for the experiences of all those who have passed through my life, both positive and negative, for they have helped shape who I am - a person I'm good with, a person I love. I'm thankful for being reborn and realizing there is so much more to this life then getting up and going to work every day. But most of all, I am thankful for still being sober, one day at a time.

David Schumann

I thank the Creator for my life and the path that led me here.

To my wife, thank you most of all. Your patience, encouragement, and love made it possible. Three years you believed and prodded me on, in the midst of all the rest, while balancing medical school and raising our son. I am in awe – humbly and eternally grateful for your magical presence by my side. Always you reminded me of why I was working with such difficulty and uncertainty, my coach, telling me not to worry and keep going, that everything would be fine.

To Elijah who lost so much time with his father, thank you for your love and gentleness. I know if the choice had been yours, you would have given twice over in even the smallest hope that a life could be rescued. Precious boy, you inspire me more than anyone.

To Sandy and Kevin, for fifteen years of friendship and family, and for everything that moved our little project together to fruition in relative ease and enjoyment.

To Ryan, the third member of our team, thank you so much for your patient excellence with illustrations, cover design, research, website, and early edits. Thank you supremely to Annalisa for the perfect cover art.

A grand thanks to our editors, first Caroline Pincus, and then Holly Lasko Skinner. Caroline gave us the confidence and guidance when we needed it most. She helped significantly to shape and refine the final drafts, and found just about every comma that Kevin missed in his lovely dialogues. Holly helped in the beginning, providing us with the most important advice along the way — that we rewrite the whole thing and take our time.

To those good friends who steered me with genuine and good counsel through these years, especially in regard to this work, Trent, Joe T, David S, my father, Greg Y, and certainly a few others. Thank you dearly for the timely words that mattered most.

Thanks to my sister, Rebecca, for her love and support of our family, and for her early read and encouragement. To my mother, of course, and to my other sisters and family that have been the highest blessings, believing in and supporting me always.

To many that Kevin already mentioned, and for others that simply thanked us for what we were doing or encouraged us by relating their interest. Thanks to Joe Braun for his efforts in raising awareness. Special thanks to Alisa for excellent and timely final revisions of the cover.

Visit us at www.recallawareness.com

Learn more about how you can help raise awareness, find recalled vehicles, and support our cause.

Find articles written by Kevin and Dave, and additional resources.

Check out Kevin's Twitter feed.
https://twitter.com/kevmichaelfitz

Glossary

13X (Zeolite): A desiccant material developed along with the X-series. Its small bead-like geometry allowed it to be easily nested between propellant tablets, and its ability to absorb moisture helped to stop PSAN from degrading to the point of rupture in the more difficult environmental tests.

2004: A phase-stabilized ammonium-nitrate (PSAN) propellant developed by Paresh's team. The first generation of inflators that included it were PSDI, SPI, PSPI, and then SDI.

2004L: Paresh's follow-up propellant succeeding '2004.' It was developed for the X-series inflators. It used a more widely available fuel and boasted 5% higher gas efficiency, but was less dense than '2004' (meaning more of it was needed in each inflator). The engineers responsible for putting the X-series into production would note that 13X desiccant was the key improved performance of the X-series, while 2004L had little to no impact.

3110: Developed by Paresh's team in 1994, '3110' was Takata's first propellant to not use sodium-azide. It was included in a very successful generation of inflators developed in 1995 and 1996, and put both Paresh and Takata on the map. However, the push for smaller inflators and higher gas efficiency propellants would eventually render '3110' obsolete.

9339: A new auto-ignition material designed along with the X-series inflators.

AIB: A booster material developed by Deb Hordos and Sean Burns that included its own autoignition function. Its tablet geometry helped reduce the initial kick that was being produced by the previous '3110' booster granules. This helped solve a serious issue that could cause the connector in the second chamber of PSDI-X to disconnect, preventing the second chamber from firing.

AMP: The successor PSAN propellant to '2004L,' represented the best of what a PSAN propellant could be. It used lower cost fuels, and contained a wax additive that formed a moisture-resistant barrier around the propellant. As with all PSAN propellants, it would still rupture in the event of a leak, and as such was only meant to be used to bridge the gap until a fail-safe propellant could be developed.

(AN) Ammonium-Nitrate: An oxidizer that is used to make very gas-efficient propellants, but is very difficult to work with. Propellants are made of both a fuel and oxidizer. Takata used PSAN (phase-stabilized AN) from 2000 through 2015 as their main propellant. *See PSAN, '2004,' and '2004L.'*

(AI) Auto-Ignition Material: Abbreviated as 'AI' and also referred to as a 'thermal-switch', auto-ignition material is a pyrotechnic included in inflators to prevent them from becoming dangerous in the event of a fire. The material is designed to trigger at a temperature lower than the melting temperature of the propellant, allowing the inflator to self-dispose before it becomes an explosive hazard. The downside for Takata was that it introduced more moisture into the inflator, which led to degradation of the PSAN propellant during environmental testing.

Armada: A city located in eastern Michigan (northeast of Auburn Hills) that housed the technical team where Paresh developed propellant and inflator designs, and Kevin and Dave worked.

ASL: Automotive Systems Laboratory was the research and development wing of Takata's airbag program. The inflator and propellant division of ASL, run by Paresh, was responsible globally for new designs.

Auburn Hills: A town in metro-Detroit that housed Takata's North American headquarters responsible for finishing modules. This office is where many of the executive managers resided.

Ballistic model: A model is a series of mathematical equations that solve for dynamic functions. A ballistician computes the thermo-chemical equations raging inside gas generators and rockets, and uses this to predict and analyze results.

Batwing: References a propellant geometry of PSAN named for its particular shape that was used in the PSDI and PSDI-4 designs.

Bonfire: A test required by the Department of Transportation to ensure that inflators are safe to be transported. This test is typically completed by placing boxes of inflators into a fire built from a specific arrangement of wood. If the inflators move too far from the center, or they explode or eject any material then they are concerned unsafe for transport.

Booster: Booster or ignition material is a critical component in the chain reaction that leads to the inflation of the airbag. When a collision occurs, the crash sensor sends a charge to the initiator that ignites the booster. This causes the pressure in the inflator to rise until the propellant is also ignited. The booster material used by Takata was typically granules of '3110' propellant, which would later be replaced by 'AIB'.

Calcium sulfate: The first desiccant used by Paresh to combat moisture intrusion. Desiccants absorb moisture before it can get to the propellant. It was superseded by 13X.

Chief Engineer, Chief Inflator Engineer, Global Organization: With the global restructuring came new titles. Claus Rudolf was named Chief Engineer of Takata, responsible for seatbelts, airbags, inflators, steering wheels, electronics, systems, configuration management, and administrative. Beneath him was the Chief Inflator Engineer position that was initially extended to Kevin Fitzgerald.

DFMEA, FMEA: Failure modes, effects, and analysis is a tool that was developed by the automotive industry to manage risk in design development. Understanding what failure modes are possible and their likelihood of occurrence provides a scoring of various potential failures that are ranked. It is used to determine potential causes of failure during real-world use, and what countermeasures can be taken to mitigate them.

(DOT) Department of Transportation: The Department of Transportation is a part of the United States government responsible for federal transportation projects and setting safety regulations. DOT regulators were required to witness and approve specific inflator transportation tests, including the bonfire test.

(DOJ) Department of Justice: Wing of the United States Government responsible for ensuring that the law is fairly applied to all citizens, and that justice is brought to those who are guilty of committing a criminal offense.

(DR) Design Review: Design Reviews occurred periodically throughout a development program. The milestone review was used in Takata to determine if an inflator design was ready to move into the next stages of development or into production.

(DV) Design Validation: An environmental test series conducted on production-intent inflators that are typically produced in the engineering laboratory with hardware that is not made with production tooling and processes. The DV is used to determine if the inflator is ready to enter production.

Dual-stage inflator: Dual-chamber inflator designs allow for varying gas output depending on collision parameters. This prevents airbags from filling too quickly and injuring occupants in low speed collisions, and became a requirement by the NHTSA in 1997.

Gas Yield: Gas yield is the percentage of gas produced for a mass of propellant, unique to each formulation. A 60% yield produces six-tenths of a gram of gas for each gram of propellant combusted.

GDI, GDI 1.7: A version of the SDI-X 1.7 inflator developed by Christophe and Heiko specifically for Nissan and Renault that utilized GuNi propellant instead of Paresh's PSAN propellant.

GM, General Motors, GM Platforms 'GMT-900,' or 'K2XX': GMT-900 and K2XX were design variations of existing inflators built specifically for General Motors. The GMT-900 was a variation of SPI, while the K2XX was a variation of PDP. These platforms were critical for maintaining relations between GM and Takata.

GuNi, GUNI: A propellant used by other inflator manufacturers which strikes a good balance between performance and aging stability. GuNi fails-safe, unlike PSAN.

Heat-aging or accelerated aging: An environmental test that subjects an inflator to elevated temperatures, typically 90°C for 1000 hours. The environment is used to simulate long-term heat exposure in the vehicle.

Internal pressure: The amount of pressure inside the inflator during deployment. This value is critical. A pressure that is too high will result in structural failure of the inflator, while a pressure that is too low means that gas output will not be high enough to safely protect the occupant.

ISI, Inflation Systems Inc: ISI was responsible for the production, manufacturing, and quality management of inflators in the Takata organization.

LAT: Lot Acceptance Tests are performed on a number of inflators from each batch to ensure product quality before the lot is shipped to the customer. LAT failures indicate that there is either a flaw in the design of an inflator, or that there was a failure during the manufacturing process.

MEOP: The Maximum Expected Output Pressure is calculated by measuring the internal pressure of a number of high temperature inflator deployments and calculating that population's upper statistical edge. It is used in determining the structure's safety factor.

Moses Lake: Moses Lake is a city in central Washington where a Takata manufacturing plant that contained production lines for both propellant and inflators was located. The operation was originally owned by Rocket Research, but was bought by Takata for $80 million in 1992.

NADI: The Non-Azide Driver Inflator is based on Paresh's '3110' propellant.

NASI, NASI-2: The Non-Azide Side Inflator is a '3110' side-impact inflator.

NHTSA, National Highway Traffic Safety Administration: Established in 1970 following the National Traffic and Motor Vehicle Safety Act of 1966, and the creation of the Department of Transportation in 1966, NHTSA is responsible for "enforcing vehicle performance standards." Through "partnerships with state and local governments, NHTSA reduces deaths, injuries and economic losses from motor vehicle crashes." Though NHTSA does not directly conduct recalls themselves, their role in the Takata recall is vital. They have the power to determine if a particular inflator model should be added to the recall list, while also overseeing automakers remediation campaigns.

PFMEA: Process Failure Mode and Effects Analysis is a document that is created before a design enters production. It is used to identify the potential causes and risk priority of failure for a product at each step of the manufacturing process.

(PM) Program Manager: Programs are typically used to achieve long term business goals, and consist of several smaller projects. A program manager is responsible for determining the overall strategy for completing the program, and overseeing and assigning roles for each of the individual projects within the program.

PNADI: Programmable Non-Azide Driver Inflator was a dual-stage, '3110' inflator with a limited production run.

PSAN, PSAN inflator: One of the final patents submitted in 1994 during the joint venture between Takata and Rocket Research protected a group of propellants developed around PSAN, or phase-stabilized ammonium-nitrate. It promised higher gas efficiency than any propellants being used at the time, which meant smaller and lighter inflators. Paresh embraced the chemistry developing '2004' and it continued to be used throughout Takata's lifespan, including '2004L' and 'AMP' propellants. PSAN, however, is incredibly susceptible to moisture, and has a low melting temperature. Most importantly, it does not fail-safe, and its use is the reason for the numerous injuries and deaths caused by Takata inflators.

PSDI: Programmable Smokeless Driver Inflator is a dual-stage driver side inflator that was part of the first generation of PSAN Takata PSAN inflators. PSDIs in the 2001-2002 Honda Accord and 2001-2002 Honda Civic are responsible for many of the deaths caused by Takata inflators.

PSDI-4, PSDI-5: The follow-up generations to PSDI. PSDI-4, like PSDI, is an independent chamber design, while PSDI-5 is a dependent chamber design. PSDI-5 used tablets instead of wafers, due to inherent variability of wafers.

PSDI-X: PSDI-X is part of the X-series of inflators utilizing '2004L' propellant and 13X desiccant.

PSPI: Programmable smokeless passenger inflator, is a dual-stage passenger side inflator that was part of the first generation of PSAN Takata inflators. As was the case with PSDI, PSPI ruptured many times during validation testing, particularly during the heat-aging environment.

PSPI-6: Paresh's follow-up design to PSPI, the PSPI-6 is a cylindrical, dual-stage, dependent passenger side inflator.

PSPI-X: The X-series version of the PSPI, PSPI-X is a dual-stage passenger inflator utilizing 13X desiccant and '2004L' propellant. The passenger side inflators of the X-series were less popular than their driver side counterparts, as they were a cylindrical geometry utilizing wafers as opposed to the industry trend of disc-shaped inflators with propellant tablets. As a result, Honda was the only customer for this particular inflator.

(PV) Process Validation: The final environmental test series that validates the mass production process and ensures the product is safe for use in customer vehicles. The parts are produced on the final production equipment, the same that will produce the mass production units, and are manufactured by plant operators at the production facility.

R&D: Research and development is the area of work within an organization that is focused on innovating new designs or products.

Restraint performance: The measured ability for an airbag to protect an occupant in the event of a collision.

PDP: Programmable Disk Passenger inflator is a dual-stage, toroidal passenger inflator utilizing 13X desiccant and '2004L' propellant. It was developed in response to Takata's poorly selling cylindrical passenger side offerings (PSPI-X and SPI-X). GM in particular, demanded the disk geometry to win future passenger business.

SABAG: A joint-venture occurring between TRW Automotive and Imperial Chemical Industries focused on the manufacturing of high-volume sodium-azide propellant. Started in 1987, this is where Paresh gained much of his experience working with propellant prior to Takata.

Safety Factor, 1.5 vs. 1.7, calculation and reason for: Safety Factor is calculated by dividing the lowest statistical failure pressure of an inflator by its maximum expected operating pressure (*see MEOP*). It is used to demonstrate that an inflator can safely withstand its operating pressure. Most of the automotive world requires a safety factor greater than 1.5 for inflators, but Europe requires greater than 1.7.

Sequential environments: Validation tests designed to expose an inflator to multiple environments before evaluating their performance. They are often the most difficult and time-consuming tests to complete during validation. An example of this is the sequential combination of heat-aging, thermal-shock, and mechanical environments like vibration and drop.

Single-stage inflator: An inflator with a single chamber. Single-stage inflators produce only one output and are therefore used less frequently in frontal airbags when out-of-position occupant considerations were mandated.

SL-20: A proposed upgrade to SSI-20 that was to use '2004L' and AIB. Despite its impressive performance, Kevin conceded the design to show his eagerness for Takata to develop a global inflator strategy.

SPI, SPI-2: Smokeless Passenger Inflator is the single-stage passenger side inflator from Paresh's first generation of PSAN inflators. Like PSPI, it also failed often during validation. SPI-2 was essentially the same design as SPI with only slight modifications.

SPI-X: The X-series version of SPI, SPI-X utilized 13X desiccant and '2004L' propellant. Like PSPI-X, it did not sell well due to its cylindrical geometry and was only used by Honda.

SDI: Smokeless Driver Inflator is the single-stage driver side inflator from Paresh's first generation of PSAN inflators. It has claimed a few of the tragic deaths with a unique failure mode that ejects the booster tube like a bullet into the driver.

SDI-X, SDI-X 1.7, SDI-X2: The X-series lineup included two single stage driver inflators utilizing 13X desiccant and '2004L' propellant, SDI-X, for driver side, and the slightly larger SDI-X 1.7 for compact passenger applications. Like PSDI-X, they were attractive inflators that sold well. After the release of SDI-X, Europe began using single stage driver side inflators with innovative cushion venting, a trend that would spread globally. This spurred Takata to create a more advanced single stage driver side inflator titled SDI-X2.

SDI: Special Devices, Inc is an energetic device company that makes the pyrotechnic squibs that initiate the inflator sequence, as well as micro gas-generators (MGG) that tension seatbelts during accidents. This is the company where David Schumann interned while pursuing his education at the University of Arizona.

Sled test evaluations: Sled tests utilize real safety parts and crash-test dummies to simulate a collision. Sensors are placed in various places on the crash-test dummy to measure the force they experience in the collision, how much the chest compresses, how fast the body accelerates after collision, and other factors. These measurements are then used to evaluate the effectives the safety product.

Smokeless propellant, *see PSAN, '2004,' and '2004L'*

Specification: Car companies produced specifications (USCAR, AKLV, Honda, etc.) that defined requirements inflators must meet in order to be approved for production.

SSI-20: Takata's first and only PSAN side-impact inflator. LAT failures in Monclova exposed critical design flaws that have never been addressed. The vast majority of SSI-20 inflators are un-desiccated and for some reason none are under recall.

Tank pressure, tank pressure results: To measure the performance of inflators, they are tested in closed-volume tanks and the pressure of the gas produced by the inflator is recorded over time. The output pressure must reside between a specified upper and lower limit in order for the inflator to pass the test.

TAIC: The Takata Aschaffenburg Inflator Center was established in Germany in 2001 to service European customers and reported directly to Paresh in ASL Armada. TAIC was first led by Stephen Kimmich and then later Heiko Kratz and is where all of Takata's GuNi inflators were developed.

TKH: TK Holding Inc. was established in 1989 as the primary North-American subsidiary, and consisted of the management team responsible for the rapidly growing US operations.

TKJ, TKC: Takata Corporation in Japan (TKC), or Takata Japan (TKJ), is the parent headquarters representing the privately held interests of the Takada family.

TRW: An American corporation that is one of the leaders in car part manufacturing. They play a major role in the development and production of inflators.

Unibody: A dual-stage passenger inflator that was part of Takata's '3110' generation of inflators. The BMW variant, in particular, highlighted the inexperience of Takata's LaGrange, GA inflator engineering.

USCAR: The United States Council for Automotive Research is an organization responsible for collaborative research between American automakers – Chrysler Group LLC, Ford Motor Company, and General Motors. They provide specifications for inflators used in cars from any of these automakers that must be met during validation.

Validation: Validation for inflators is a two-step process including design validation and process validation. Design validation is a test series conducted on final design inflators that are produced in the engineering laboratory and are typically built with hardware that is not made with production tooling and processes. Process validation is the final test series that validates the design for mass production and use in customer vehicles.

X-Series: The X-series generation of inflators were designed around Paresh's new PSAN propellant '2004L', and also included a new desiccant, 13X, and a new autoignition material called 9339. It included the PSDI-X, SDI-X, and SDI-X 1.7 driver inflators, as well as the PSPI-X and SPI-X passenger inflators. Kevin and his team were responsible for ensuring the designs were production ready.

Timeline

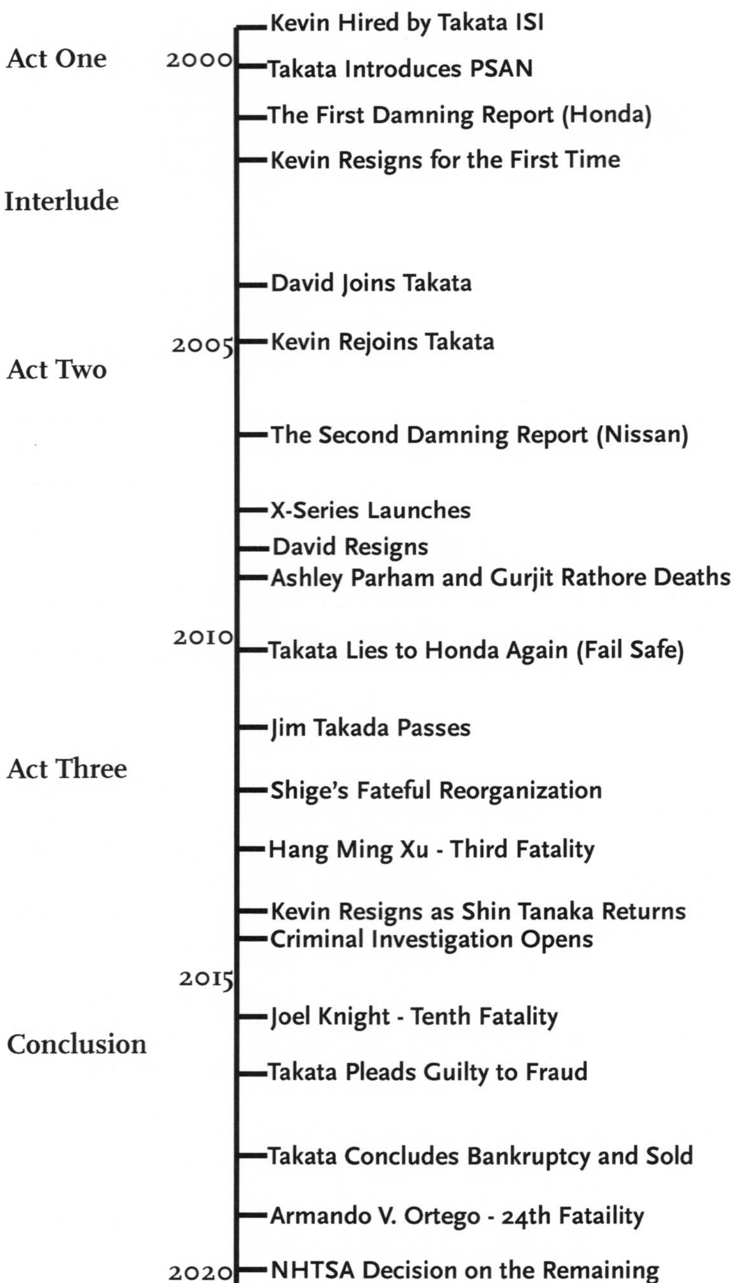

Act One
Interlude
Act Two
Act Three
Conclusion
2000
2005
2010
2015
2020
Kevin Hired by Takata ISI
Takata Introduces PSAN
The First Damning Report (Honda)
Kevin Resigns for the First Time
David Joins Takata
Kevin Rejoins Takata
The Second Damning Report (Nissan)
X-Series Launches
David Resigns
Ashley Parham and Gurjit Rathore Deaths
Takata Lies to Honda Again (Fail Safe)
Jim Takada Passes
Shige's Fateful Reorganization
Hang Ming Xu - Third Fatality
Kevin Resigns as Shin Tanaka Returns
Criminal Investigation Opens
Joel Knight - Tenth Fatality
Takata Pleads Guilty to Fraud
Takata Concludes Bankruptcy and Sold
Armando V. Ortego - 24th Fataility
NHTSA Decision on the Remaining

Endnotes

1 Klayman B., Kubota Y. "How Takata Crossed 'Dangerous Bridge' on Airbag Quality, Safety." *Automotive News*, 16 January, 2014. https://www.autonews.com/article/20140116/OEM11/140119727/how-takata-crossed-dangerous-bridge-on-airbag-quality-safety.
2 Air Bags Overview. (n.d.) https://www.nhtsa.gov/equipment/air-bags. Accessed May 2019.
3 1 foot divided by 88 feet per second (60MPH) equals 11.3 milliseconds.
4 The two major acquisitions were Irvin and Gateway Industries.
TK Holdings Inc. https://opencorporates.com/companies/us_de/2213152
5 Called Canadian Industries Limited (CIL)
6 Gas yield is the percentage of gas produced for a mass of propellant, unique to each formulation. 3110 was near 55%, a little better than sodium-azide at 50% – a half a gram of gas for every gram of solid propellant. Also see Gas Yield in Glossary.
7 At the time, one and two biggest were GM with $170 billion in revenue, and Ford with $150.
8 The Challenger Space Shuttle disaster was attributed to a faulty O-ring designed by Morton-Thiokol, the progenitor of Autoliv.
9 Sit J. "Teen Dies After Possible Honda Malfunction." *News 9*, 29 May, 2009. http://www.news9.com/story/10441178/teen-dies-after-possible-honda-malfunction
See also:
The Ashley Parham Foundation: http://theashleyparhamfoundation.org/
10 Kastner P. "Decision to make air bags has marred family legacy." *The Columbus Dispatch*. 19 January, 2014. http://www.dispatch.com/content/stories/insight/2014/01/19/1-blowing-up-in-a-companys-face.html
11 Variable airbag gent holes were being used to move from dual to single stage inflators.
12 Shows the welding at Armada is much more robust.
13 Takt time is the maximum time an assembly line's 'bottle neck' station can run at and still meet customer demand.
14 *Yokoten* is a Japanese word that roughly means 'best practice sharing.'
15 *Akiko* – Jim Takada's wife, often called *Aki*.
16 *Skosh* is from the Japanese word '*sakoshi*' that means 'a little bit.'
17 "Takata admits defective air bags, will recall over 33 mn vehicles." *San Diego Tribune*. 19 May, 2015.
http://www.sandiegouniontribune.com/hoy-san-diego/sdhoy-takata-admits-defective-air-bags-will-recall-over-2015may19-story.html

18 Kessler A., and Tabuchi H. "Lawmakers Press Takata on Propellant in Airbags." *The New York Times*. 2 June, 2015.
https://www.nytimes.com/2015/06/03/business/takata-hearing-airbag-recall.html

19 Soble J. "Takata Chief Executive to Resign as Financial Pressure Mounts." *The New York Times*. 2 June, 2015.
https://www.nytimes.com/2016/06/29/business/international/japan-takata-ceo.html

20 Spector M. "U.S. Auto Regulator Hits Takata With $70 Million Fine in Air-Bag Settlement." *The Wall Street Journal*. 3 Nov, 2015.
https://www.wsj.com/articles/federal-regulators-set-to-hit-takata-with-70-million-fine-1446568993

21 Tabuchi H., Ivory D. "Takata Discarded Evidence of Airbag Ruptures as Early as 2000." *The New York Times*. 12 Feb, 2016.
https://www.nytimes.com/2016/02/13/business/takata-discarded-evidence-of-airbag-ruptures-as-early-as-2000.html

22 Department of Justice, Office of Public Affairs. "Takata Corporation Agrees to Plead Guilty and Pay $1 Billion in Criminal Penalties for Airbag Scheme." *The United States Department of Justice*. 13 Jan, 2017.
https://www.justice.gov/opa/pr/takata-corporation-agrees-plead-guilty-and-pay-1-billion-criminal-penalties-airbag-scheme

23 Banville L. "3 Takata Executives Indicted In Criminal Probe Of Airbag Safety Tests." *The Legal Herald*. 18 Jan, 2017.
https://legalherald.com/takata-executives-indictment/

24 "GM Asks Fed for Exemption to Avoid Yet Another Takata Air Bag Recall." *Associated Press*. 19 June 2019.
https://www.marketwatch.com/story/gm-asks-feds-for-exemption-to-avoid-yet-another-takata-air-bag-recall-2019-06-19

25 "Report: 16.7M Faulty Takata Air Bags Still on US Roads." *Associated Press*. 21 Dec, 2018.
https://www.detroitnews.com/story/business/autos/2018/12/21/report-faulty-takata-air-bags-still-us-roads/38781195/

26 Sherpardson D. "Honda, Acura will recall 1.2M vehicles in N.A. with Takata airbags for second time." *Automotive News*. 12 Mar, 2019.
https://www.autonews.com/regulation-safety/honda-acura-will-recall-12m-vehicles-na-takata-airbags-second-time

Made in the
USA
Monee, IL

13917034R20180